AMERICAN HUSBANDRY

COLUMBIA UNIVERSITY STUDIES
IN THE HISTORY OF
AMERICAN AGRICULTURE
NUMBER 6

AMERICAN HUSBANDRY

EDITED BY

HARRY J. CARMAN

PROFESSOR OF HISTORY
COLUMBIA UNIVERSITY

NEW YORK : MORNINGSIDE HEIGHTS

COLUMBIA UNIVERSITY PRESS

1939

COLUMBIA UNIVERSITY STUDIES
IN THE HISTORY OF
AMERICAN AGRICULTURE

EDITED BY

HARRY J. CARMAN

*Professor of History in
Columbia University*

And

REXFORD G. TUGWELL

FOREWORD

PROBABLY because of the already strained relations between Great Britain and her New World continental colonies, *American Husbandry*, at the time of its publication (1775), apparently was unknown or ignored in America. Nor did it attract very much attention on this side of the Atlantic until the twentieth century when American scholars began to give more attention to agriculture and other economic aspects of American development. Finally in 1918, in a review essay, Dr. Lyman Carrier, long a laborer in the field of American agricultural history, not only emphasized the great historical value of the book, but pointed out that the number of copies available for use in this country was highly limited. It is for these two reasons that the editors of the Columbia University Studies in the History of American Agriculture have deemed it advisable to bring out a new edition of this book together with such supplementary data as will add to its usefulness.

For the convenience of the modern reader some changes have been made in spelling, punctuation, and typography. Notes appearing in the original text are indicated by an asterisk; those inserted by the editor are indicated by a number.

The editors of the Series are indebted to Miss Matilda L. Berg of the Columbia University Press for her numerous suggestions and helpful criticisms and to Professor Samuel McKee, Jr., of Columbia University for research assistance.

H. J. C.

R. G. T.

COLUMBIA UNIVERSITY

AUGUST 1, 1939

CONTENTS

CONTENTS xiii

INTRODUCTION

I N 1775, J. Bew, a bookseller in Paternoster Row, London, published a two-volume work entitled *American Husbandry*. Although appearing in the list of "New publications" in *The Gentleman's Magazine*, May, 1775, this important work—which, along with Jared Eliot's *Essays upon Field Husbandry* (1747), constitutes today the most significant source of information concerning American colonial agricultural practices—went almost unnoticed at the time. Indeed, a careful examination of the leading contemporary periodicals including *The London Magazine*, *The Scots Magazine*, and *The Annual Register* failed to reveal a single review of this book. *The Monthly Review* formed a notable exception; in the issue of this magazine for January, 1776, one finds a long, unfavorable review, detailed in its criticism of one aspect of *American Husbandry*.

In the pages immediately following, the reader will find, reproduced in full, the anonymous critical essay from *The Monthly Review;* he will find also a review of *American Husbandry* by Dr. Lyman Carrier, reprinted from the *Journal* of the American Society of Agronomy (1918), and a discussion of the authorship of *American Husbandry* by Professor Harry J. Carman.

Review of

AMERICAN HUSBANDRY

from

The Monthly Review

THIS work contains some very serious errors which we[1] think the Writer must have avoided, had he really visited the several colonies to which his account extends. Whether he be an American born or not, is of little importance*; but certainly the present performance is not merely the result of his own observations: it consists chiefly of accounts obtained from different persons very differently qualified for information; and therefore a considerable inequality is discoverable in the merits of their respective communications.

So far as this work (in common with every other publication of the kind) comprehends any remarks which may tend toward the general improvement of agriculture, &c., it may, exclusive of the danger to be apprehended from mistakes and misrepresentations, (and these it will be the business of a Reviewer, as far as he is able, to detect) prove an acquisition of some value to the Public: for of all the sciences which contribute toward the earthly happiness of mankind, this, we

---

* A correspondent, who seems impatient for our sentiments concerning this work thinks "every passage of it discovers the industrious hand of that eminent Book-builder Mr. A——r Y——g:" how far the Letter-writer is warranted in this conclusion, we cannot pretend to determine.

[1] An anonymous writer, reviewing *American Husbandry* in *The Monthly Review* or *Literary Journal* (printed for R. Griffiths), Vol. LIV (London, 1776), Art. VII.

think, stands foremost in point of importance. The subject, indeed, has been of late greatly cultivated, and prodigious practical improvements have been made; yet much remains to be done. Husbandry ought to be more generally understood as a science. Experiments, growing out of public patronage, would direct and instruct rude labour in the right application of his powers; and we may rest assured, that the culture of the earth will always flourish and increase in proportion as the sure means are discovered of rendering it more and more profitable—The *Board of Agriculture*, proposed by Mr. Donaldson in his valuable letter to the King on this subject* seems to be that grand *disederatum*, the public reservoir of agrarian policy, from whence new and most important meliorations would derive their source, and be distributed, by ten thousand channels, to every part of the Kingdom; nor would the current stop there, but flow on, uninterruptedly, to fertilize the bogs of Ireland, and even the wilds of America. Contemplation wanders with delight, and feels no lassitude in attending this diffusive progress. Like the inhabitant of Cairo, who watches with transport the risings of his Nile, and rejoices to behold the fruitful stream expatiate far beyond its native bed, we see around us in different parts, the barren heath, the dreary forest, or the desert marsh, changed by the magic touch of skillful husbandry, into luxuriant pastures or waving fields of corn!—The subject would transport us beyond the limits and proper province of a Review; but we must return to the work before us.

As we are little acquainted with the practices of North American farming, we shall not detain our Readers on the Continent; but as we are somewhat *more at home* in the West Indies, we shall at once set sail for Jamaica, in order to see

* See Review for July 1775.

in what manner our Author hath acquitted himself in his dissertation upon that island.

And here we are sorry to observe, that the mistakes of this pretended American are, we had almost said innumerable. We shall not try the patience of our Readers by any detail of the most trivial defects, but confine our remarks to a few of those more distinguished errors into which he could not have fallen, if he had been at the pains of obtaining any degree of authentic information.

Without any just idea of the cane-plant, or the face of the country in that island, he finds great fault with the present method in use there, of cleaning the canes with the hand instead of the horse-hoe—To reform this supposed erroneous and ignorant practice, he says, (Vol. II, p. 129) "*He* would carry the ideas of the improved husbandry of England into that of sugar in Jamaica; *he* would run a Berkshire shim through the intervals, in order to cut down the weeds; and *he* would run a double-winged plough through each interval, to mould up the roots of the plants."

We are persuaded, that if this Author was a planter, and should carry his threats into execution, *he* would very soon uproot all his canes, and be taught to know, that although some particulars of the improved husbandry of England might be admitted with propriety in Jamaica, yet that others are inadmissible, and this among the rest. But he enters copiously into the superior advantages to be gained by this new practice; and heated with his hypothesis, proceeds to answer, in form, all the objections which he tells us, "he has heard against it."—In this operation he meets with no difficulty, as he seems in reality to have no antagonist but himself to encounter; for the objections he has stated are such as no planter would probably offer; but at the same time he omits a material and most obvious one, which *every planter* would naturally suggest, viz. That it is *impracticable,* and that this impracticability arises from the very manner of the cane's growth, in which it differs essentially from all those plants which are the subjects of culture in the English farms—Mr. American having conceived a wrong idea from some imperfect description he has read of the sugar cane in *Ligon's* account of the Barbadoes, or some other obsolete author, compares a cane-piece in Jamaica to "a grove of oaks" (p. 137) as if he supposed them so many single stems, ranged upright in a line, like a regiment of guards drawn up for a review in Hyde-park; and hence concludes it very feasible to traverse the interval between each rank with his horses and ploughs—If, upon inquiry, he had learned that a very great number of stems, shoots, or suckers, spring from every stool, spreading in every direction, and extending across the intervals so luxuriantly, that hand-hoeing only can be applied, and this too with some care and caution, to avoid bruising or injuring the shoots; he would never have thought of recommending this branch of English husbandry to our West-India planters.

He asserts (p. 138), that "the negroes in Jamaica never do *task work*"—In this he is mistaken again—The work there on every plantation, or settlement of any importance, is proportioned to the known ability of the field labourers. But for this no specific rule can be prescribed, without doing them very great and manifest injustice; because their ability on different estates is various. Experience of what they can conveniently do, is the only reflective guide; consequently the measure of the task must vary on different plantations according to soil, and various other relative circumstances. If a different conduct is, as he affirms, pursued in South Carolina, and Virginia (the rice and tobacco colonies), we cannot think it deserving of the commendation he gives it. But his comparing the usage of negroes in Jamaica, to that "of horses in England" (a stale reproach against the planters there), is equally absurd and untrue.

He gives us (p. 139), what he calls, a calculation for a *considerable* plantation in Jamaica. This, he says, is founded upon "repeated inquiries among the *Jamaica planters;* and "will yield every *satisfactory information.*"—Where this assiduous investigator picked it up, we know not, but when upon examination, it appears not at all adapted to the plantations in that island, there is great room to suspect, that no such inquiries, as he pretends, were ever made. We find in it some appellations which are not in use there; such as, a *stove,* an *agent,* a *farrier.* This induces us to believe, that he has culled the statement out of different tracts relative to Barbadoes, or others of the Leeward Isles, where those heads of expence occur.—He has told us (p. 126) that the planters divide their cane-land into three parts: one of which is in young plants; the second in first rattoons (or plants of the second year); the third in fallow. In his estimate he proposes an estate, consisting of 600 *acres* of land, and he makes the produce of each year 400 hogsheads.—But the lands in Jamaica do not yield for plants and rattoons, at an average, more than one hogshead of sugar per acre, *on a general calculation* (which his is supposed to be), and it follows, that his allowance does not quadrate in this point with our Jamaica properties.—Further, we must allot 400 of the 600 acres (agreeable to his rule) for land planted in canes, and the other 200 for fallow; so that here remains no allowance whatever, for woodland, for pasture, for provision-grounds, and waste.—If his estimate of the produce is unjustifiably too high, his calculation, on the other side of the account for *charges,* is enormously too low.

Still further to evince his entire ignorance of Jamaica, whose affairs he affects to understand so thoroughly, he acquaints us, that the rate of interest there is 8£. per cent. (p. 140).

He goes on in his reveries, and (p. 141) computes the gain which the planter makes on his capital at from 15£. to 30£. Pursuing this idea, he treats with much seeming contempt, the *New History of Jamaica;* which, he says, allows the planter to gain no more than 10£. per cent.; an allowance which Mr. American considers "so very inadequate," that, if true, "the *planter must very soon be in goal*" (p. 142).

As this is a direct attack upon the reputation of a work which we have very much commended (see Review for August and December 1774), the cause of this ingenious Writer* becomes our own, and we must be allowed to defend, at once, that Historian and ourselves.—But the Public are still more concerned in the question.

At the close of his detail (Hist. of Jamaica, Vol. I, p. 464), Mr. L. mentioned, that his opinion would probably be found to differ from that of others; but he knew, at the same time, that most of his brethren, the planters, were apt to gaze at their West India possessions through the wrong end of the telescope. It does not, therefore, seem, that he would have intended any delusive estimate, which might cause a particularly hurtful effect, by not undeceiving those who are too apt to take every opinion upon trust, and by misleading young

* Edward Long, Esq.

and inexperienced proprietors belonging to the island, to form too extravagant a notion of their fortunes: he appears rather to have done all in his power, to come at the truth, or near to it; but in order to satisfy ourselves how far he is, or is not entitled to this praise, we have reconsidered the subject with fresh attention, and we are still more strongly persuaded that he is as right, as his censurer is wrong: and that the Reader may judge this matter fairly, as umpire between them, we will present him with three estimates of different estates in Jamaica, with which the present Reviewer happens to be so perfectly well acquainted, as to be able to produce the most unquestionable vouchers for their exactness. We must premise, that the sugar made on these estates, is of nearly equal goodness, and has generally a prompt sale at the London market.

The first of these examples, is a plantation situated on the *north side* of the island, within a short distance of the sea; and consists of the following articles, all fairly valued:

Acres	Rs	Ps		£. Jamaica Cur.
225	0	10	land in canes	4,506.6
248	0	0	ditto—pasture and provisions . .	3,428
453	1	30	ditto—wood-land, worth 1813£.	
926	2	0		

	£. Jamaica Cur.
Mill, distilling-house, curing ditto and all other buildings and offices, complete	3,600
Implements and utensils of all sorts in store, or in use	300
146 Negroes	8,760
82 Head of cattle (horned) old and young .	943
35 Mules	1,050
Add for the wood-land	1,813
Total £.	24,400

The produce of this estate (one year with another) has been

Hhds. sugar	Punchs. Rum
100	56

The nett proceeds (*communibus annis*), the
medium being taken of the last four years,
and deducting every contingency, except as
below, was .... £. 2,200 per An.
From this deduct annual interest
at 6 per cent. on 1813£.
being the value of the wood-
land lying unemployed, viz. £. 108–15–7
Allow for purchase of four new
negroes, supposed annually
put on, young and middle-
aged, with the duty, cloathing, and all other charges in-
cluded 251– 4–5   360

Remains clear for the proprietor .... £. 1,840

This estate, however, (in fact) had *no negro recruits*, during the space above mentioned.—The clear gain ought therefore to be stated at 2,091£. which is about equal to 9£. per
cent. on the capital.

If this estate was brought to a sale, and its books of account
carefully examined by the purchaser, we are confident, that
he would not give more for it than 24,000£. including the
price of the wood-land. If, however, the capital was to be
rated agreeably to the bubble-practice lately introduced into
the *Ceded Islands* (with a sinister view to raise the value of
property there above its natural pitch) it would be an easy
matter, by a supervaluation upon every article on one side of
the estimate, and by a diminution of charges on the other, to
describe it as a capital of 30,000£. Such a capital, according to
the rule of 10£. per cent., ought to yield a clear income of

3,000£. Our American, reckoning at 20£. per cent. would call it 6,000£. whereas, in truth, it is found to be little more than one-third of his calculation.—It is evident then, that the higher the computation of the capital is carried, the more reduced in proportion will be the apparent gain per cent. on that capital.

Our second example is a larger estate, in the same quarter of the island. We need not descend into particulars, but only state, that it has a complete water-mill, and other works, and necessary appendages; 290 negroes, a short carriage to the sea, and has been settled a great many years.

The produce of this estate, on an average of four late years, was, at a medium, 150 hogsheads of sugar, and 84 puncheons of rum.

Jamaica Currency

The annual gross proceeds at a medium ...... £. 4,300 – –
The annual contingent charges (Negroes included) at the like medium ....   1,300 – –

Nett proceeds per annum about £. 3,000 – –

We apprehend that no intelligent person would bid more for this estate than about 30,000£.—But if another, thinking differently of its value, should give 60,000£., the consequence must be this: if he has no superior skill in the management, or does not put on additional labourers to augment or improve the produce, his income from it will still be 3,000£. which is only 5£. per cent. on the capital sum he has expended in the purchase of it.

Our third example is a plantation on the *south side* of the island, well circumstanced in every respect.—The medium of its produce, on a computation of four late years, was 271 hogsheads of sugar, and 133 puncheons of rum.

Jamaica Currency

	£.	s.	d.
The medium of gross proceeds per annum	8,455	11	1¼
Medium of contingent charges and supplies including new negroes purchased	3,505	15	7
Clear proceeds £.	4,949	—	6¼

We should rate the value of its capital at
about £.50,000

10£. per cent. on this is . . . . £. 5,000

Deduct for interest at 6£. per cent. on
3,200£. the value of wood-land and
waste ditto, lying unoccupied   192

Clear balance to the proprietor per an-
num   4,808

We will not conceal, that this estate (which is Mr. *s in
Clarendon parish) yielded in one of these four years, a profit
of 16£. per cent. and in another, not more than 3£. per cent.
This great disparity happened from the casualty of irregular
seasons; from uncommonly favourable rains in the one, and
a severe drought in the other; which may serve to demonstrate the fallacy of any positive mode of calculation taken
from one year, or not founded on the medium of several
years taken in a series.

But to bring the question more home to our author, he
gives us (p. 149) an account of Mr. Kennion's estate, in the
parish of St. Thomas in the East, sold not long since to Mr.
Simon Taylor.—The capital here is put at 100,000£. which
is the price it sold for.—Yet it appears, on the very face of
it, that the profit it yielded to Mr. Kennion for a series of
seven years preceding the sale, was no more than 32,000£.
The medium of which *per ann.* is about 4,570£. which is *not*
5£. *per cent.* on the capital.—Every addition of negroes, &c.,
which the present owner may heap upon it, will augment the

capital, and in proportion augment the profit.—Yet we believe, if he could gain 10£. per cent. on his purchase money,
or 10,000£. per ann. he would be very well satisfied.

In reply to the latter part of Mr. American's reflection
on the Jamaica History, we shall recur to the *third* example,
above cited, of an estate valued at 50,000£. Let us suppose
that the proprietor of it is indebted to his merchant even
20,000£. This is a large sum, and equal to two-fifths of the
capital. If he owes this money to a person in Jamaica, he pays
6£. per cent. interest on it. If to a merchant in Britain, 5£.
per cent. We shall take the larger interest, and suppose he
pays 6£. This amounts per annum to 1,200£. and reduces the
clear income to 3,608£. We admit further, that the proprietor
resides in Britain, and allow a further deduction of 6£. per
cent. on the *gross proceeds*, for the attorney's, or manager's
commission. This is about 507£. and reduces the income to
3,101£. which at 4£. per cent. exchange, is sterling 2,215£.
—Will Mr. American assert, that such an income is not sufficient to keep the proprietor from starving? On the contrary,
may he not live in Britain in a respectable style, and if he is
frugal, save 1,000£. a-year to be applied in reducing the
principal and interest of his debt?—Our American (in the
same note) alleges that "if the planter resides in England,
and makes 6£. per cent. on his capital, he ought, *if he resided
in Jamaica*, to make 20£." But, why, or how this is to be expected we cannot discern. He would save (it is true) the
commission paid to an attorney, and if he confined himself
in general to his plantation, some retrenchments might also
be made, in the articles of dress, furniture, equipage, and
house-keeping; all which might enable him to lay up somewhat the more out of his income annually, towards reducing
his debt.—Or (if not in debt) he might make a greater an-

nual addition to his capital, by the purchase of labourers. But his gain will still regularly keep its due proportion with the value of his capital, whatever it may be. He will not, in fact, gain more, but only spend less; and even this implies that the estate is equally well managed when he resides upon it, as when he is absent, which, however, is very far from being always the case. If the planters gained 15£. to 30£. per cent. as our American presumes, they would be in very happy circumstances indeed! But the sad truth is, that almost all of them are in debt; and the major part have to struggle with it their whole lives. They exist in a kind of splendid poverty, subsisting chiefly by the credit they receive from the merchant, "still in hopes to get the better," and perhaps still disappointed. Their negro recruits, the duties and excise, the heavy freight, the insurance, and many other defalcations, commonly swallow up one half of the gross proceeds, and sometimes more; their taxes in the island are often very high; their works costly, as well as their implements; and the expences of manufactures, and carriage great. Their estates are continually changing hands; so that some have been under three different owners, in the course of seven years. Yet we have known a few retrieved from very heavy incumbrances of debt; but this happened by a long minority and honest active guardians. Others, less loaded, have been recovered by a timely recourse to a strict parsimony, and a steady perseverance in it for many years. The fluctuations of the market, is another circumstance, which may show the impropriety of rating the gain upon our capitals there; any otherwise than by a series of crops, and their *net proceeds;* for sugar and rum are extremely irregular in their prices. To illustrate this by examples, we shall mention, that the planter's sugars (of equal quality or nearly so) were sold last

year at 10s per hundred weight less than in the year 1773;
and 5s. less than in the year 1774. So that the income, which
in 1773 was 2,870£.—became reduced in the following year
to 2,520£.—and in the last to 2,170£.

These commodities are likewise very perishable in their
nature, inasmuch that every hour of their continuance on
board ship, and in the warehouse, takes somewhat from their
substance. At the same time various exigencies often require
a prompt sale, and when the market is so glutted, as that no
demand appears, nor a reasonable price can be got, the planter
is forced to anticipate their proceeds, by borrowing of the
merchant, for payment of bills drawn, or to supply his ordinary expences of living.

Let us add to these considerations, that while sugars, from
their greater plenty, are falling in price, the rates of all the
necessaries sent out from Britain, for annual plantation-use,
are enormously advanced, and negroes more so than any
other. The price of the latter has risen in the space of the last
20 years, 50£. per cent. and upwards, and British wares in
general at least 25 to 30 per cent. At present the unhappy
conflict with North America presages a similar advance upon
the articles of supply usually drawn from that continent;—
for by late advices from Jamaica we are informed, that hogshead staves which used to be sold for 12£. per thousand, are
now raised to 30£.—And the misfortune is, that when the
price of any of our plantation-supplies has been once height-
ened, it has rarely, if ever, sunk again to its former standard;
but the cause is very different in respect to West Indian staple
commodities; the reason of which is, that they are obliged
to buy their supplies, and sell their produce, at whatever price
is imposed upon, or offered to them; and this truly indicates
the situation in which the Colonies stand with Britain, and

the despotic control which she holds over all the fruits of labour. Those among them who possess very large estates, as Mr. Dawkins, Beckford, Pennant, &c., may bear up very well under these and other additional pressures; but many of the multitude must, and do sink, particularly in the Ceded Islands. Ruin, it is true, does not fall abruptly upon them; but interest, and yearly increase of principal, gradually creep on, and continue spreading and eating away, like a leprous ulcer, till the whole capital is consumed past recovery. Many, no doubt, have deceived themselves by golden dreams and visionary computations. It is almost the constant custom of the planters of Jamaica to compute their incomes, and regulate their expences, by the number of hogsheads and puncheons they expect to make every year; without ever inquiring into the state of debts, or examining the sum they may really be entitled to spend, deducting interest and charges. Their debts they settle by a note, bond, or mortgage, and then conclude them paid. Nothing, in any other part of the world, can equal their absurdity, and their delusion. But hence it is, that such numbers continue involved as long as they live, and that so many estates are every year sacrificed to creditors. The appearance of wealth, is there mistaken for the reality of it, and the *Ignis fatuus* still continues to dazzle, and invite fresh adventurers, who run the same round for a while, and then get fast stuck in the swamp, like their predecessors.

We would not be thought to speak with contempt of a West-India property. We think it has been proved, that with care and frugality, the planter's occupation will be very profitable. We mean only to shew, that the profits are not so enormous as many half-informed arithmeticians imagine. That, in fact, they are such as will yield a very comfortable maintenance to a proprietor who acts with constant circumspection and economy, and agreeable to the unerring counsel, which his annual state of accounts will present to his view. We ought by all fair methods to encourage new adventurers to improve our settlements, by forming plantations; but we cannot think it honest to tempt them with exaggerated prospects of immoderate gain; and by that means, mislead them into fallacious opinions, and a plan of living, which may terminate in beggary, and thus defeat the original design of establishing useful, permanent settlers.

To conclude with Mr. American;—if we might judge of the rest of his work, from what he says of the West Indies, we should pronounce it a compilation hastily put together, after raking for materials in a book called "Political Essays," and every other tract that has contained anything relative to colony-husbandry. Some imperfect hints he may have carefully picked up from persons conversant with the Plantations; but as to the bulk of his farrago, the Author seems to be largely indebted to his own fertile genius, his own theories, and the observations he has drawn from long and sedulously applying his mind to the system of British Husbandry. His opinions, therefore, upon American and west-Indian culture, must in general be regarded as merely speculative and arbitrary. It would have been commendable, perhaps not unuseful, to collect and reduce into order, all that lies scattered in different volumes and essays upon this subject; and the Compiler, *as such* would have been allowed no small degree of merit. But when we find this *pretended Yankee* attempting to foist himself upon us for the genuine *Simon Pure*, assuming airs of self-sufficiency, and dictating to us with intolerable presumption; he deserves the severest castigation, for his imposture, his arrogance, and his folly.

AMERICAN HUSBANDRY

A Much Overlooked Publication

By Lyman Carrier

THIS review [from the *Journal* of the American Society of Agronomy, II (1918), 206–11] is written to call attention to a 2-volume publication on American agriculture issued in London in 1775. The author does not give his name, but uses the pseudonym, "An American." Unfortunately, this publication, *American Husbandry*, has been generally overlooked by bibliographers of English and American literature. Allibone[1] does not mention it, neither does Loudon,[2] or McDonald,[3] nor does it appear in the review of Colonial writings in the *American Cyclopedia of Agriculture*. Sabin[4] has an entry "American Husbandry, see Arthur Young," that may refer to these books or that may have meant a chapter by that title in Young's *Annals of Agriculture*, as Sabin's bibliography was never completed. Cushing[5] lists 38 different writers who used the pseudonym "An American," but does not mention *American Husbandry*, and none of the authors given is at all likely to have written this work. The Farmers'

[1] S. Austin Allibone, *British and American Authors* (Philadelphia, 1870).

[2] John C. Loudon, "Agricultural Bibliography of North America" in *Encyclopedia of Agriculture*, 4th Ed. (London, 1839).

[3] Donald McDonald, *Agricultural Writers from Sir Walter of Henly to Arthur Young* (London, 1908).

[4] Joseph Sabin, *Dictionary of Books Relating to America* (New York, 1868).

[5] William Cushing, *Initials and Pseudonyms* (New York, 1885–88).

Magazine of 1801 refers to Bordley's[6] book as "the first American work upon practical husbandry which has come into our hands."

An extensive criticism of *American Husbandry* appeared in the London *Monthly Review* of January, 1776. Obadiah Rich[7] lists it. Flint[8] speaks of it as "an exceedingly interesting work," and Trimble[9] refers to it as "an indispensable source" of information on colonial agriculture.

SCOPE OF THE WORK

The author describes the soil, climate, and agricultural practices and products of the English colonies in America, beginning with Nova Scotia and Canada, and following in geographical order with New England, New York, New Jersey, Pennsylvania, Maryland, Virginia, the Carolinas, Florida, and the West Indies. The agricultural possibilities of the Ohio and Mississippi valleys were emphasized. In addition to this descriptive matter the objectionable farm practices are mentioned and remedies suggested. The staple commodities which each colony produced or was capable of producing are discussed from the standpoint of their value to Great Britain. Statements showing the capital necessary to establish a farm and the probable receipts and expenditures connected with its operation are given for most of the colonies. Direct comparisons are frequently made between the agricultural possibilities of America and England, with the advantages and disadvantages pertaining to each country.

[6] J. B. Bordley, *Essays and Notes on Husbandry and Rural Affairs* (Philadelphia, 1799).

[7] Obadiah Rich, *Bibliotheca Americana* (New York, 1846).

[8] Charles Flint, *Report of United States Commissioner of Agriculture, 1866* (Washington, 1868), p. 25.

[9] Wm. Trimble, *Introductory Manual for the Study and Reading of Agrarian History* (Fargo, N. D., 1917).

Purpose of the Work

These books appear to have been written largely for the benefit of England, and it was probably intended that they would be read in England more than in America. The author states "I particularly mean to explain everything in my power concerning the country management of America from its being so little known in England." This publication would have been very valuable to English emigrants to America, but a deeper political purpose appears back of its composition—to clear up the dense ignorance in regard to the colonies which prevailed in the English government at that time. Had they [these volumes] been published earlier and given wide circulation they might have changed the histories of two great nations. At the time they appeared the Boston Tea Party and the Battle of Lexington and Concord had put a stop to sober reasoning on both sides of the Atlantic.

Literary Style

One of the most striking features of these books is the directness with which the author goes at his subject. There is a happy absence of the chapter of the apologetic excuses for undertaking the great task of writing a book so customary in eighteenth century publications. Neither is there the misplaced theological discussion so common in the writings of the early preacher-agriculturists. They are as easy to read as any modern book on the subject, and are far superior to any other colonial agricultural writings. Another feature is the thoroness with which the different matters are discussed.

A fault which is quite noticeable is the unnecessary repetition of the same observations under different phases of the subject.

CHARACTER OF THE PUBLICATION

The value of these books at the present time is due to the agricultural and not the political information which they contain. Compared with the agricultural books published in the last half of the eighteenth century either in America or Great Britain, they stand far in advance of their time. They are also of much value from a historical point of view. The agriculture of the colonists, as described in *American Husbandry*, differs considerably from that described in the agricultural histories and retrospects written in the past half century. In many of the latter, conditions have been colored to show a wonderful advancement in farming since the United States became a nation. As a matter of fact there has not been any great improvement except in the invention and wider use of farm machinery. The ordinary farm practices of his period did not meet the approval of the author of *American Husbandry* any more than present practices meet the standards of modern writers. The distinctly American practice of cropping a piece of land until it would not give a profitable yield and then turning it out for nature to restore the fertility while the same process was repeated on another area was strongly condemned. The closing chapters of the second volume, which deal with the possibilities of the colonies becoming independent and with the British colonial policy, must be classed among the most remarkable writings of pre-Revolutionary times. They should be read by every student of colonial history.

Perhaps the nature of these books may be best shown by a few direct quotations.

I need not observe here that in all countries one great principle of husbandry is the procuring and using as much dung and manure as possible. The farmers of New Jersey cannot raise hemp for exportation in large quantities for want of more manure; yet do they give in to one practice which is very negligent; they leave the straw of much of the buckwheat they cultivate about their fields in heaps; they find their cattle will not eat it and so think there is no other use for it; but surely these men might reflect on the importance of the *litter*, as well as *food* for cattle; in the consumption of their hay and other straw they might certainly use far more than they have, or perhaps can have; but to possess it on their farms without using it is unpardonable; nor is it a universal practice which keeps the whole country in countenance, for there are some planters who have better ideas, use all their straw carefully for litter; and the advantage which these men reap from the practice ought surely to make the rest follow their example. There is no error in husbandry of worse consequence than not being sufficiently solicitous about manure; it is this error that makes the planters of New Jersey and our other colonies seem to have but one object, which is the plowing up fresh land (Vol. I, p. 143 [This edition, pp. 104–5]).

In discussing the agriculture of the New York colony he states:

They should never exhaust their lands; and when they were only out of order they should give them what ought to be esteemed the most beneficial fallow; that is, crops which while growing received great culture at the same time that they do not much exhaust the soil; such as all sorts of roots and pulse and every kind of leguminous plant with the various kinds of clovers.

A cropping system he recommended for one of the North Central colonies was: 1, Indian corn; 2, potatoes; 3, Indian corn; 4, peas or beans; 5, barley; 6, clover; 7, wheat.

In this system no two exhausting crops came together, peas or beans and in general the plants which bear a leguminous flower being of a different nature from corn in this respect (Vol. I, p. 457 [This edition, p. 322]).

An experiment station was another of the things he advocated for the improvement of agriculture. He says:

It is impossible to know what the merit of the plants indigenous in these colonies is unless there is a plantation established at the public expense under the direction of a skillful botanist and one perfectly well acquainted with the practical as well as the theory of agriculture. In such a plantation improvements might be made in the culture of tobacco; vineyards might be planted and cultivated, both of the native vines and also of foreign ones. Experiments might be made on the culture of silk. All the native plants like those I have just mentioned which promised anything of utility might be brought into culture and trials made of their worth as materials for manufacture. Such a plantation well supported would be attended with some if not all those excellent consequences which flowed from the gardens of the Dutch East India Company at the Cape of Good Hope (Vol. I, p. 275 [This edition, p. 196]).

Cotton we import from Turkey at the expense of above two hundred thousand pounds a year; this commodity agrees well with the soil and climate of Georgia, especially those of the back parts of the province. I am sensible that our West India islands would produce it, but the land which is so occupied there would produce more valuable staples; there we want land, but on the continent is more land than we know what to do with (Vol. II, p. 40 [This edition, pp. 357–58]).

The cotton they cultivate here (eastern Louisiana) is a species of the white Siam. This East India and annual cotton has been found to be much whiter than what is cultivated in our colonies which is of the Turkey kind; both of them keep their color better in washing and are whiter than the perennial cotton that comes from the islands though this last is of longer staple (Vol. II, p. 84 [This edition, p. 390]).

THE AUTHOR

It would appear from a study of *American Husbandry* that the author had lived both in England and America, and that he was loyal to Great Britain. He evidently had a scientific training, including a knowledge of botany, and was most familiar with the agriculture of Virginia and Maryland, but had also visited Pennsylvania and probably New England. A reasonable assumption would be that he had some connection with the British government as evidenced by the continual economic discussion of a political nature, and one might reasonably suppose that these two books were not his first and only literary production.

The only man who seems to answer all these requirements is Dr. John Mitchell, best known as a botanist and memorialized by *Mitchelli repens*, the pretty little partridge berry. As another paper bearing on the life of Doctor Mitchell has been prepared for publication elsewhere, only a brief account will be given here, see p. . . . Doctor Mitchell was born and educated in Great Britain and graduated an M.D. He came to America early in the eighteenth century and settled at Urbanna on the Rappahannock River in eastern Virginia. His first literary work seems to have been a small treatise on botany and zoology in 1738, followed by another in 1741 in which he proposed 30 genera of plants. These were published in 1748 by Doctor Trew of Nuremburg. Doctor Mitchell sailed for England in 1746 with an extensive botanical collection, but a Spanish privateer captured the ship and took his possessions. Mitchell reached England, but was compelled to give up his botanical work. He was made a fellow in the Royal Society in 1748 and two of his papers may be found in the Philosophical Transactions of that Society. About 1753 he was employed by the British Ministry to prepare a map of North America which was published in 1755. This map has been recognized as the most authentic of the colonial period and was the one used at the peace council at the close of the Revolutionary War. Accompanying this map Mitchell submitted a report which was published in 1757 entitled "The Contest in America between Great Britain and France, by An Impartial Hand." Another anonymous book which has generally been credited to Dr. Mitchell was entitled "The Present State of Great Britain in America," 1767.

In addition to the publications mentioned above this study has revealed two other anonymous publications which were undoubtedly the work of Doctor Mitchell. The first of these was "An Account of the English Discoveries and Settlements in America" in the revised edition of Harris' Voyages and Travels published in 1748, and which may be found also in Pinkerton's Voyages and Travels (1819). The second was entitled "A New and Complete History of America." This was issued in 1756 and consists of three volumes. The third volume ends abruptly in the middle of a word and the set was never completed. This is a very rare and little known publication.

As Dr. Mitchell died in 1768 or seven years previous to the publication of *American Husbandry*, the manuscript must have been edited by another. There is evidence of an attempt to disguise Doctor Mitchell's part in its preparation. A careful comparison of these books with the other books generally credited to Doctor Mitchell, together with those anonymous books mentioned above, leaves no reason for doubting that Dr. Mitchell was the author of *American Husbandry* and that the manuscript was in a fairly complete condition at the time of his death.

AUTHORSHIP OF
AMERICAN HUSBANDRY

By Harry J. Carman

THE authorship of *American Husbandry* is a matter of speculation, for the creator of this two-volume work, for some unknown reason, chose to hide himself in anonymity. The title, with its long explanatory sub-title, is followed by a single line which reads "By An American." Whether it was the product of an American or not is apparently beyond absolute proof. Dr. Carrier after much painstaking research came to the conclusion that it was written by Dr. John Mitchell, author of the famous Mitchell map which appeared in 1755. As we have seen, Mitchell emigrated from England and settled in Virginia about 1700. As a distinguished botanist who carried on correspondence with Linnaeus and as a collector of plant specimens he had occasion to visit several of Virginia's neighboring colonies. In 1748 he was back in England, where he gained the friendship of the Duke of Argyle, Lord Bute, and Benjamin Franklin, all of whom were interested in America. He died in 1768 without having revisited the colonies. Dr. Carrier's reasons for crediting Mitchell with the authorship of *American Husbandry*—even though the book was not published until seven years after Mitchell's death—are herewith set forth at length.[1]

[1] Summarized from the *Annual Report of the American Historical Association, 1918* (Washington, 1921), I, 211–18.

Seven years after his death Mitchell's greatest work was printed in London. It was in two volumes and sold for 11 shillings. The title was "American Husbandry," by "An American." The title page gives the further information that the volumes were printed for J. Bew, in Paternoster Row, London, 1775. It was unfortunate that the publishing of these books was delayed until that time—the beginning of the Revolutionary War. They evidently had a very limited sale and were soon forgotten. For some unaccountable reason this publication has been consistently overlooked by bibliographers of British and American books. The only one to which the writer has had access which mentions it is Rich's *Bibliotheca Americana Nova*, 1846. There are no confirmatory statements that Mitchell wrote *American Husbandry*, and this is probably the first time he has ever been credited with its authorship. Mr. B. B. Woodward, assistant in charge of the general library of the British Museum, was unable to ascertain anything about the author or the history of the books.

That Dr. Mitchell had in mind the preparation of just such a work as *American Husbandry* is shown in the following extract from the preface to *The Present State:*

To form a better judgment concerning the colonies it would be necessary to give an account of every one of them in particular: to consider the nature of the soil and climate and what it produces or is fit to produce for the benefit of the nation, this we have endeavored to supply by a few notes in order to explain many things which appear to be but little understood. But as these can give but an imperfect idea of many subjects treated of in them a more particular account shall be given in a second part of this discourse if we find that design is approved of. We may then also consider more particularly the several staple commodities that may be made in the plantations for the benefit of the nation and the ways of making them and give a more particular account of what they now make or of the produce of the colonies as well as their exports and imports.

Statements to the same effect may be found on pages 135, 138, and 246. *American Husbandry* describes the several British colonies in America, beginning with Nova Scotia and taking them in geographic order to the Bahama Islands. The order followed in *American Husbandry* is almost identically the same as the outline proposed for the *History of North America.*

Of all our colonial literature, *American Husbandry* is the most accurate and comprehensive account of the English colonies in America and gives by far the best description of their agricultural practices. The recommendations for the improvement of farming compare favorably with those of any modern textbook on the subject and are much superior in style and presentation to any other English or American agricultural books of the eighteenth century.

The *Monthly Review* of January, 1776, given above, in full, devoted 10 pages to a scathing denunciation of this work. The critic states:

As we are but little acquainted with the practice of North American farming, we shall not detain our readers on the Continent.

The review is taken up almost wholly in picking flaws in the recommendations for the sugar planters of Jamaica. Whether this tirade is justified or not the writer is not sufficiently informed on sugar-cane culture to say. The closing lines of this criticism, however, show which foot the shoe pinched.

It would have been commendable, perhaps not unuseful, to collect and reduce to order all that lies scattered in different volumes and essays upon this subject, and the compiler, *as such,* would have been allowed no small degree of merit. But when we find this *pretended Yankee* attempting to foist himself upon us for the genuine *Simon Pure*, assuming airs of self-sufficiency and dictating to us with intolerable presumption, he deserves the severest castigation for his imposture, his arrogance, and his folly.

In a footnote to this review is the statement:

A correspondent who seems impatient for our sentiment concerning this work thinks that every passage of it discovers the industrious hand of that eminent book builder, Mr. A———r Y———g.

This evidently refers to Arthur Young. The correspondence between George Washington and Arthur Young after the Revolution discloses such an unfamiliarity with American agriculture on the part of Young as to prove beyond doubt that he was not the author of this work. The only reason for thinking that Young might have prepared these books is that he was the best and most prominent agricultural writer in England at the time of their publication.

That *American Husbandry* has the appearance of being the work of a compiler is due to the large number of quotations which it contains, Dr. Mitchell's name appearing some 15 times. It would seem to have been the intention of the one who presented the manuscript for publication to cover up Dr. Mitchell's part in its preparation by frequently quoting *The Present State* and by paying a nice tribute to Dr. Mitchell's ability. It was very unlike Mitchell to say anything about himself, although in his writings he frequently used the same material more than once without quotation marks. As there is no description of a colony in *American Husbandry* to which parallel passages may not be found either in *The Present State* or in Mitchell's histories, the manuscript must have been in a fairly complete condition at the time of Mitchell's death. The absence of serious errors is also strong evidence that it was not the work of a mere compiler.

There is a marked improvement of literary style in this publication over Mitchell's previous works, credit for which may be due the editor. A fairly good index is also added, a feature which does not appear in any other of Mitchell's books. There are evidences of some additions. Quotations from two reports with dates subsequent to Mitchell's death are to be found in the second volume. These may have been inserted as "filler," as the second volume lacks 150 pages of being as large as the first.

It would be interesting to know who was responsible for the publication of this work, and why it was put out anonymously, but these are problems which do not now seem possible of solution. That the editor knew little of American affairs appears almost certain or he would not have followed so blindly Mitchell's thoughts and recommendations.

It is never easy to prove the authorship of an anonymous publication by a comparison of literary styles. When it comes to proving the parentage of a whole family of literary orphans the task is still more difficult. Literary style is an elusive thing not easily described, but it is a reality to a student of any writer's books. We shall give a number of quotations from these several books under discussion. While the claim may be raised that the author of the later publications wrote with the earlier books at hand, this argument will scarcely hold in the present case. The successive publications in some instances contain passages quite closely following those of the earlier books, yet each has additional information which shows the author possessed a definite knowledge of the subjects treated equal to that possessed by the writer of the first. Dr. Mitchell had a peculiar literary habit of expression.

He was diffuse, using long sentences and many unnecessary clauses, phrases, and words. His writings abound in quotations for which due credit is made. He was given to repeating the observations which he had made under one phase of his subject while discussing something else even in the same publication. Another characteristic of his, no matter whether he was writing on potash, yellow fever, agriculture, or history, was that he went to the bottom of his subject in an exhaustive, scientific manner. A careful study of all these books reveals the same original argumentative discourse, similar observations, similar iteration, the same likes and prejudices, recommendations for the encouragement of the production of the same staple commodities by the colonists for Great Britain, and (in the last two publications) the same forceful arguments for the peaceful settlement of the disputes which were fast separating the colonies from the mother country, and the same charges of ignorance and bad policies on the part of the British government which were responsible for this estrangement.

To give all the parallelisms which occur in these voluminous publications would necessitate the reproduction of a large part of all of them. A few of the most striking passages follow. On the subject of tobacco growing, for example, these quotations may be adduced.

The tobacco seeds are first sown in beds where having remained a month, the plants are transplanted into little hillocks, like those in our hop-gardens, the first rainy weather; and being grown a foot high there, within the space of another month they top them, and prune off all the bottom leaves, leaving only seven or eight on the stalk, that they may be the better fed; and these leaves, in six weeks time will be in full growth; the planters prune off the suckers, and clean them of the horn worm twice a

week, which is called worming and suckering; and this work lasts
three weeks or a month, by which time the leaf from green begins to brownish and to spot and thicken; which is a sign of
ripening; as fast as the plants ripen they cut them down, heap
them up, and let them lie and sweat a night, and the next day
they carry them to the tobacco-house where every plant is hung
up at a convenient distance one from another, for about a month
or five weeks; at the end of which time they strike or take them
down in moist weather, when the leaf gives or else it will crumble
to dust, after which they are laid upon sticks and covered up
close in the tobacco-house for a week or a fortnight to sweat;
and then opening the bulk on a wet day, the servants strip and
sort them, the top leaves being the best, and the bottom the worst
tobacco; the last work is to pack it in hogsheads, or bundle it up,
which is also done in a wet season; for in curing of tobacco, wet
seasons are as necessary as dry to make the leaf pliant. (1748,
Harris, II, or Pinkerton, II, 242.)

The Virginia planters sow the tobacco-seeds in beds, as the
gardeners in England do colwort seeds; they leave them there a
month, taking care all that time to have them well weeded.
When the plants are about the breadth of ones hand, they are
removed the first rainy weather, and transplanted into what they
call tobacco hills. In a month's time the plants will be a foot high,
and they top them, and then prune off all the bottom leaves,
leaving only seven or eight on the stalk, that they may be the
better fed by the top, and these leaves in six weeks time will be
in their full growth. The planters prune off the suckers, and clear
them of the horn-worm twice a week, which is called worming
and suckering; and this work lasts three weeks or a month; by
which time the leaf from green begins to turn brownish and to
spot, and thicken, which is a sign of its ripening. As fast as the
plants ripen you must cut them down, leave them in the field
for half a day, then heap them up, let them lie and sweat a night,
and the next day carry them to the tobacco-house, where every
plant is hanged one by another, at a convenient distance, for about
a month or five weeks; at the end of which time they strike or
take them down in moist weather, when the leaf gives, or else

it will crumble to dust; after which they are laid upon sticks and covered up close in the tobacco-house for a week or a fortnight to sweat, and then opening the bulk in a wet day, the servants strip and sort them, the top leaves being the best and the bottom the worst tobacco. The last work is to pack it in hogsheads or bundle it up, which is also done in a wet season; for in the curing tobacco, wet seasons are as necessary as dry, to make the leaf pliant, which would otherwise be brittle and break. (1756, *Hist. of America*, III, 163–64.)

In addition to this there is a botanical description and a colored drawing of the tobacco plant not found in the other books. The description follows:

It is called by the botanists, *Nicotiana major latifolia, Nicotania major,* five tobacum majus; or, Tobacco. It is an annual plant; when it is at its full growth, it is about the height of an ordinary man; the stalk is straight hairy, and clammy, like that of the hyascy amus niger vel vulgaris, or common black henbane; the whole habit is of an absolete yellowish green; the leaves alternate; some of the lower leaves are a cubit long and nine inches wide entire, but waved; the lateral costae of the leaf arch into one another near the margin; the leaves have no pedicles, and by an auriculated base embrace the stalk; towards the top, the stalk branches from the sinus's of the leaves, and higher from the sinus of a slender foliculum proceed fasciles of flowers: the flower is slender and tubulous, one and a half inch long, yellowish, with an obsolete diluted purple brim, not divided but expanded into four or five angles: the calix is tubulous of four or five narrow segments; the pistillum becomes the seed-vessel conoidal, bicopsular with a middle spongy double placenta, and contains many small round brownish seeds; the seed is ripe about the end of September. (*Hist. of America*, p. 165.)

Tobacco is raised from the seed, which is sown in spring upon a bed of rich mould; when about the height of four or five inches, the planter takes the opportunity of rainy weather to transplant them. The ground which is prepared to receive it, is, if it can be got, a rich black mould; fresh woodlands are best; some-

times it is badly cleared from the stumps of trees, that they can
not give it any ploughings; but in old cultivated lands they plough
it several times, and spread on it what manure they can raise.
The negroes then hill it; that is, with hoes and shovels they form
hillocks, which lie in the manner of Indian corn, only they are
larger, and more carefully raked up: the hills are made in squares,
from six to nine feet distance, according to the land; the richer
it is the further they are put asunder, as the plants grow higher
and spread proportionably. The plants in about a month are a
foot high, when they prune and top them; operations, in which
they seem to be very wild, and to execute them upon no rational
principles; experiments are much wanting on these points, for
the planters never go out of the beaten road, but do just as their
fathers did, resembling therein the British farmers their brethren.
They prune off all the bottom leaves, leaving only seven or
eight on a stalk, thinking that such as they leave will be the
larger, which is contrary to nature in every instance thro'-out all
vegetation. In six weeks more the tobacco is at its full growth,
being then from four and a half to seven feet high: during all
this time, the negroes are employed twice a week in pruning off
the suckers, clearing the hillocks from weeds, and attending to
the worms, which are a great enemy to the plant; when the
tobacco changes its colour, turning brown, it is ripe and they then
cut it down, and lay it close in heaps in the field to sweat one
night: the next day they are carried in bunches by the negroes to
a building called the *tobacco house,* where every plant is hung up
separate to dry, which takes a month or five weeks: this house
excludes the rain, but is designed for the admission of as much
air as possible. They are then laid close in heaps in the tobacco
houses for a week or a fortnight to sweat again, after which it is
sorted and packed up in hogsheads; all the operations after the
plants are dried must be done in moist or wet weather, which
prevents its crumbling to dust. (1775, *American Husbandry,* I,
222–25.)

   This account is followed by about 20 pages describing the
equipment, management, and profits of a tobacco plantation
—material not to be found in the other books. Similar pas-

sages might be quoted in regard to the culture of corn, cotton, and indigo, the raising of silkworms, manufacture of potash, and the production of tar-pitch, but they would extend this account to an unnecessary length. One point is worth noting: In discussing corn culture for New England the author describes the methods of topping and plowing, which are typical of Virginia and not of New England.

Since Mitchell was a physician, it is to be expected that items pertaining to his profession would be found if he was the author of these books. Nor are they wanting, as the following quotations illustrate:

The acute diseases in these unhealthy parts of North America generally turn to intermittents which are not mortal even in 20 months but in a few months more they may bring on that cachexy, with an emaciated habit, a swelled belly, and a pale sallow complexion which is characteristic of the bad state of health in all the southern and maritime parts of North America. (*Present State*, p. 191.)

To take at one view the state of the small-pox in Boston from January 1752 to July the 24th, the following table may serve:

	Whites.	Blacks.
Small-pox in the natural way	5,059	485
Whereof died	452	62
By inoculation	1,970	139
Whereof died	24	7
Sick in seventeen families	23	....
Persons who have not received it	174	....

There died of inoculation thirty-one persons not including dubious deaths. (*Hist. of America*, I, 382.)

The next three extracts are taken from discussions in regard to the natural products of Virginia. There is nothing to indicate that anyone was quoted.

We come to speak of what is produced by their soil. And first with respect to trees; of which we may affirm, few countries are better stocked, or afford greater variety. As to timber, they have oaks, cedars, firs, cypress, elm, ash, and wallnut; some of their oaks measure two feet square, and sixty feet in height. They have also beach, poplar, hazel, &c., besides sassafras, sarsaparilla, and many other sweet woods and such as are used in dying. (Harris, II, or Pinkerton, II, 241.)

The chief productions of the soil are oak, cedar, cypress, firs, two sorts of elms, walnut, and ash. The oaks are commonly of such prodigious bigness that they will measure two feet square and sixty feet high. (*Hist. of North America*, III, 161.)

As to timber and wood, they have all the sorts that are found upon the Continent: many sorts of oaks, cedars, firs, cypress, elm, ash, and walnut; some of their oaks are said to measure two feet square and sixty feet in height. They have also beech, poplar, hazel, besides sassafras, sarsaparilla and other dy[e]ing woods. (*American Husbandry*, I, 219).

Reference has been made to Dr. Mitchell's prejudice against Nova Scotia and Florida. To illustrate:

Canada can be nothing but a factory for the fur trade and Nova Scotia only a fishing settlement both of which this nation already has too many. (*Present State.*)

We engaged in the war for those fruitful territories on the Ohio and Mississippi, which we got by peace; but by the regulations after it we are deprived of them and thereby conspire with our enemies to deprive ourselves of those very advantages which it was their aim to do by the war; while we got no more by Canada and Florida than to relieve them of a burden and charge, and to saddle ourselves with it. (*Present State.*)

Neither the fisheries nor the export of lumber prove advantageous enough to render the settlers [of Nova Scotia] comparable in ease and wealth to the people of New England. (*Am. Husbandry.*)

But will any planter we have in North America remove either to Canada or Florida? Is it not obvious to every one that such a removal would be from bad to worse? (*Am. Husbandry.*)

From 143 to 170 years have passed since these anonymous publications were issued and as no just claim for writing them has been made in behalf of anyone else it would seem that cataloguers and bibliographers should give credit for authorship to John Mitchell; this has already been done in the case of *The Contest in America* and *The Present State of the British Empire in America.* One thing is certain, either Dr. Mitchell wrote all of these books or there was another man with Dr. Mitchell's education, ability, experience, and opportunities, and one who thought exactly as he did. The known events in Dr. Mitchell's life dovetail too closely with the preparation of these works to be assigned to chance. The part played by the publisher of *American Husbandry* was too trivial to deserve serious consideration as far as the question of authorship is concerned, although a critical study with a view to determining additions made by him might be valuable.

The evidence submitted by Dr. Carrier and outlined above is, as Dr. Carrier himself admits, not absolutely conclusive. In fact, several reasons lead one to believe that Mitchell was not the author. In the first place, the lapse of seven years between Mitchell's death and publication of the book weighs heavily against him. Were he the author, the delay in publication could not, it would seem, be explained by his inability to find a publisher. A botanist of repute, member of the Royal Society, maker of the Mitchell map, and well known to prominent persons in Britain both in and out of the government, anything he might write would be unlikely to go begging for a publisher. Moreover, the great interest in England in the colonies and in their relation to the Empire between the close of the Seven Years War and the American Revolution would, in all probability, make any London publisher or bookseller eager to have this manuscript. There is of course the possibility that if Mitchell were the author, he may have completed the manuscript just before his death and that his relatives or executors—if he had any—either did not immediately find the manuscript, or, finding it, did not realize its importance.

No one who carefully examines *American Husbandry* will seriously doubt that Dr. Carrier is correct in stating that the book has the appearance of being the work of a compiler. It abounds in quotations, some of considerable length. Dr. Carrier's argument that in quoting frequently from his *Present State* Mitchell was merely covering up his own part in the preparation of *American Husbandry* does not seem to be of particular weight. Whoever prepared these volumes cited and quoted other authors as well as Mitchell. Excerpts from the writings of Arthur Young, for example, appear no less frequently in the pages of these two volumes than do those from Mitchell's writings. In this connection it is important to note that no fewer than seven of the quotations borrowed from Young's writings were taken from his *Political Essays,* which were not published until four years after Mitchell's death. It is also to be remembered that reference is made to approximately a dozen works not written by either Mitchell or Young—including *Account of European Settlements, Candid and Impartial Considerations on the Nature of the Sugar Trade,* and Peter Kalm's *Travels*—although these references are less frequent than those to works of Mitchell and Young. Would not Dr. Carrier's explanation of the author's reason for hiding his connection with the preparation of the work apply equally well to Arthur Young or to the other authors cited?

Nor does Dr. Carrier's recourse to a comparison of literary styles prove very much. As Dr. Carrier himself says, the task of identifying anonymous authorship by this method is not always easy. Especially is this true when we know that, during the quarter of a century preceding the outbreak of the American Revolution, anonymity among British writers was quite fashionable. Mitchell was not the only one to hide his identity. Furthermore, during these years a great deal of literary compilation prevailed with the result that several writers obtained their materials from the same sources, even to the extent of copying the same mistakes. Recourse to parallelism, therefore, is in this case somewhat vitiated. Take, for instance, portions of the account of sugar-cane culture in Jamaica as it appears in *American Husbandry* (II, pp. 122–29):

Before I give any account of the expences and profit of the culture, I shall make some observations of the essential faults with which their agriculture in this article abounds. First the preparation of the ground, which is generally fallowed with hoes; though ploughs are used by a few planters, yet the number is inconsiderable. In clearing a piece of fresh ground, they destroy the wood in the manner practiced in the colonies, that is, saw it off and leave the stump to rot in the ground: this effectually precludes the plough. The hoeing culture is more trivial than can easily be credited; for in strength and efficacy it is not comparable to the same operation given by the farmers in England to several crops. Three, four or five hundred negroes have been seen hoeing a piece of forty acres; they cut about an inch deep, sometimes if the soil is loose a little deeper, and at others not half an inch; if the planter attains any depth that approaches that of ploughing, the expence he is at to get it is enormous. Now it should not be forgotten, that the cane roots at a depth proportioned to the loosened mould upon soils that have any tenacity, indeed in very friable sandy loams, or loose hazle mould, the roots strike much deeper than the hoe has been, or they would not thrive at all; and to remedy these evils it is that holing is practiced in which they dig small holes where the canes are to be set, to receive the dung and cane set: but such methods in every article of husbandry throughout the world are bad. . . .

In the preparation of my ground, I would carry the ideas of the improved husbandry of England into that of sugar in Jamaica; I would, in clearing my fresh land, remove all obstacles which might stop the plough, such as roots or large stones; this expence would be well repaid by my successive advantages. I would then plough the fallow of a depth proportioned to that of the soil; in rich lands I would go a foot, but in shallower soils eight inches. . . . (See pp. 418–20 this edition.)

The canes are cut when in full maturity. . . They are cut with hand-bills as close to the ground as possible, then cleared from their leaves, &c., and cut into shorter pieces, from two feet and a half to four feet in length. The chief precaution here is, that the cane be cut off smooth, without hacking the root, which in the dry season is of great prejudice to it. . . . (See p. 416 this edition.)

On cutting the canes they are immediately carried to the mill, usually a windmill, in which, being ground between iron cylinders, the juice is pressed out, and flows through a tube into a vat; thence it is conducted through a pipe into another vat, and after that to the cauldron in the boiling house; it is then boiled, and as fast as any scum arises it is taken off; it runs from this boiler through four or five more, smaller and smaller, in all which it is likewise boiled till it becomes a thick glutinous consistence: when boiling can be carried no farther, a fermentation is raised by lime water, which is subsided by a small piece of butter, after which it is taken into coolers, where it dries and granulates. . . . (See p. 416 this edition.)

After the sugar is dried and granulated, it is put into pots of a sugarloaf form, open at the point, through which aperture the dregs of the sugar falls; these dregs are melasses, or treacle; when it has sufficiently purified itself, it is called muscovado sugar, . . . (See p. 417 this edition).

From the melasses rum is distilled, by means of fermentation in the common method of gaining all other spirits.

Now compare with this the account of the same process as explained by Arthur Young in his *Political Essays* (pp. 278–80):

The whole process is performed by negroes, with hoes; and, upon that plan, the disposition of the plantation into squares, as above mentioned is judicious. But I apprehend a little reflection will point out a more advantageous method of cultivation. Why cannot the grounds be prepared with ploughs? The expence would, beyond all doubt, be reduced greatly; and the plough will command at various depths as the hoe, and even stir the ground as superficially, if that is wanted. But as rich *deep* soils are the best for the cane, there is great reason to believe that deep tillage would be infinitely the most advantageous wherever the staple would admit it. Then I should apprehend, that a disposition of the field into oblong squares would be much better than perfect squares; and particularly for this reason, horse-hoeing upon the principles of the new husbandry in Europe might be substituted for the common hoeing, and certainly would be performed for a tenth of the expence, and more probably would be found more efficacious; but for this purpose the canes must either be planted by a line in regular rows, or in a furrow struck with a plough, which would be equally straight and much cheaper. . . .

The canes are cut with hand-bills, and carried in bundles to the mill, which is now generally a wind-mill; it turns three great cylinders or rollers, plated with iron, set perpendicularly, and cogged so as to be all moved by the middle one. Between these the canes are bruised to pieces and the juice runs down through an hole into a vat, which is placed under the rollers to receive it; from whence it is carried through a pipe into a great reservoir, in which however, for fear of turning sour, it is not suffered to rest long, but is conveyed out of that by other pipes into the boiling house where it is received by a large cauldron; here it remains until the scum, which constantly arises during the boiling, is all taken off; from there it is passed successively into five or six more boilers, gradually diminishing in their size, and treated in the same manner. In the last of these it becomes of a very thick, clammy consistence. They then ferment it with limewater, and subside it with a piece of butter; after which it is placed in a cooler, where it dries, granulates, and becomes ready to be put in pots; it is strained through these, the molasses running off into a receptacle made to receive it, and from that rum is made.

Apparently, neither the author of *American Husbandry* nor Young had ever seen a Jamaica sugar plantation. Young cites the *Art of Making Sugar* as the source of his information and inasmuch as his *Political Essays* were published in 1772 we may infer that if Mitchell were the author of *American Husbandry* then he, in all probability, secured his information from the same source as did Young. On the other hand, the criticism of the hoe method of sugar cane cultivation is so similar in both *American Husbandry* and the *Political Essays* that one might reasonably conclude that the author of *American Husbandry* obtained his information on this particular subject at least, directly from the Young volume. If this be so, then Mitchell was not the author of this portion of *American Husbandry*. Finally, by way of emphasis, we should note Dr. Carrier's comment that in literary style *American Husbandry* was markedly superior to Mitchell's earlier writings.

Some authorities have been inclined to attribute the authorship of these volumes to Arthur Young (1741–1820). At the date of their publication Young was well started on a career which was to stamp him as one of the most gifted and voluminous agricultural writers of all time. A person with a zeal for agricultural improvement, he traveled up and down England, and toured Ireland and France in the interest of agricultural betterment. Critical of what he deemed to be bad practices, he was outspoken in his condemnation of swamps, wastes, common open fields, fallows, small farms, short leases, and antiquated methods. His industry as a writer was amazing; in the short space of three years he produced sixteen volumes, not to mention numerous pamphlets.[2] In the early seventeen-seventies he seriously considered emigrating to America, but did not do so. Evidence is also abundant that he was deeply interested in Britain's overseas domains. In his *Political Essays* volume, for example, almost half of its 550 pages are devoted to "The Present State of the British Colonies." This long essay is subdivided into seven sections:

1. Present State in respect of Situation, Population, Manufactures, and Labour.

2. Staple Commodities.

3. Benefits resulting to Britain from their Settlements.

4. Defects in their Establishment, and the means of remedying them.

5. Security of their remaining under the Dominion of Britain.

6. Comparison between them and the Colonies of other Nations.

7. Of forming New Settlements.

Much that is contained in the *Political Essays* and particularly in the essay on the colonies is strikingly similar, as noted, to the material in *American Husbandry*. Yet no absolute proof has been found which would warrant crediting Young with the authorship of the latter work. If he was the author, he makes no mention of it in his autobiography; nor

[2] Consult *The Autobiography of Arthur Young* edited by M. S. Betham-Edwards (London, 1898); C. S. Haslam, *The Biography of Arthur Young F. R. S. from His Birth until 1787* (Rugby, 1930); G. D. Amery, "The Writings of Arthur Young," in Royal Agricultural Society of England, *Journal*, LXXXV (1924), 175–205.

do his biographers—although one of them, as we shall presently observe, endeavored to clear up this question. As noted elsewhere, when *American Husbandry* was reviewed shortly after its first appearance, the reviewer, as Dr. Carrier points out, appended a footnote to the effect that a correspondent thought he saw in every passage of *American Husbandry* the handiwork of Arthur Young. Neither in this note nor in the review, however, does the reviewer confirm the opinion of the correspondent, though in the last paragraph of his review he does italicize the statement that the author was a "*pretended Yankee.*" A careful examination of all the numbers of the magazine for a two-year period after the publication of the unfavorable review shows no word of rebuttal from Young. In the Department of Manuscripts in the British Museum reposes a mass of unpublished manuscripts by Young on various agricultural subjects. A thorough survey of this material failed to disclose anything that might lead to Young's identification as the author of *American Husbandry*. A number of letters from Young to various people, dated in and about 1775, furnished no clue. A painstaking perusal of several volumes of the Hardwicke Papers also was without avail. In one volume of letters in the British Museum written *to* Young, a passage from one letter is highly suggestive. From this letter written by John Reinhold Forster it is possible that Young may have been encouraged to produce a book on American husbandry. Unfortunately the rest of the correspondence—assuming that there was any—does not appear in the volume and has thus far not been located. The excerpt from the letter follows:

London, Feb. 4, 1771

. . . . I am now publishing a work on the natural History and husbandry of North America translated from Prof. Peter Kalm at Aobo in Sweden. These observations show the Infancy of Husbandry and Cultivation in these climates, which when properly cultivated would do honour to the Mother Country and be at the same time useful to America and to Old England. I do not doubt you are best capable to superstruct upon these observations of my Author, the best Instructions for the Improvement of your Fellow-Subjects beyond ye Atlantic, who will be desirious to receive them as benefactions, what they really are. In this view I take the liberty to recommend you my Publication and am with the greatest Esteem,

Sir, . . . &c

Jno. Reinhold Forster

The book to which Forster refers is evidently Kalm's *Travels into North America,* which appeared, in Forster's translation, in 1772. *American Husbandry* quotes from Kalm's book once or twice, notably in Volume I, pages 132–34 [this edition, pp. 106 ff.].

In a further effort to ascertain whether the author of *American Husbandry* was Young, I went through *Notes & Queries* in the British Museum. In Series 9, Volume VII, page 508, I found the following note:

American Husbandry. Can anyone inform me if a work entitled as follows, a copy of which is in the British Museum Library [Number 43. C. 20, 21] is by Arthur Young? If not, by whom was it written?

[Then follows title, date &c. of book.]

The reference in Sabin's Dictionary of Books Relating to America indicates Arthur Young as the author of this work, which, though purporting to be by "An American" was very evidently written by an Englishman. The query has been put to me by the Sub-Librarian of the Cornell University Library, Ithaca, New York.

M. Betham-Edwards.

Unfortunately, not a single letter appears in reply to this appeal. Nevertheless the evidence in support of Young as the author of these two volumes seems to be more convincing than that advanced in favor of Mitchell.

It may well be that the author was neither Mitchell nor Young. Interest in the colonies and the stimulus for agricultural improvement, both of which were characteristic of eighteenth-century England, gave rise to a voluminous literature, much of it anonymous in character. Among the many writers who were concerned with both of these problems during the ten-year period ending in 1775 were Dr. John Campbell and the kinsmen, Edmund and William Burke. Campbell, a prolific writer, published much of his material anonymously. His memoir entitled *Candid and Impartial Considerations on the Nature of the Sugar Trade; the comparative importance of the British and French islands in the West Indies; with the Value and Consequences of St. Lucia and Grenada truly stated* was published in London in 1763 without his signature. This work, a classic in the field of colonial literature, not only sets forth the value to the mother country of colonial holdings in general and the sugar islands in particular, but embodies one of the clearest statements of eighteenth-century philosophy regarding the relations which should exist between a metropole and its outlying possessions. Broadly considered, the same philosophy pervades *American Husbandry*. The contention, however, that Britain was not in danger of losing her American colonies so long as there was fresh land which settlers might open and thus keep out of commerce and manufacturing is much more in keeping with Arthur Young's *Political Essays* than with anything that Campbell wrote. Two other works by Campbell, namely, *A Treatise upon the Trade of Great Britain to America* (London, 1772), and *A Political Survey of Great Britain* (2 vols., London, 1774), devoted much space to Britain's overseas possessions. Moreover, in March, 1765, Campbell was appointed His Majesty's agent for the province of Georgia, an office he held until his death ten years later. The source of the material in *American Husbandry* relating to Georgia is based upon letters from unknown planters. These letters may have been addressed directly to Campbell in his capacity as agent. The fact that he died in 1775—the year *American Husbandry* appeared—and that his biographers agree his health was impaired and his death hastened by the hardship of preparing *A Political Survey of Great Britain* and its cool reception by the public, would seem to rule him out as "An American."

Evidence that the author may have been either Edmund Burke or his kinsman, William Burke, is very slight. In 1757 Edmund Burke published *An Account of the European Settlements in America*. Although there is proof that he contributed a great deal to this book in its final form, he himself admitted that it was written by his brilliant but somewhat erratic cousin, William Burke.[3] Neither Edmund nor William Burke visited America, though William held the office of secretary to Guadaloupe in 1762 pending peace negotiations between England and France. Edmund Burke, however, did at one time consider coming to the New World, for in a letter to R. Shackleton, under date of August 10, 1757, he speaks of himself as having been "sometimes in London, sometimes in remote parts of the country, sometimes in France, and shortly, please God, to be in America."[4] Richard, a brother of Edmund Burke, visited the West Indies and speculated in land in St. Vincents. But a careful examination

[3] See James Boswell, *Letters Addressed to J. W. Temple* (London, 1857), p. 318.
[4] Edmund Burke, *Works* (London, 1837), I, 17.

of the writings of these three men fails to give a single clue that any one of them wrote or directly inspired the compilation of *American Husbandry*.

A final attempt to identify the author by tracing his contract with Bew, the publisher, has also been without avail. Apparently none of Bew's letters or papers found their way into the manuscript division of the British Museum. Bew appears to have been one of the first booksellers to move to Paternoster Row. From there he published in 1774 *The Ambulator*, a guide book to the environs of London. *The Ambulator* seems to have been his most successful venture as he brought out a third edition in 1787. However, the fifth edition, in 1793, no longer bears Bew's name but is "Printed (by Assignment from the Assignees of J. Bew) for Scatcherd and Whitaker, Ave Marie Lane. 1793." Bew died therefore between 1787 and 1793. He published a number of religious and political pamphlets, mostly anonymous, but does not seem to have issued any work which at the time was regarded as outstanding.

Though the methods of historical detection have failed thus far to identify its author, *American Husbandry* will, in all probability, continue as the principal source of information concerning one of the leading economic activities of colonial America.

AMERICAN HUSBANDRY

CONTAINING AN ACCOUNT OF THE

SOIL, CLIMATE,

PRODUCTION AND AGRICULTURE

OF THE

BRITISH COLONIES

IN

NORTII AMERICA AND THE WEST INDIES

WITH

Observations on the Advantages and Disadvantages
of settling in them, compared with

GREAT BRITAIN AND IRELAND

BY AN AMERICAN

IN TWO VOLUMES

VOL. I

LONDON
Printed for J. BEW, in Pater-noster-Row
MDCCLXXV

CHAPTER I

NOVA SCOTIA

Soil and climate of Nova Scotia—Agriculture—Fishing—Lumber—State of the settlers—Islands of Cape Breton and St. John—Observations

TO JUDGE the climate of Nova Scotia[1] by the latitude would lead any person into the most egregious mistakes. Between 44 and 50 degrees of latitude in Europe we find some of the finest and most pleasant countries in this quarter of the world; but in Nova Scotia the case is very different. The winter lasts seven months and is of a severity that is dreadful to new comers, the deepest rivers are frozen over in

---

[1] Nova Scotia has an area of 21,428 square miles. It has an annual rain fall of about 44 inches. Despite its severe winters its growing season is long, the climate being tempered by the proximity of the ocean and the Bay of Fundy. Originally a place of French settlement, it was in 1621 granted by James I, under the name of Nova Scotia, to Sir William Alexander who proceeded to settle a small Scottish colony there. The region was restored to the French in 1632 and by 1713, when it was transferred to the English by the Treaty of Utrecht, it had a population of 2,500, almost entirely French. By 1755 the number had risen to 10,000. In that year the fanaticism accompanying the French and Indian War expressed itself in the English expulsion of nearly 7,000 of these peaceful farming people from their land and homes. They were distributed along the Atlantic Coast from Maine to Georgia. Because of limited transportation, the men were forced to go first, their families being left to follow later. Many tragic cases of separation of loved ones ensued. The exodus of these French families has been immortalized in Longfellow's *Evangeline*. See J. B. Brebner, *New England's Outpost, Acadia, before the Conquest of Canada* (New York, 1927), and A. G. Doughty, *The Acadian Exiles* (Toronto, 1916). [All numbered notes have been added by the editor.]

one night, so as to bear loaded waggons; the snow lies in some places ten feet deep, and upon level tracts it has been known to be six feet deep: the inhabitants are shut up in their houses, and except in the towns, lead a miserable life; are almost in as torpid and lifeless state as the vegetables of the country; much of the summer is spent in laying in fuel for the winter, and brandy and rum are then the greatest luxuries the people indulge in. Such a degree of cold as is then felt benumbs the very faculties of the mind, and is nearly destructive of all industry. When this severe winter goes, at once comes a summer (for they have no spring) of a heat greater than is ever felt in England. The snow is presently melted, and runs in torrents to the sea; the ground is thawed, the trees are presently in leaf, and the little husbandry here practiced is then begun. But what is almost as bad as the extremes of heat and cold, are the perpetual fogs, which render the country equally unwholesome and unpleasant; and, what is peculiarly provoking to the inhabitants, last far into summer. Such is the climate; it is bad almost in excess; but we are not to imagine that it banishes husbandry, which might be the first conclusion of such as were unused to northern latitudes.

The soil varies greatly: in many parts it is thin and gravelly on a bed of rock; for many years this was what they endeavoured to cultivate, but ill success taught the inhabitants a change which has proved very advantageous. They fixed[2] in the salt marshes on the Bay of Fundy, which, although they required a very expensive drainage, yet, from the fertility of the soil, repaid the farmer much better than other tracts gained with much less difficulty. The soil in these marshes is a white or blue clay, mellow when in culture and marly; if

[2] That is, settled.

the water is well conveyed off, it is capable of producing great crops, being suitable to the heat of the summer. But the expence of getting this land is not small; the sea is to be dyked out, those dykes are to be kept in repair, and the temporary flashes[3] conveyed off. Further, only the line next the coast is of value, as that only has the benefit of harbours for boats and schooners, and for carrying off lumber for the West Indies. Most of the advantageous tracts were patented several years ago; but the lotts change hands often, and at present many of them are to be sold cheap enough, though under culture.

An idea of their management may be gained from the following particulars: upon the settlers first going[4] they fix upon a piece of marsh, with an adjoining one of woodland, seldom less in the whole than from five hundred to eight hundred or a thousand acres: if the marsh is already banked, they pay an annual tax for that work; if not, they must execute it before any profit can be made. They build the house on the edge of the woodland; a work that costs nothing in materials from the plenty of wood, which is fine, consisting generally of oak, pine, or black birch: but all the trees are grubbed,[5] which makes the labour heavy.

Three years are nominally given to settle the tracts assigned; but this is not strictly adhered to, but extended by favour to six or seven. After ten years a quitrent[6] is paid to the king of two shillings for every fifty acres; also a covenant

[3] Streams of water.

[4] "First going" is here used in the sense of "arrival."

[5] Dug up by the roots.

[6] A fixed rent. In feudal times it was payable by a freeholder or copyholder to his feudal superior in commutation of services. In British North America the quitrent was modeled upon English precedent. See B. W. Bond, *The Quit-Rent System in the American Colonies* (New Haven, 1919).

entered into of planting two acres with hemp of every fifty taken up: the planters are kept to this article, but with very little effect, for the climate is utterly improper for that production.

The marsh land is fine, and wants little more after draining but to set the plough to work for sowing wheat: it is all covered with a short but thick and spongy moss, which they plough in, and on one ploughing harrow in their wheat. This work they perform as soon as the weather breaks, and the snow is all gone; they do it in a very clumsy manner, attending not the least to their lands being laid neat and regular. In September the corn[7] is ripe: they usually mow it, and the crops they get, notwithstanding the soil being good, scarce ever amount to middling ones in England. I have been assured that two quarters[8] of bad wheat in quality are a great crop. They have hardly any idea of fallowing,[9] but in the succeeding year plough up the stubble for another wheat crop, which they continue as long as the land will yield it, and then leave it to recover itself, sometimes, however, changing for beans. The woodland, when cleared, they plant with pease, potatoes, cabbages, &c. the latter production is very useful to them, [as] they keep under the snow in winter very sound.

As to inclosures, they have only a ring fence, and one or two near the house; not always that; sometimes none but what parts their marsh land from the woods. Cattle, in sum-

[7] As used here "corn" means grain or kernel or wheat.

[8] A quarter equals eight bushels.

[9] Fallow land is land ordinarily used for crop production but which is plowed and not seeded for a season. Fallowing was regarded as an extremely sound method of allowing the land to rest and thereby regain its fertility and vigor. It was also used as a method of conserving moisture and of killing weeds. In modern agricultural practice rotation of crops is often substituted for fallowing. While fallowing helps conserve moisture, it is considered wasteful of humus and nitrogen.

mer, are turned into undrained marshes and the woods, and in winter are three parts starved.[10]

That I may give as clear an idea of this management in all its relations as I can, I shall insert the expences of settling the plantation of Reeves's on the Bay of Fundy, as it was put into my hands by a gentleman on whom I can depend.

	£.	s.	d.
Freight, &c. of five persons from England .	105	0	0
Patents, fees, &c. for nine hundred acres .	37	8	6
Dyking	172	0	0
Building the house, barns, boat-houses, &c.	67	10	0
Stock of the farm	70	0	0
Grubbing two hundred and thirty acres of wood-land, at 25s.	287	5	0
Seed, and putting in the crop	52	0	0
A schooner, seventy tons, at 40s.	140	0	0
A shallop	26	8	0

[10] There is general agreement today that Nova Scotian agriculture on the eve of the American Revolution was pretty haphazard and slovenly. Two substantial Yorkshire farmers who visited the region in the early seventeen-seventies found its farmers "in general, ignorant, indolent, bad managers"; nothing, they reported, "can be said in favour of the inhabitants, as to their management in farming. They neither discover judgment or industry. Such of the New Englanders, into whose manner and characters we particularly inspected, appeared to be lazy, indolent people. In general, they continue in bed till seven or eight o'clock in the morning; and the first thing they do, after quitting it, is to get a glass of rum after which they prepare for breakfast, before they go out to work, and return to dinner by eleven. They go out again about two, and at four return to tea. Sometimes they work an hour or two after, and then return home, both masters and their servants, amongst whom there seems to be no distinction; and you can scarce know one from the other." J. Robinson and T. Rispin, *A Journey through Nova Scotia* (York, 1774), p. 36. This complaint of the class-conscious European who had cultivated expensive land intensively against the lavish, careless exploitation of cheap land which characterized North American agriculture, occurs repeatedly in the literature of this period. See J. B. Brebner, *The Neutral Yankees of Nova Scotia* (New York, 1937), pp. 138–46, for a scholarly account of Nova Scotian agriculture during the eighteenth century.

	£.	s.	d.
A whale boat	10	10	0
Netts, lines, twine, and sundries	98	15	0
Seamen's wages for a season	27	8	6
Bread, seventy hundred, at 15s.	52	10	0
Pork, three barrels, at 50s.	7	10	0
Beef, six barrels, at 40s.	12	0	0
Arms and amunition	26	0	0
Furniture and sundries	156	0	0
	1,348	5	0

The annual produce after a few years was calculated at:

Six hundred quintals[11] of cod fish, at 14s. . .	420	0	0
Mackarel and shads, sixty-seven barrels at 20s.	67	0	0
Jamaica fish, twenty-two quintals, 9s. . . .	9	18	0
Refuse ditto, eighteen quintals, at 6s. 6d. . .	5	17	0
Ship timber and lumber	63	0	0
	565	15	0

It is much to be regretted, that the annual expenditure was not known; but if the high price of labour is considered—the wages of the fishermen—the repairs of the vessels—nets—implements — ammunition — wines — rum — tea — sugar, and other luxuries, &c. all these articles would certainly make a considerable deduction from this annual product. As to the products of the land, they are more than consumed at home. Can any unprejudiced person suppose that the sum of thirteen hundred pounds might not be expended on waste lands in Great Britain to much better advantage? I will not so far anticipate the subject as to calculate here, but most assuredly we may determine that, in point of *profit*, such a sum might

---

[11] A weight of one hundred pounds. In Great Britain where the long ton of 2240 pounds legally prevails, the quintal equals one hundred twelve pounds or a hundredweight.

be more beneficially expended in British husbandry than in that of Nova Scotia.

I say, in point of *profit,* as to that of pleasure, there are other circumstances to be considered, which are material; these particularly concern the great plenty of game in the country, and the general freedom of all sporting and fishing. It has been asserted, and not upon bad authority, that a boy of twelve or fourteen years of age, with his gun, would maintain ten or twelve in family the year round, pork and bread excepted. Two boys have been known to catch above two hundred hares in one winter with twine snares. Six boys, in three canoes, shot, in four days, one hundred and fifty wild geese, and four hundred black ducks. To this may be added, that eels are in the little rivers so plentiful that they keep immense quantities of them frozen for winter provision.

These particulars, indeed, indicate not only pleasure, but also a considerable degree of profit; for a country which will admit of such circumstances must yield no trifling advantages in housekeeping: and however insignificant such a point m[a]y seem in a general account of a country, yet is it of importance in the eyes of those who quit their own to settle in America. In Britain, the game laws are so strict that unqualified persons must give up all thoughts of the pleasure of shooting and fishing, as well as the advantage in feeding their families, or be liable to severe and infamous penalties;[12] and

[12] Game legislation in England may be divided into three periods. The first dating from early times and regulated by the Forest Laws, confined the rights of hunting and fishing to the King and his favorites; the second, during which the famous Game Laws replaced those of the forest, admitted the owner of the soil to the pleasures of the chase on his own estate; the third, ushered in by the Game Act of 1831, repealed a large number of earlier statutes and destroyed the seignorial monopoly. As long as the landed interests were protected in their seignorial rights, the mass of the English population were legally debarred from hunting and fishing. See

that this monstrous contrast sends no trifling number of people to the colonies I have not a doubt.

In the preceding accounts the reader finds that the whole
product of the new plantation (and that a considerable one)
consists in fish and lumber. It is remarkable, that without the
fishery the inhabitants of this colony would starve; their husbandry is insufficient to feed them; a circumstance strongly
characteristic of the merit of Nova Scotia as a colony. In this
respect the farmers somewhat resemble the inhabitants of
Devonshire, Dorsetshire, and Cornwal[1], before the northern colonies almost beat the mother country out of her share
of the fishery; a very great portion of the English Newfoundland fishery was carried on by little farmers on the above-
mentioned coasts, who went out as soon as their spring
feed[ing] was over, and returned before harvest: but in Nova
Scotia it is the principal dependance of the people for their
subsistence; and the only sale by which they can supply themselves with manufactures and other necessaries.

Their other export is lumber to the West Indies, but of
this the whole province does not send out more than sells for
five thousand pounds, and sometimes not so much. A part of
the winter season is applied to cutting and sawing trees, but
from the severity of the season the progress made in this work
is inconsiderable, and yields no great profit to the farmer. The
distance of those islands, with the vast superiority of the more
southern colonies in climate for the winter execution of this
work, lessen the profit of the Nova Scotians greatly.

Neither the fishery nor the export of lumber prove advantageous enough to render the settlers comparable in ease
and wealth to the people of New England, New York, &c.

R. M. Garnier, *History of the English Landed Interest* (London, 1893),
II, 467–72.

or, I may add (and this is what I mean particularly to in-
culcate) to the same class of men among our farmers in
Britain; except in the articles, not immaterial I allow, of
shooting and fishing: but when the difference of climate is
considered; the agreeable and healthy life which is lead even
in winter in England; the friendly society enjoyed by our
lowest classes of farmers in our country towns and village
alehouses, upon market days and other meetings—the goodness of our roads, and the security of living, what can tempt
any that feel such advantages to leave them in pursuit of
imaginary happiness in the woods of Nova Scotia? Where the
winters are miserably severe, where society is scarcely any
where to be found—without a road in the country—and where
a hostile race of Indians, till very lately, rendered the whole
colony unhappily insecure. But the great superiority remains
to be mentioned: promotion,[13] if I may so express myself, is
cheaper in England; for it ap[p]ears from the preceding
calculation, that a much larger sum is necessary to go to, and
settle, with any advantage in Nova Scotia, even on the smallest scale, than would be sufficient to stock a good farm in
England. The fishing apparatus is expensive; and if that
employment is neglected, the most profitable branch in the
country is lost: the planters must degenerate into mere tartars,
without a commodity for sale wherewith to buy manufactures.
Let these circumstances be considered, and I think it must be
apparent that many of the emigrants who go to Nova Scotia
with a view to practice a husbandry, &c. more profitable than
that of Europe must find themselves miserably deceived.

What sort of a country must it be where government is
forced to give a bounty on raising corn to keep the people
from starving? Yet this is the case with Nova Scotia. On all

[13] Establishing one's self in business or as a farmer.

wheat raised it is one shilling a bushel; on barley, oats, and pulse,[14] nine pence, and on roots six pence.

Relative to the islands of Cape Breton and St. John I must observe that the former has only a few plantations made by connivance by fishermen, merely for the convenience of its situation for the cod fishery. But the island of St. John was granted to some well known noblemen, since the peace,[15] with a view to colonize the whole: the scheme was originally formed by the late Earl of Egmont; but he did not live to see any success attend the plan, which yet was laid as well as most could be for such climates, and the execution begun with great spirit, at an expence that would have brought into culture no inconsiderable tract of waste in England or in Scotland; and that the success would have been greater and infinitely more beneficial at home than in America, cannot for a moment be doubted. Several hundred of settlers have been fixed there, yet they are at present supplied with food from New York: instead of a beneficial system of pasturage and planting hemp, they have already, like all these northern colonists, taken to the fishery as the only means of paying for the necessaries of life, in direct contradiction to the designs of their patrons. This is, and ever will be, the consequence of colonizing in such northern latitudes, where agriculture must ever be carried on with feebleness; where the climate is to the last degree rigorous; and where every spot is inhospitable and frigid. To plant colonies in such situations is acting contrary to every rational idea of colonization.

[14] Pulse is the name used for any leguminous plant and its fruit, such as peas and beans.

[15] The Peace of Paris (1763) by which France ceded to England all of Canada and all the region east of the Mississippi. France retained only two insignificant islands—St. Pierre and Miquelon—on the coast of Newfoundland for drying fish. See C. P. Nettels, *The Roots of American Civilization* (New York, 1938), pp. 590–92.

I am sensible that the original idea of planting Nova Scotia was not so much upon a plan of *agriculture* as *defence*. The encroachments of the French made settlements and fortresses necessary; and the neighbourhood of Louisburg[16] rendered a safe port, as a retreat for the the navy, indispensable: upon this plan garrisons were necessary; and these could not be supported without an adjacent agriculture. There is something rational in this, but it extends no further than the necessity of the case, and not to the immense expence which the nation has suffered on account of the colony, amounting to considerably more than a million sterling; besides, this argument, since the peace, has no longer any validity, whereas we have acted as if it continued in full force; and after feeling the unprofitable expence of one snowy desart, have planted a second. This conduct would have been excusable had we possessed no other territories in America, but while such immense districts remained uncultivated to the south, it was really inexcusable upon every principle of good policy.

[16] The fortress of Louisburg was located on Cape Breton Island at the northeastern extremity of Nova Scotia. It commanded the rich fisheries off the banks of Newfoundland. It controlled the traffic through the Gulf of St. Lawrence, the Great Lakes, and the northern approaches to the valley of the Mississippi. The strongest fort in the New World prior to the nineteenth century it was held almost continuously by the French from 1713 to 1758 when it finally passed into the hands of the English. Only once during the intervening years had it changed possession. In 1745 New England troops under William Pepperell, a wealthy Maine merchant, had taken this French stronghold in a surprise attack. Much to the disgust of the colonials and particularly the New Englanders, who had long suffered from continued forays from Louisburg, it was given back to France in 1747 by the Treaty of Aix-la-Chapelle. See J. S. McLennan, *Louisbourg from Its Foundation to Its Fall, 1713–1758* (1918).

CHAPTER II

CANADA

*Soil and climate of Canada—Agriculture—Inhabitants—
River St. Lawrence—Nature of the country not yet
settled—Exports—Importance of this acquisition—
Observations*

CANADA is much colder in the winter than Nova Scotia,
which may be accounted for by the distance from the
sea; yet is the climate greatly preferable: the air is clear and
pure, and the inhabitants in general enjoy as good health as
any set of people in all America. That the climate is better
we may likewise gather from the productions; pumpions[1] and
melons, apples and pears, are cultivated in common; whereas
in Nova Scotia, though we cannot say the country is absolutely without them, yet is the vegetation weak in comparison.
In this I speak of the northern part of Canada about Quebec;
for as to the south of it, in the neighbourhood of Montreal,
it is far more mild, as appears by several plants commonly
found there and to the south, which will not live at Quebec.

The north-west wind blows, through winter, with a severity
that is scarcely credible: it plainly comes through all walls
that are not very thick; a candle is blown out when held
against a wall that is only a brick and a half thick: all the in-
side of such walls are covered with snow blown through, on
the side against the north-west; and the walls must be of a

[1] Pumpkins.

vast thickness, at the same time that the house is well sheltered by wood and hill, for people within not to feel the wind
blow on them. This dreadful north-west [wind] is felt
throughout the continent, even to Charles Town, in South
Carolina; and it has been absolutely asserted that it has blown
over the whole Atlantic ocean, and been felt in Europe. It
is this wind which renders the climate of all North America
so peculiar that no other is similar to it. Hence, arises the
severe frosts felt there in such southern latitudes that the like
is never known in Europe. Sharp frosts are sometimes felt
in Florida, in latitude 30, which is that of Egypt and
Morocco. This is owing to the north-west winds. They acquire
their extreme coldness from the immense extent of snowy
continent over which they blow, possibly from the North pole,
whereas the continent of Europe and Asia ends in latitude 75,
an open sea being to the north. This has been well explained
by a late writer, from whom, candour demands I should
acknowledge, that I borrowed the hint.*

This wind in Canada is more severe than in Nova Scotia,
the snows are also as deep and as universal, but the air is clear,
being free from the fogs which render the latter country so
extremely disagreeable. The winter is not, however, absolutely without employment; wrapt up well in furs, winter
expeditions are undertaken, and sawing and cutting lumber
go on, though not with near such alacrity and effect as in the
more southern colonies, where the workmen are employed as
regularly in that season as in summer.

The soil in Canada is of two sorts, the stoney, and the pure
loam, or mould without stones; both are cultivated, but the
latter is much the best; it is black or reddish, and is certainly
as fine land as any in the world; and were it in a more favour-

* Dr. Mitchel's *Present State of Great Britain and North America*. [All
notes indicated by symbols are in the original text. Ed.]

able climate would yield as rich productions. There are vast
tracts of it in Canada which would, in many parts of England,
let at twenty-five shillings an acre, but here are uncultivated;
all the settlements and farms in this country being only on the
banks of the rivers, principally on that of St. Lawrence; the
cultivated country is only a narrow slip on each side the river,
scarcely any where half a mile broad, unless it spreads on
account of other streams that fall into the principal one. In
some places, however, the cultivated country is some miles
broad, particularly near the three towns.

Respecting the vegetable productions of this colony there
are found almost all the useful plants that are cultivated in
Scotland, and many that succeed better in England than in
Scotland. The common crops are wheat, barley, rye, and oats;
several sorts of peas and beans; many sorts of roots, particularly carrots, parsnips, and potatoes, but the latter are not
in plenty, from the French not much affecting them. Many
of the farms have an orchard, though not so commonly as in
the old English colonies to the southward: apples, pears, and
plums succeed well; but peaches they get with difficulty, nor
are they of a good flavour: mullberries will not grow here.
Walnut trees, carried from France, dye every year to the
root, but shoot out again in the spring.

Their husbandry is very bad; the system is taking a crop
and what they call a fallow, that is, they take a crop of wheat
and after it leave the land at rest for a year, not for ploughing, but that the weeds may grow and be eaten off by the
cattle: this method can arise from nothing but the plenty of
land, for surely common sense might tell them that a field,
answering the purpose of a meadow by the quantity of weeds
on it, must be a strange preparation for corn. If they left it
for ten or twelve years, till the grasses came so thick as to

choak the weeds, it might, when ploughed up, become at once good corn land, as we find in many places is the case in England. In general they let the lands rest only one year, but some who have more land than the rest leave it sometimes for two, three, or four years, before they sow it again: white clover, by that time, comes in great plenty.

No crop gets more than one ploughing, which is in April, after the frost breaks; then all their sorts of corn[2] are sown, wheat as well as the rest, consequently they have only a spring wheat: however, a few farmers have of late years got into the way of sowing the same grain in autumn; they do not thereby get an earlier harvest, but the grain is weightier and better, and the crop more abundant. As soon as the weather breaks, all the ploughs in Canada are at work to get in the corn, waiting very rarely, and but on small spaces of land, for carrying on the manure; and on one ploughing, which is performed with oxen or horses indiscriminately, they sow all sorts of grain and pulse. Their crops are as good as moderate ones in England; from four to six or seven septiers per arpent[3] are commonly gained of wheat, that is, about two or two quarters and a half per English acre: oats yield very large crops, they sow them for their horses and other cattle; barley is a poor crop with them; and peas a very uncertain one, but sometimes they get a fine product of them.

Every farmer has annually a small piece of flax, but it is only for the use of his family: they have none that is good, whether owing to their management of it, or the climate, I know not. They have also a piece of tobacco in every farm, for the family: all smoak it here.

---

[2] "Corn" as used here means grain.

[3] A septier equals about twelve bushels. Arpent is an old French measure of land varying in value with the locality.

They have in all parts of Canada very fine meadows of natural grass, of a fine sort,* with great plenty of white clover; not low marshy spots, but high upland meadows, the soil dry, sound loam; these are great advantages to the farmers; they yield fine crops of good hay which is mown in August.

The country inhabitants of Canada are all little farmers, very few of them having large farms, at least if we give that term only to the land they usually keep in any culture. Villages are rarely met with, and the few there are consist only of here and there a mechanic, or a schoolmaster: they are a chearful, hospitable people, and have behaved themselves with much good sense and politeness to the English that have settled amongst them since the conquest. At Quebec and Montreal they are remarkably gay and social, which indeed is the case in a good measure in most countries that are so cold as to confine the inhabitants to their houses for a long winter; without a social disposition, such winters would be insupportable. They are further a very happy people; yet their enjoyments are by no means numerous, and the whole country lies under two evils which almost entirely prevent increase; the want of communication in winter with the rest of the world; and the want of money for circulation. This affects the whole colony equally, and makes their share of chearfulness an absolute necessary of life.

Was it not for the river St. Lawrence the whole country would be so destitute of communication, as to be next to uninhabitable: but that noble river, which is navigable for the largest ships to Quebec, and every where deep enough for

---

* *Poa Angustifolia.* A large genus of perennial grasses of low growth with copious rootstocks, long, soft, radial leaves forming an abundance of foliage. Excellent pasturage. Common wire grass (June grass), and Canadian and Kentucky blue grass are among the best known species.

all the inland navigation of Canada, quite to the falls of Niagara, is the great channel of communication between the different parts of the country. Indeed Canada is but a narrow slip of cultivated land along the banks of this river, which to such parts answers every purpose that can be wished, of travelling and the conveyance of merchandize, and the produce of the farms to the towns of Quebec, Montreal, and Trois Rivieres, in each of which are regular markets. No slight part of the demand in those markets is formed by the troops who both enliven and enrich the colony.

The unsettled country, which includes all but the banks of the river, is a forest, generally filled with various sorts of pines, oak, birch, &c.; many of the trees are large. In parts of these forests the underwood is thick; in others, there is none at all. The soil in them has the same varieties as in the cultivated fields. Large tracts are excellent, and would, if cleared of wood, produce as good crops as any of the fields already in culture; but there are not inhabitants enough to extend the cultivation; and there are many reasons for this, which I shall mention by and by. I may observe that all that immense country to the south of the river St. Lawrence, which is part of New England and Nova Scotia, has very few tracts in it, by the report of the Indians, which are not capable of cultivation. It forms a square of three hundred miles every way, which is much larger than Great Britain; and consists of forests on a good soil, or rich marshes. Cultivation would improve the climate, drive away the fogs, and make the country much more inhabitable than at present. But such improvements must be some centuries off, and in the mean time the whole will remain, except on the coast and river, a mere inhospitable desart, like Nova Scotia. The southern parts of Canada, north of the great lakes about Niagara, &c. possess

a climate infinitely superior to that tract, and also the line
of country from Crown Point to the river St. Lawrence,
equals any part of North America for fertility of soil, and
agreeableness; at the same time that the climate is so much
superior to that even of Montreal, which I before observed
was preferable to that of Quebec. Were it not for the country
to the south of the lakes drawing away the people, these
territories would soon be cultivated.

For the further information of the reader I shall transcribe
the table of the annual exports from Canada since the peace
of 1763.

Skins . . . . £.	76,000
Whalebone and oil	3,500
12,000 quarters of wheat, at 20s.	12,000
Geneseng,[4] snake root, &c.	3,000
Timber and lumber	11,000
£.	105,500

Which exports, with the import of manufactures, &c. employ thirty-four ships, and about four hundred seamen. But
the wheat has for the last three or four years been at thirty-
two shillings a quarter. As far as the skins can be gained, this
colony will admit of increase, but the common idea is, that
it has for some time arrived at its zenith, as the game, &c.
from which they are taken, rather declines than increases; the
wheat and lumber are the surplus of the colony consumption,
raised by the hands which are fixed in their farms, and from
habit, love of their native country, poverty, want of ability to
move, or other motives, remain in it; but the export I do not
apprehend is likely to increase, because new settlements are

---

[4] Ginseng is an aromatic perennial plant whose roots are used for
medicinal purposes, especially in China. The American species is native to
the areas north of the Ohio River and extending from Maine to Nebraska.

rare, but many families leave the country and move to the southward. This export is all the means which the whole body of the inhabitants have of purchasing manufactures, wines, spirits, India goods, and sugar, excepting alone the expenditure of the military and civil government, a part of which may be reckoned *profit* to the colony, and supposed to go for the same commodities.

But notwithstanding the small prospect of improvement, yet is not Canada to be esteemed a slight acquisition to the British empire. Indeed it is, with the territories on the Ohio, a very important one; and which, with good management on our parts, might be made of much greater consequence, even to the commercial interests of Britain, than the acquisition either of Guadalupe [Guadeloupe] or Martinico [Martinique], supposing there was a necessity of giving up both these islands if Canada was retained; a supposition which may be stated, but which can never be believed. I have read many accounts of North America, in which the importance of this country has been pretty extensively considered, yet did I never meet with a just idea of the main strength of the argument. Dr. Mitchel seems to have understood it, but he wrote in so confused a manner, that it is difficult to gain his meaning.

The most important commercial interest of Great Britain is the supplying her colonies with manufactures, in exchange for their staple commodities. This trade, far the greatest that is carried on by England, depends on the colonies having room, not for common husbandry and farming, but for raising immense quantities of staples, lumber, &c. to enable them to pay for the British manufactures; a sort of agriculture which we shall by and by find requires very different *room* from the husbandry of Europe, being incompatible with a country that is fully, or even half peopled. It further depends on this plenty of land being also great enough for every person without much difficulty to become a planter or farmer; for if such a difficulty arises, the overplus of population must betake itself to common labour, which at once establishes manufactures, for people will not starve, and if they cannot have employment in one thing they must in another; but, on the contrary, while land is very plentiful no manufactures (further than for private use, which should not go by that name) can be fixed, because labour must be immoderately dear, where every man may with so much ease become a little farmer.

Now what I would deduce from this circumstance is that the French policy in hemming in our colonies to a narrow country along the sea coast by that well known chain of forts which they had built quite from Crown Point to New Orleans, was admirably calculated for the absolute destruction of all our settlements, as *colonies supplied by Britain with manufactures*, for they cut off the increase of plantations so effectually by their forts and the incursions of their Indians, that some hundred thousand people were, at the opening of the war, deprived of their agriculture, and would in a few years have all become manufacturers for sale, had not the evil been destroyed. And if a different event of the war had taken place to secure them in their encroachments, that evil would have arisen to a magnitude that would have explained in a manner too striking to be doubted, how the possession of Canada might be of more importance than a sugar island; though one exported six times more in value than the other.

It was said, I remember, that confining the French to their just bounds would have had the same effect. But this was weakly urged; for while they had Indians left them, they would always have had it in their power to prevent that necessary extension of the agriculture of our settlements upon which our whole interests in America depend. The Indians the French collected about Fort Duquesne, though near two hundred miles from our settlers, deprived us in six months of near an hundred miles of territory; for so far did our backsettlers quit their habitations upon the cruel excursions of their enemies.

It is therefore plain, that they who rest the comparison of Canada against a sugar island, merely on the ballance of an account of exports and imports, much mistake the matter, since they overlook therein the essential distinctions which form the real importance of this colony. But in the present case there is something further than mere extent and security; for the southern districts of Canada, those of the lakes, down to the Ohio, contain as valuable a territory as any possessed by us in America. The most fertile part of that continent, in a fine climate, and admirably adapted for the production of hemp and tobacco, commodities, I will venture to assert, is of more consequence to this nation than even sugar; and yet I am very far from derogating from the great and undoubted importance of sugar colonies to Great Britain.[5]

[5] The question of whether England at the close of the Seven Years' War (1756–1763) should retain Canada in preference to the rich French sugar-planting island of Guadeloupe and the Spanish island of Porto Rico aroused wide and protracted debate between those who asserted that colonies were chiefly valuable as sources of raw materials, and those who asserted that they were chiefly worth while as markets for English manufactures. The decision to retain Canada resulted in part from the opposition of the British West Indian planters who strongly opposed the acquisition of additional sugar-producing territory lest it destroy their monopoly of the home market. It was also in part the result of the fact that as England was becoming less and less an agricultural and more and more a manufacturing nation, the temperate zone colonies with their rapidly expanding population afforded a better market for manufactured goods than the tropical possessions with their fewer numbers. See C. W. Alvord, *The Mississippi Valley in British Politics* (Cleveland, 1917); W. L. Grant, "Canada *versus* Guadeloupe," *American Historical Review*, Vol. XVII (July, 1912).

CHAPTER III

CANADA

Defects in the agriculture of Canada

THE husbandry practiced in this colony is in many respects so very defective that I think it will not be an impropriety to point out the most material branches of their management in which they act contrary not only to the common ideas of good farmers in England, but also to the dictates of the climate and other circumstances of the country.

First I shall remark that their system is essentially faulty. It is this,

1. Wheat or other grain.
2. Fallow, that is weeds for one, two, or three years.

There is no greater error in farming, whatever may be the country, than taking many successive crops of corn without the intervention of a fallow, or some crop which, from an extraordinary culture while growing, answers the purpose of a fallow; but I shall venture to assert that even this fault is less than the management of the Canadian: the food gained by their cattle is too trivial to mention; but what condition of freedom from weeds can land be in, when the crop is sown only on one ploughing, and the land, after that crop, left to run to weeds for a twelve-month? Yet is this the management of these people.

Let me, instead of such mistaken conduct, recommend to them never to fail of ploughing the land they design for corn[1] in September; the succeeding frosts and snow will meliorate it much; if their plan is to leave it to weeds by way of a fallow after the corn, let them never fail of sowing plenty of white clover seed with the corn: the country in general runs naturally to it; it can never be supposed therefore to fail; but when the ground is left to seed itself, it is three, four, or five years, before a tolerable plant comes; in the management I propose, they would have a rich meadow the first year.

Secondly. Instead of letting the land rest only one year, I would advise them to leave it under clover three or four; during that, or even a longer time, it would constantly improve, until it gained a thick rich turf, after which the ploughing it up for corn would be attended with great advantage, at the same time that the meadow thus gained would pay the farmer as well as the best in his farm. Suppose the white clover left four years, the system would then be

1. Corn.
2. Clover four years.
3. Corn.

But I should propose improvements in the corn years of the system. The Canada farmers are very inattentive to the change of their corn crops, making very little distinction between successive ones of wheat, barley, and oats, and pease and beans; whereas they ought most certainly, according to the principles of the best English husbandry, interchange them by following white corn[2] with pulse, and that again with white corn.

[1] Grain.
[2] That is, white oats. White oats delights in a dry land and does especially well in gravel or sand. In England white oats was considered best for lands subject to quack grass and other weeds. See *A Dictionary of Country Affairs* (London, 1765), Vol. II.

Thirdly, I must remark that our French husbandmen do not properly attend to the winter support of their cattle: the climate agrees very well with cabbages of two or three sorts, turneps, carrots, kale, &c. plants which are hardy enough to stand extremely well the field culture in that climate. These would be of very high advantage in the winter support of their cattle, and would, with the help of a greater quantity of hay (gained by means of clover on their fallows instead of weeds) enable them not only to increase their profit by these cattle, but at the same time answer a purpose equally beneficial in raising manure, a business in which their long winters might be of great efficacy. In this climate, where the soil is so chilled with intense frost, and drenched in snow and rain, it must have a coldness in its nature much demanding that warmth which manure gives, and consequently no business would be more profitable than raising plenty of it. The population of the towns of Canada is insufficient to yield the farmers much assistance in this way; nor indeed would it be of much consequence were this otherwise, unless the countrymen had better ideas of the nature of their business, since they do not carry away near so much from Quebec and Montreal as they might; for want of attention in them, no slight quantities are annually thrown into the river, which is utterly inexcusable considering their having water-carriage to every farm almost in the colony.

Were the ideas of the farmers upon this object of keeping cattle, with a view to raising the more manure, of the nature they ought to be, the articles of winter food for cattle abovementioned, such as cabbages, turneps, and other roots, would be introduced in the arable fields interchangeably with corn, in the manner turneps are in the systems in England and Scotland: this would keep the lands in much better order than they are at present, besides being the means of raising manure and making a greater profit from the increase of cattle. Upon these principles the following system might be recommended to the farmers of this country:

1. Wheat.	6. Cabbages.
2. Pease.	7. Wheat.
3. Oats.	8. White clover.
4. Turneps.	9. White clover.
5. Barley.	10. White clover.

This system for ten years would answer all the purposes of good husbandry—would keep the land clean from weeds—would raise great plenty of winter food for cattle—and improve by their manure the products of corn.

Had I not extended this chapter to a length I did not expect, I should expatiate on other articles of their management, which I have reason to think not a little faulty, particularly in their methods of ploughing and laying their lands, which is done here in a manner more awkward and clumsy than can be conceived in England; also in the way they have of getting in their hay and corn harvest; but these and other particulars may be esteemed too insignificant for particular notice.

CHAPTER IV

CANADA

The agriculture of Canada compared with that of Britain

I AM sensible that the number of emigrants that go from Great Britain and Ireland to Canada is not considerable, nor to be compared with those who every day go to our colonies to the southward, yet as some future advocates, even for the northern settlements may arise—and as a worse country than this, viz. the island of St. John, has lately been attempted to be settled—I think it may prove of use to draw a comparison between the profit and advantages which may be expected from agriculture in Canada and in Britain, that all may, in future at least, know (if they will leave their native country) which are the parts of America that emigrants had better go to.

Much of the happiness and many of the comforts of life among the farmers or planters of any country depend on their raising a sufficiency of saleable products, not only to pay the expences of cultivation, but also to purchase such commodities as they cannot raise themselves; such for instance as many articles of cloathing, furniture, and food, not to speak of luxuries, which hardly deserve that name from the generality of the use. Some idea may be formed of the state of life in Canada from the exports being compared with the population. No list of the inhabitants has been taken since it came under the dominion of Britain;[1] but I have reason to think them not decreased. We are told by a good writer that before the war they amounted to 100,000*.[2] I have already shewn that they export to the amount of 105,000£. which may be called 20s. a head for the people. Now this is the whole amount of the manufactures and commodities which they consume, further than what they grow and make at home; an amount in a country that has only one manufacture (of iron); which shews how slender those enjoyments of life must be which depend on foreign imports; and that such a dependance must be absolutely necessary and essential, any one will see who considers the climate.

But we are further to remember that only about 23,000£. of this export is in the products that can have anything to do with the farmers, viz. the corn and the lumber: the skins and furs, to the amount of 76,000£. are almost all bought of the

* *An Account of the European Settlements in America*, II, 30. [This anonymous two-volume work, now generally attributed to Edmund Burke, was first published in London in 1757. Its popularity led to its publication in several later editions, both in England and on the continent. Although looked upon as the joint production of Edmund Burke and his cousin, William Burke, it is usually accredited to the former, who, however, is said to have referred to himself as merely the reviser of his kinsman's work. —Ed.]

[1] The first Census of the Dominion of Canada was taken in 1871. In the year 1666, however, a Census was taken of the colony of New France. This initial Census was repeated no fewer than fifteen times during the French régime which ended in 1763. From the date of British occupation, a series of less elaborate census reports by colonial governors took the place of these records. Eventually the census reappeared at regular intervals. There was a Census of Canada, for example, in 1765, and others followed in 1784 and 1790. See Canada, Bureau of Statistics, *Sixth Census of Canada, 1921*, "Report on the Census of Population and Agriculture, 1921" (Ottawa, 1924), I, x–xi.

[2] This figure is too high. In 1760 the white population of all Canada was only 62,000. Cf. A. L. Burt, *The Old Province of Quebec* (Minneapolis, 1933), p. 1.

Indians for woollen goods, brandy, guns, and ammunition, consequently a great part of this sum goes to the Indians instead of the Canadians, a circumstance which will reduce the consumption of manufactures and foreign products in Canada to a sum far short of 20s. a head, or even of 10s. and will prove clearly enough that what we have here been calling the enjoyments of life dependant on importation must be confined in a surprising degree.

Examining the affair in this light points out the nature of the country and of its agriculture. Land is in plenty, and so cheap that every man may have as much of it as he can stock or cultivate; but labour must be extravagantly dear, as it is in every country where land is granted to all that will have it. Wood is plentiful; and food of most sorts that are produced by the country, such as fish and fowl, very cheap, and flesh not very dear. In this case we see at once the state of a farmer, or a new settler; he has land, and wood to build him a house; and after he has stocked his farm with cattle, and implements, and feed, he has the product of it in corn and roots to feed himself and family; with fish and fowl for the trouble of taking; his flax, and his family's labour supply linen; and iron being the produce of the country, he may buy it with corn; some coarse woollens are also made, but the quantity is very trifling: there remains for him to purchase rum or brandy, several articles of cloathing, guns, ammunition, parts of household furniture, sugar, tea, wine, and India goods, if he consumes any; and in order to procure these he has no way to gain them but by his share of the export of wheat and lumber, that is 4s. or 5s. per head of his family, supposing the Indians carried off none of the import—but as they take off the most, the share of the farmers must be yet less.

It is very evident therefore that the life and enjoyments of a new settler in Canada must be strangely confined and wanting in what we should call the necessaries of life; but this objection is not of weight with those whose previous state of life was inferior, such as disbanded soldiers, servants, labourers, and some others, such may certainly make a shift to get fixed in a farm, and find in it most if not all the necessaries of *their* life: but even these must be such as are on the spot; for it would answer to none to go thither in order to gain this. When a man receives his discharge in a country where he can have land for nothing, it is his business to take it, for another colony being far more advantageous is nothing to him who may not have money to move himself one hundred miles, instead of five hundred, which may be necessary for him to go.

That the comparison between the number of people, and the exported produce, is, in respect of Canada, a just rule to judge of the consumption of foreign products, &c. will appear from reflecting that in this colony they have no other means of gaining them: a case which is different in our maritime ones, where a trade is carried on, and other means of bringing money into the country besides their mere agriculture.

The circumstance that must keep down this colony, and make it unprofitable to settle in, is the want of a short and regular navigation. At first sight it might be urged, that if 12,000 quarters of wheat are exported, more might also be, and then the farmer would find a sale for all he could raise: but the situation of the colony is such that I should rather suppose those 12,000 quarters [to be] owing to an accidental more than any regular demand—or to the conveniency of loading ships with it going out with furs, &c.—for the colonies to the southward on the coast enjoy a navigation so superior, and are so much nearer to market, that I should apprehend they would entirely undersell the Canadians.

Let it be considered as an universal rule, that agriculture can no where be a profitable employment—or one that will even yield all the necessaries of life—where the farmer has not a regular sale for every thing he raises; for if he possesses not this, he cannot with any advantage increase his cultivation, upon however small a scale it might have been before; nor can he without this scale command the money which is necessary for purchasing those things which his farm cannot produce. This is equally a fact, whether his product be wheat, tobacco, rice, or sugar. A regular market for all he raises is the soul of the farmer.

This is the distinction that must ever be made; in those colonies that have a market for the farmer's productions, he may practice his business with profit. But in those that have it not, like Canada, he can only live; he cannot get money nor can he, if he increases his culture, gain proportionably the comforts or agreeablenesses of life.

From this state of the case, how can it ever be adviseable for any person employed in agriculture in Europe, to leave it for practicing the same art in Canada? Whoever has in England, or Scotland, money enough to pay their passage and expenses to Quebec, to stock a farm, and go thro' the expenditure of the first year, small as it is, might certainly employ that money in farming at home to better advantage: since in the latter case they are in the way of improvement, and may by industry increase their capital while they live comfortably; but in the former, they can gain only a certain point, which is living comfortably, but as to increase or improvement very little is to be looked for. Yet in this we do not exclude exceptions, which there will ever be in all cases; there are certainly men who make money in Canada—but a few instances are not what should, in such an enquiry, be attended to, but the general nature of the country, and the situation of the greater number.

If money is to be expended on the passage, stocking the farm, &c. in which works two or three hundred pounds would very soon be laid out even for a small tract of land, in such case we may readily determine that the money might be laid out to far greater advantage in England, or in Scotland or Ireland: at the same time that we deduce this, we must also allow that there is a case in which Canada may be preferable to England, though not comparable to several other colonies: if a family in Britain have an opportunity of getting a free passage to Quebec, which may happen from more accidents than one;[3] and they have a small sum of money to buy a few cattle and implements when they arrive there, in that case they will be able to get into a business sufficient for their maintenance and support, which they could not be able to do in England. This is a case clearly in favour of Canada, but it is not one that can happen often.

[3] After the Treaty of Paris (1763) the Crown conferred numerous large tracts upon merchants, army officers, and wealthy landowners, all residents of Great Britain. These tracts were located in Canada, Nova Scotia, Florida, and Prince Edward Island. Undoubtedly the new owners in search of opportunities to make their new holdings profitable may have provided free passage for Old World families. See C. P. Nettels, *The Roots of American Civilization* (New York, 1938), p. 610.

CHAPTER V

NEW ENGLAND

Climate of New England—Soil—Present state of the several counties of that province—Agriculture—Observations on the exports of New England

THIS province lies between 41° and 45° north latitude, but like all the territories of America, it must not have an idea formed of its climate by a comparison with the European parallels: that latitude in the latter is the southern parts of France and the northern ones of Spain, countries in which the climate is unexceptionable: but in New England the winter is much longer than it is here, and at the same time severe beyond any thing we ever experience in the sharpest frosts: the summer in heat exceeds that of Spain, and it comes, as it does in most parts of North America, without the intervention of a spring: but what is worse, they sometimes experience, tho' not near so often as farther to the south, sudden changes from hot to cold when the north-west wind blows; but in general the weather is pretty uniform; in both summer and winter the sky is clear and serene, and for months together exhibits a pure azure expanse, without a cloud or speck to be seen. The climate has been vastly improved since the country has been cleared of wood and brought into cultivation. The cold in winter is less intense, the air in summer purer, and the country in general much more wholesome. It is the climate of this province which entirely regulates its agriculture, and therefore should be well attended to; the great heat in summer and the severe frosts in winter, with the north-west winds which blow with such sharpness, these render the culture of common wheat not near so advantageous as that of maize.

The soil of the province differs considerably, as may be supposed in a country of such great extent. The south and eastern parts are the most fertile, such as Massachusets Bay, Connecticut, Rhode Island, and the whole tract that borders on New York, quite to the Lake Champlain. In these territories are found very considerable tracts of fine and rich land. It consists of a black mold on a red loam or clay: of loams, some stoney, but not therefore unfertile; and parts of clay alone which is not their worst land. They have also very good sandy lands, which soil agrees best with their capital production, maize.

New England being the oldest of our American colonies, the best parts of it may be supposed to be granted away or purchased, which is the case; but it is not thence to be apprehended that the greatest part of this large province is cultivated: in the southern divisions the country is well settled, so as for many miles together to have some resemblance of old England, but even in these there are very large tracts of forest left, which are private property and consequently cannot now be patented. The richest parts remaining to be granted are on the northern branches of the Connecticut river towards Crown Point, where are great districts of fertile soil still unsettled. The north part of New Hampshire, the province of Main[e], and the territory of Sagadahock[1] have but few settlements in them compared with the tracts yet unsettled; and they have the advantage of many excellent ports,

[1] Early name for the Kennebec river.

long navigable rivers, with all the natural advantages that are
found in other parts of this province; I should further observe
that these tracts have, since the peace, been settling pretty
fast: farms on the river Connecticut are every day extending
beyond the old fort Dummer,[2] for near thirty miles; and will
in a few years reach to Kohasser,[3] which is near two hundred
miles; not that such an extent will be one tenth settled, but
the new comers do not fix near their neighbours and go on
regularly, but take spots that please them best, though twenty
or thirty miles beyond any others. This to people of a sociable
disposition in Europe would appear very strange, but the
Americans do not regard the near neighbourhood of other
farmers; twenty, or thirty miles by water they esteem no
distance in matters of this sort; besides, in a country that
promises well the intermediate space is not long in filling up.
Between Connecticut river, and Lake Champlain, upon Otter
Creek, and all along Lake Sacrament[4] and the rivers that
fall into it, and the whole length of Wood Creek, are numerous settlements made since the peace, by the Acadians, Canadians, and others from different parts of New England. This
whole neighbourhood is a beautiful country, and possesses as
rich a soil as most in New England. Let me also remark
here that the new settlers in these parts have cultivated common wheat with good success, so that they have more fields

[2] Fort Dummer was erected on the site of what is now Brattleborough,
Vermont, to protect the English settlements of that region against Indian
attacks.

[3] In the upper Connecticut Valley.

[4] Lake George was discovered in 1642, on the eve of Corpus Christi,
by a French Jesuit missionary, Isaac Joques, who gave it the name of
Lac du S. Sacrament, by which it was known till 1755, when William
Johnson called it Lake George, after George II of England. It is 33 miles
long, from three-fourths of a mile to three miles wide, and 300 feet above
the sea. It is 205 feet above Lake Champlain into which it empties over
very rough country. Unlike Lake Champlain, its shores are not suitable for
agriculture.

of it than of maize, which is not the case in the southern parts of New England; to what this difference is owing I have not been informed.

In the province of Main[e], particularly on the rivers which fall into the sea near Brunswic[k], there are many settlements made by Germans who have come over since the war; they are in general in a thriving condition, as most of the settlers are in North America that are well situated for an immediate communication with the sea; ships come very regularly to all the ports on this coast to take in loadings of corn, salted provisions, and lumber for the West Indies; by which means the farmers (who also are engaged pretty deeply in the fishery on these coasts) have a ready opportunity of conveying all their surplus products to a regular market, the great thing wanted in Canada. But still these northern coasts of Main[e] and Sagadahock are under the fatal influence of that freezing climate, which is bad enough in the south parts of New England, but here approaches to the severity of Nova Scotia, though not so much involved in fogs.

The particulars of the husbandry of this province are extremely worthy of attention, because it is as it were between the most northerly colonies and the central ones, which are of an acknowledged merit in climate, &c. The crops commonly cultivated are, first, maize, which is the grand product of the country, and upon which the inhabitants principally feed. It is not however to the exclusion of common wheat, which in a few districts is cultivated with success. It would be useless to give a particular description of this plant, which is so generally known. Its culture has something particular in it, and therefore should be mentioned more particularly. It is a very large branching plant, which requires a great share of nourishment, so as to be planted singly at the distance of four or five feet square; it requires good land, and much dung, if plentiful crops would be gained; and the soil must be kept clean from weeds, by frequent hoeings, besides ploughing cross and cross between the plants: this is practiced only by good farmers, but it is pity it is not universal among all the cultivators of this plant, for none in the world pays better for good treatment, proportioned to the value of its produce. Had Mr. Tull,[5] the inventor of the horse-hoeing husbandry, known it, or rather had he lived in a country where it was commonly cultivated, he would have exhibited it particularly as the plant of all others which was most formed for his method of culture: even common farmers in some parts of New England have been [so] struck with the excellency of the practice of ploughing between the rows of this grain, that they have been presently brought to practice it in common, so that it is now no longer an unusual method. One peck of the feed is the common quantity for an acre of land; and the produce varies from twenty to forty bushels, but from twenty-five to thirty are very generally gained. The expences of this culture per acre have been thus stated:

	£.	s.	d.
Seed	0	0	6
Culture	0	11	8
Harvesting, &c.	0	3	6
Conveyance to market	0	4	6
Sundries	0	2	6
	1	2	8

[5] Jethro Tull (1674–1741), English agriculturist, writer, and inventor, has been called the greatest individual improver of agriculture. He believed in the importance of pulverizing the soil, and the two books in which he advocated the practice, *Horse-Hoeing Husbandry* (London, 1731), and *Horse-Hoeing Husbandry or an Essay on the Principles of Tillage and Vegetation* (London, 1733), revolutionized British agriculture. He also invented a machine drill and made other improvements in farm methods. Cf. T. H. Marshall, "Jethro Tull and the 'New Husbandry,'" in *Economic Historical Review* (1929), II, 41–60.

And the value, straw included, amounts to from 50s. to 4£. sterling per English acre, which is certainly very considerable: but then their management in other respects renders the culture not so cheap as it may appear at first sight, for the New England farmers practice pretty much the same system as their brethren in Canada; they have not a just idea of the importance of throwing their crops into a proper arrangement, so as one may be a preparation for another, and thereby save the barren expence of a mere fallow. Maize is a very exhausting crop; scarce any thing exhausts the land more, and this to so great a degree, that their being obliged to depend on this for their food renders them more than any other circumstance unable to raise hemp and flax in sufficient quantities for exportation, or even for rigging their own ships, and cloathing themselves with linen. Nor have they sufficient quantities of rich land upon which they can practice a management that would include both.

Besides maize, they raise small quantities of common wheat; but it does not produce so much as one would apprehend from the great richness of the soil: this is owing to the peculiarity of the climate, for we have lands in Europe that, to appearance, could bid fairer to produce large crops. But as I before observed, the new settlers in the north-east part of the province have found that wheat is to be raised with no contemptible success.

Barley and oats are very poor crops, yet do they cultivate both in all parts of New England: the crops are such as an English farmer, used to the husbandry of the eastern parts of the kingdom, would think not worth standing; this I attribute entirely to climate, for they have land equal to the greatest productions of those plants. Their common management of these three sorts of grain, wheat, barley, and oats, is to sow them chiefly on land that has laid fallow for two or three years, that is, left undisturbed for weeds and all sorts of trumpery to grow; though at other times they sow oats or barley after maize, which they are enabled to do by the culture they give the latter plant while it is growing: all their corn here is in general sown in spring, from the common idea that the climate will not admit of an autumnal sowing: but this is with exceptions; for of late years some of the more intelligent *gentlemen farmers* have, in various instances, broken through the old methods and substituted new ones in their room. These have, in various parts of the province, substituted the autumnal instead of the spring sowing, and with great advantage. In some parts of Connecticut and Rhode Island, they have introduced the English system of making clovers a preparation for corn; they leave the grass upon the land as many years as it will yield tolerable crops, and then plough it up, and sow wheat, which is found a much better management than the common one. The clover affords good crops of hay once a year, besides an advantageous eatage for their cattle, which is much better than leaving the land to cover itself with weeds.

Summer fallowing is in some parts of the province not an uncommon practice, but it is not executed so well as in England; they give this preparation to land that is pretty much exhausted, and which they design for maize or for hemp, which latter also requires the addition of much manuring. What they produce is good, though not equal to the Russian, or even to that of old England; but its requiring the very best rich lands in the province, and also dunging, prevents them raising even enough for their own use, as their numerous shipping demands large supplies of it. They have been urged by several counties, even to a large amount, to go largely into the culture of hemp, which would certainly be a very national object, since there is no staple that any colony could raise [that] would be more advantageous to Great Britain, or save her the expenditure of larger sums of money.

Flax they raise with much better success, as it does not demand near so rich a soil as hemp; but the more southern colonies much exceed New England, even in this article, for what is there raised is not sufficient for the home consumption of this very populous colony, whereas more to the south they export considerable quantities of flax-seed.

In the best cultivated parts of New England, turneps are introducing in [being introduced into] the field culture, but not in the manner they ought to do. This is an article that demands their attention greatly, but as I shall be more particular on them when I speak of the defects of their husbandry, I shall not enlarge on it here.

Pease, beans, and tares[6] are sown variously through the province, but scarcely any where managed as they are in the well cultivated parts of the mother country. But every planter or farmer grows enough of the food for fattening hogs, for supplying his own family, and [for] driving some fat ones to market. Hogs are throughout the province in great plenty, and very large; a considerable export from the province constantly goes on in barrelled pork, besides the vast demand there is for the fishery, and the shipping in general.

Apples may be mentioned as an article of culture throughout New England, for there is no farmer, or even cottager, without a large orchard: some of them of such extent that they make three or four hundred hogsheads of cyder a man, besides exporting immense quantities of apples from all parts

[6] Name popularly applied to several varieties of the vetch, especially the common vetch.

of the province. The orchards in New England are reckoned as profitable as any other part of the plantation. Among the other productions of this province, I should not forget the woods, which, in the parts not brought into culture, are very noble; they consist of oak, ash, elm, chestnut, cypress, cedar, beech, fir, ash, sassafras, and shumac. The oak is very good, and employed chiefly in ship-building; and the fir yields very greatly for masts, yards, and plank; even the royal navy is supplied from hence with masts of an extraordinary size; and the export of lumber to the West Indies is one of [the] greatest articles in the province.

A large portion of every farm in New England consists of meadow and pasture land; wherein it much resembles the better parts of the mother country. In the low lands, the meadows are rich, yielding large quantities of hay, which, though apparently coarse, is yet much liked by all cattle; the common herbage of many of these is a grass which has made much noise in England under the name Timothy grass.[7] Two or three tons of hay an acre are not an uncommon produce in these meadows. The farmers find great advantage in keeping a large part of their farms for pasturage, as they are thereby enabled to support large herds of cattle and flocks of sheep, which much improve their farms.

The cattle commonly kept here are the same as in Great Britain; cows, oxen, horses, sheep, and hogs; they have large dairies, which succeed quite as well as in Old England; oxen they fat to nearly as great a size; their mutton is good; and the wool which their sheep yield is long but coarse, but they

[7] A perennial, bunchy grass with deep roots and a spiked or panicled head; often called Herd's grass after John Herd who is supposed to have found it growing wild in New Hampshire about 1700 and cultivated it. The name "Timothy" comes from Timothy Hanson who introduced the seed into Virginia in 1720.

manufacture it into coarse cloths that are the common and only wear of the province except the gentry, who purchase the fine cloths of Britain: no inconsiderable quantities of these coarse New England cloths are also exported to other colonies, to the lower people of whom, especially to the northward, they answer better than any we can send them. The horses are excellent, being the most hardy in the world; very great numbers are exported to the West Indies and elsewhere.

It is proper to observe that the unsettled parts of the province, which northwards extend almost from the coasts to the river St. Lawrence, are, with an exception of some open meadows and marshes, one continued and thick forest of the above-mentioned trees, but particularly of pines; and though such parts are not brought to that value and population as the rest, yet are they to be esteemed highly valuable and a great treasure for future exportation, whenever the legislature shall in their wisdom give a bounty sufficient to enable the New Englanders to undersell the Baltic in the ports of Great Britain; an object of infinite importance, than which there is scarcely any in the economy of our colonies that demands more earnest endeavours. This vast forest, which is in size equal to that of the whole island of Great Britain and extends into the greatest parts of Nova Scotia, belongs to the crown, but grants are made constantly to all such persons as apply for land, of such parts of it as they demand, under condition that they settle it in a given time and proportion; also under a reserve of all timber fit for masts for the royal navy. If there is a navigation, and application is merely made for grants in any other parts, the rest of the timber is of no slight value to the new settlers, as it yields a certain price and is a commodity regularly exported from the province.

I shall conclude this account, with a table of the exports of this province since the peace.

Cod-fish dried, 10,000 tons, at 10 £. . . . . £.	100,000
Whale and cod-oil, 8500 tons, at 15 £.	127,500
Whale-bone, 28 tons, at 300 £.	8,400
Pickled mackarel and shads, 15,000 barrels at 20s.	15,000
Masts, boards, staves, shingles, &c.	75,000
Ships about 70 sail, at 700 £.	49,000
Turpentine, tar, and pitch, 15,000 barrels at 8s.	600
Horses, and live stock	37,000
Pot-ash, 14,000 barrels, at 50s.	35,000
Pickled beef and pork, 19,000 barrels at 30s. .	28,500
Bees-wax, and sundries	9,000
Total £.	485,000

Upon this table I must observe that the fishery amounts to 250,900£. of it, or rather more than half the total, which shews what a great proportion of the people of this colony are employed in it. The other half is the produce of their lands, for so both ships and pot-ash[8] must be esteemed. Cattle and beef, pork, &c. came to 65,500£., all the rest is timber, or what is made of timber; this is a proportion that gives us at once a tolerable idea of the colony. We are not from hence to suppose that the great body of the landed interest in this country has, like Canada, no other resource to purchase foreign commodities with, than this small export. The case is very different; New England enjoys a vast fishery and a great trade, which brings in no slight portion of wealth. The most considerable commercial town in all America is in this province; and another circumstance is the increase of population. These causes operate so as to keep up a considerable circulation within the colony. Boston and the shipping are a market which

[8] Wood ashes.

enriches the country interest far more than the above mentioned export, which, for so numerous a people, is very inconsiderable. By means of this internal circulation, the farmers
and country gentlemen are enabled very amply to purchase
whatever they want from abroad.

CHAPTER VI

NEW ENGLAND

*State of the inhabitants—Country gentlemen—Farmers—
New settlers—Lower classes*

THERE is in many respects a great resemblance between
New England and Great Britain. In the best cultivated
parts of it, you would not in travelling through the country,
know, from its appearance, that you were from home. The
face of the country has in general a cultivated, inclosed, and
chearful prospect; the farmhouses are well and substantially
built, and stand thick; gentlemen's houses appear every
where, and have an air of a wealthy and contented people.
Poor, strolling, and ragged beggars are scarcely ever to be
seen; all the inhabitants of the country appear to be well fed,
cloathed, and lodged, nor is any where a greater degree of
independency and liberty to be met with; nor is that distinction of the ranks and classes to be found which we see in
Britain, but which is infinitely more apparent in France and
other arbitrary countries.

The most ancient settled parts of the province, which are
Rhode Island, Connecticut, and the southern part of New
Hampshire, contain many considerable land estates, upon
which the owners live much in the style of country gentlemen in England. They all cultivate a part of their estates;
and if they are small, the whole: this they do by means of
their stewards, who are here generally called overseers: the

rest is let to tenants, who occupy their farms by lease in the
same manner as it is in the mother country, the rents paid
for such farms being the principal part of the landlords income.

Here therefore we see a sketch of one class of people that
has a minute resemblance to the gentlemen in England who
live upon their own estates, but they have in some respects a
great superiority: they have more liberty in many instances,
and are quite exempt from the overbearing influence of any
neighbouring nobleman, which in England is very mischievous to many gentlemen of small fortunes. Further, they pay
what may be almost called no taxes; for the increase of people
and farms is so great that the public burthens are constantly
dividing; besides their being in all instances remarkably low.
This is an advantage to be found no where but in America,
for all the rest of the world groans under the oppressive
weight which bad governments and absolute monarchs have
laid on mankind. They have also the advantage of living in
a country where their property is constantly on the increase
of value. Trade, navigation, fisheries, increasing population,
with other causes, have operated strongly to raise the value of
all the estates under cultivation, whose situation is favourable;
for in proportion as the wild country is taken up good lands
and convenient situations rise in value, till we see they come,
near the great towns, to as high a value as in the best parts
of Great Britain; for near Boston there are lands worth
twenty shillings an acre. Another circumstance in which the
estates of the gentlemen in New England have a great advantage is that of being exempted from the payment of tythes and
[of] rates for the support of the poor, which in Britain make
a vast deduction from the product of an estate. The plenty of
timber and the cheapness of iron and all materials for building

are also advantages to all country estates of a most valuable nature; in England this article, which is what goes under the general name of repairs, swallows up a large portion of rent, and with those already mentioned, and land-tax, leaves him, out of a large nominal rental, but a small neat [net] income.

With these advantages, the New England gentlemen are enabled to live upon their estates in a genteel, hospitable, and agreeable manner; for the plenty of the necessaries of life makes housekeeping remarkably cheap, and counter-ballances the small rents they get for such parts of their estates as they let. This circumstance is owing to the ease of every man setting up for a farmer himself on the unsettled lands: this makes a scarcity of tenants; for those who have money enough to stock a farm, have enough to settle a tract of waste land, which is more flattering than being the tenant of another: one would suppose that such a circumstance would prevent their being a tenant in the country; but this is not the case, low rents and accidents sometimes induce them to live rather than to settle: nor, upon the whole are tenants common in New England; there are more estates that are under the management of overseers than that are let to tenants.

Upon the whole, we may determine that the country gentlemen of New England are in many respects very fortunately situated, and as well stationed in all respects for living comfortably and at their ease as any set of people can be: and this circumstance does not extend merely to the points which I have now mentioned, but to another which deserves attention; it is the growth of timber and increased value of forest land: in New England, any gentleman may have a grant of whatever land he pleases upon complying with the common terms of settlement, which are the grant of fifty acres for every white person fixed on the estate; this, to a person in the country, is a condition so easily performed that they have it in their power to command almost what part of the ungranted land they please: this is an advantage unparalleled in any country of the world except our other colonies. By this means the gentlemen of New England have an opportunity of constantly increasing their estates. Those of fortune erect saw mills on their new grants, by which means they are enabled to make a very considerable profit by the woods at the same time that they lay the foundation of future estates for their posterity.

Some modern writers, very well informed in the affairs of our American colonies, have been particularly attentive to the circumstance of the mortgages which the merchants and others of London have on their estates. This wants an explanation: the country gentlemen of New England are as free from this as any men in the world: it concerns only those who have dealings with London, these are the tobacco and rice planters; but as to the people of property in New England it is not the case with, I may say, any man in the province that is not engaged in trade.

The next class of the country inhabitants of which I am to describe is the farmers; but I must previously observe, that by farmers we are to understand not only the men who rent lands of others, but also the little freeholders who live upon their own property, and make much the most considerable part of the whole province. These are the posterity of former settlers who, having taken in tracts of waste land proportioned to their ability, have died and left it to their descendants equally divided among all the children, by the gavelkind custom,[1] which is prevalent throughout this province. These

[1] A custom of inheritance of lands whereby all the sons of a holder of an estate in land share equally in such lands upon the death of the father. Most of the lands of England were held in gavelkind tenure prior to the Conquest of William in 1066. The custom of dividing lands among the male heirs is still preserved in parts of England, notably Kent.

countrymen in general are a very happy people; they enjoy many of the necessaries of life upon their own farms, and what they do not so gain, they have from the sale of their surplus products: it is remarkable to see such numbers of these men in a state of great ease and content, possessing all the necessaries of life, but few of the luxuries of it: they make no distinction in their agriculture from the tenants of the gentlemen, only live more at their ease, and labour with less assiduity. I should observe that this set of men near resemble a similar class which we knew in England very generally, before our wealth grew so considerable as to destroy all moderation; the great, when grown wealthy as well as powerful, have purchased all such little freenolds as joined their estates, and thereby exterminated one of the most useful sets of men that could be found in this or any kingdom, an event which the law of gavelkind secures the New Englanders from.

These freeholders of small tracts of land which compose the greatest part of the province, have, almost to a point, the necessaries of life and nothing more, speaking however according to our ideas of life in Europe. Their farms yield food —much of cloathing—most of the articles of building—with a surplus sufficient to buy such foreign luxuries as are necessary to make life pass comfortably: there is very little elegance among them, but more of necessaries—a greater capability of hospitality and decent living than is to be found among the few remains of their brethren in England: a class which taxes, tythes, rates, and repairs, with the increased expences of living, have almost driven from the face of the earth. It is not therefore difficult to draw a parallel between the little freeholders of Old and New England: in the former, a variety of causes have almost swept away the race; whereas in the latter they flourish as much as such a set of men can any where flourish.

Before I take my leave of the two different ranks of landlords in New England, let me observe that there is a very material difference between the country gentlemen of this colony, and the mother country, in respect of that branch of luxury which induces men to leave their estates in order to squander the rents of them in a capital. Of late years there are few men in England who call themselves gentlemen that do not at least pay an annual visit to London with their wives and families, and spend as much in one month upon pleasure as they do in the other eleven upon utility: In a word, the country gentry of small fortunes in England starve upon their estates in order to make a figure at the Pantheon and Almack's;[2] and, if their rental is something above mediocrity, will not content themselves without a town house in which to spend the better half of the year. This is a custom which wastes and destroys half the estates in the kingdom, and makes beggars of many families that might with prudent management live genteely and independently in the country.

To enter into a full account of the consequences of this branch of luxury would be unnecessary; suffice it here to observe that the gentlemen of New England are almost entirely free from a profusion which could not but be fatal to their estates. It is very rarely that any families from the country make a winter residence at Boston for the sake of the small degree of pleasure which that capital affords. I know there are instances of it, but in general the thing is otherwise. The country gentlemen live the year round upon their estates,

[2] These were leading places of entertainment in London. Of the two, the Pantheon was perhaps the more famous. It was opened in 1772.

going to town only when business calls them. And thereby they escape an expence which is equally useless and consuming.

The new settlers upon fixing themselves in their plantations enter at once into the class of these freeholders; but from poverty in the beginning of their undertakings fall naturally into a class below them, unless they begin with a considerable sum of money that raises them in the consideration of their neighbours. There are many of these who begin with such small possessions that they are some years before they can gain the least exemption from a diligence and active industry that equals any of the farmers of Great Britain. Such men, although they may be in the road of gaining as comfortable a living as any of the old freeholders, yet rather fall into an inferiority to them; not from the manners of constitution of the colony, but from modesty and the natural exertions of a domestic industry.

Respecting the lower classes in New England, there is scarcely any part of the world in which they are better off. The price of labour is very high, and they have with this advantage another no less valuable, of being able to take up a tract of land whenever they are able to settle it. In Britain a servant or labourer may be master of thirty or forty pounds without having it in their power to lay it out in one useful or advantageous purpose; it must be a much larger sum to enable them to hire a farm, but in New England there is no such thing as a man procuring such a sum of money by his industry without his taking a farm and settling upon it. The daily instances of this give an emulation to all the lower classes, and make them point their endeavours with peculiar industry to gain an end which they all esteem so particularly flattering.

This great ease of gaining a farm, renders the lower class

of people very industrious; which, with the high price of labour, banishes every thing that has the least appearance of begging, or that wondering, destitute state of poverty, which we see so common in England. A traveller might pass half through the colony without finding, from the appearance of the people, that there was such a thing as a want of money among them. The condition of labourers in England is far from being comfortable, if compared with their American brethren, for they may work with no slight diligence and industry, and yet, if their families are large, be able to lay up nothing against old age: indeed the poor laws are very destructive of any such provident conduct. Those laws have the effect of destroying prudence without giving an adequate recompense; the condition of the aged or diseased poor who depend on their support is in many cases lamentable; or at least much inferior to what their own previous industry would have procured them had they not been seduced by the idea of this worse than no dependance. And without extending our reflections to this part of their lives we may determine that the pay they receive for their work does not rise proportionably with the price of all their necessaries; the consequence of which is to them great oppression. On the contrary, the New England poor have no delusive poor laws to depend on: they aim at saving money enough to fix them into a settlement; their industry rarely fails of its end, so that the evening of an industrious life is universally that of a little planter in the midst of all necessaries. The public consequence of this may be easily deduced; it is a very high price of labour, and an amazing increase of people; since marriages must abound greatly in a country where a family, instead of being a burden, is an advantage.

I have more than once mentioned the high price of labour:

this article depends on the circumstance I have now named; where families are so far from being burthensome, men marry very young, and where land is in such plenty, men very soon become farmers, however low they set out in life. Where this is the case, it must at once be evident that the price of labour must be very dear; nothing but a high price will induce men to labour at all, and at the same time it presently puts a conclusion to it by so soon enabling them to take a piece of waste land. By [with] day labourers, which are not common in the colonies, one shilling will do as much in England as half a crown in New England. This makes it necessary to depend principally on servants and on labourers who article[3] themselves to serve three, five, or seven years, which is always the case with new comers who are in poverty.

[3] That is, to apprentice.

CHAPTER VII

NEW ENGLAND

Remarks on the errors in the rural management of New England

CHAPTERS of such a nature ought not to be esteemed impertinent in such a work as this, wherein I particularly mean to explain every thing in my power concerning the country management of America, from its being so little known in England. And it is so of consequence to understand the defects of their agriculture as well as the advantages of it, since we are almost equally concerned in both.

The cultivated parts of New England are more regularly inclosed than Canada, but the planters do not sufficiently attend to this circumstance; many estates and farms are in this respect in such condition that in Great Britain they would be thought in a state of devastation; yet here it all arises from carelessness. Live hedges are common, yet the plenty of timber in many parts of the province is such that they neglect planting these durable, useful, and excellent fences, for the more easy way of posts and rails, or boards, which last but a few years and are always out of repair. This is a negligence and a want of foresight that is unpardonable: but though the new settlers see the inconvenience of it on the lands of the old ones, and find live hedges in many places substituted, yet do they go on with the practice, as if it was the best in the world. In many plantations, there are only a few inclosures about the houses, and the rest lie like common fields in England, the consequence of which is much useless labour in guarding crops from cattle.

Respecting their system, a distinction is to be made between the parts which have been many years in culture, and which, from the neighbouring population, are grown valuable; in these, lands are much better managed than in the frontier parts of the province, where land is of little value and where all the new settlers fix. In the former, the farmers lay down a system which they seem tolerably to adhere to, though with variations. They sow large quantities of maize, some wheat, barley, oats, buckwheat, pease, and beans, turneps, and clover: hemp and flax in small parcels. And these they throw after one another with variations, so as to keep the land, as well as their ideas permit, from being quite exhausted; which they effect by the intervention of a ploughed summer fallow sometimes. When the land has borne corn for several years, till it threatens to yield no more, then they so[w] clover among the last crop and leave it as a meadow for some years to recover itself. But all this system proceeds too much on the plan of the worst farmers of Great Britain, to get corn from their fields as long as ever they will bear it.

Instead of such management, I shall venture to recommend the following system:

1. Summer fallow.
2. Maize.
3. Pease or beans.
4. Barley or oats.
5. Turneps.
6. Wheat.
7. Clover for three, four, or five years.
8. Wheat.

I think such a system is well adapted to their climate and soil. But I am sensible many objections will be made to it, particularly there being twice as much wheat as maize; in this point I am doubtful. They say they cannot grow good wheat; that they *do not* grow good wheat I am sensible, but I attribute it to their throwing it into such systems as this, 1. maize, 2. maize, 3. wheat, 4. oats, 5. wheat, &c. &c. In which case, the wheat may be thin, shrivelled, and husky, without its being the fault of the climate; I am of the opinion, under such culture, it would be the same in Britain. But if in this point I should be mistaken, let the sixth crop be changed for maize. In this system I consider maize, barley, oats, and wheat, as crops that exhaust the land; but pease, beans, turneps, and clover,[1] as such as rather improve than exhaust it, provided they are cultivated in the manner they ought.

Maize is reckoned a great exhauster in New England, and they have some reason for the idea, though I think they carry it too far. The culture is something similar to that of hops; being planted in squares of about five feet, and when up, the plant is earthed into little hillocks: they ought, during the whole growth, to proceed on the exact principle and practice of the Tullian culture of horse-hoeing it incessantly and cutting up such weeds as grow about the plant, out of the reach of the horse-hoes; these are not many, as the plants standing in squares, the horse-hoes work both ways. The misfortune is [that] they do not always keep the plantations of maize clean, or the earth so loose in the intervals as it ought to be, in which case one may easily conceive that the land may be left totally exhausted; but this effect would be vastly lessened by being

---

[1] Peas, beans, and clover, but not turnips, being legumes added nitrogen to the soil. In agriculture various legumes are frequently used as green manures.

more assiduous in the culture, while the crop was growing, [and] absolutely to destroy all weeds, and keep the vacant spaces in garden order: points in which the New England farmers (some few excepted) are not by any means perfect.

Turneps,[2] and other articles of winter food for cattle, they are extremely inattentive to; the great want of the country, which almost prevents their planting hemp in quantities, is the want of dung, and yet they will not take the only method of gaining it, which is the keeping great stocks of cattle, not ranging through the woods, but confined to houses or warm yards. This can only be done by providing plenty of winter food: at present, they keep no more than their hay will feed, and some they let into the woods to provide for themselves, not a few of which perish by the severity of the cold. Great stores of turneps, or other roots, and perhaps cabbages better still, would make their hay and straw go much further, and by means of plenty of litter, for which this country is in many respects very well provided, they might raise such quantities of manure as would double the fertility of all their lands, and give them the command even of hemp in much greater quantities than it is now raised. A more general culture of the various sorts of clovers would also increase the means of keeping cattle, and consequently raising more dung, which is in all parts of the world, whatever may be the climate, the only means of getting good arable crops. Besides, turneps or other roots, cabbages, clover, &c. in their growth and the culture which such receive as stand single, much improve the land, as all good farmers in England have well known these hundred years. Nor have the New Englanders any reason to fear

[2] The turnip is a native of Europe where it has long been used as a stock feed as well as for human food. In America it is cultivated usually as a garden rather than as a field crop.

the having too much cattle for the constant export of beef,
pork, and live stock of all kinds, to the West Indies, which
is a market that will never fail them, let their quantity be
almost what it may. And this mention of cattle leads me to
observe that most of the farmers in this country are, in whatever concerns cattle, the most negligent ignorant set of men
in the world. Nor do I know any country in which animals
are worse treated. Horses are in general, even valuable ones,
worked hard and starved: they plough, cart, and ride them
to death, at the same time that they give very little heed to
their food; after the hardest day's works, all the nourishment
they are like to have is to be turned into a wood, where the
shoots and weeds form the chief of the pasture; unless it be
after the hay is in, when they get a share of the after-grass.
A New Englander (and it is the same quite to Pennsylvania)
will ride his horse full speed twenty or thirty miles; tye him
to a tree, while he does his business, then re-mount, and gallop
back again. This bad treatment extends to draft oxen; to their
cows, sheep, and swine; only in a different manner, as may be
supposed. There is scarce any branch of rural economy which
more demands attention and judgment than the management
of cattle; or one which, under a judicious treatment, is attended with more profit to the farmer in all countries; but the
New England farmers have in all this matter the worst
notions imaginable.

I must, in the next place, take notice of their tillage, as
being weakly and insufficiently given: worse ploughing is no
where to be seen, yet the farmers get tolerable crops; this is
owing, particularly in the new settlements, to the looseness
and fertility of old woodlands, which, with very bad tillage,
will yield excellent crops: a circumstance the rest of the province is too apt to be guided by, for seeing the effects, they are

apt to suppose the same treatment will do on land long since broken up, which is far enough from being the case. Thus, in most parts of the province, is found shallow and unlevel furrows, which rather scratch than turn the land; and of this bad tillage the farmers are very sparing, rarely giving two ploughings if they think the crop will do with one; the consequence of which is their products being seldom near so great as they would be under a different management. Nor are their implements well made, or even well calculated for the work they are designed to perform; of this among other instances I may take the plough. The beam is too long; the supporters ought to be moveable, as they are in ploughs in England and in Scotland; the plough share is too narrow, which is a common fault; and the wheels are much too low; were they higher, the draft would be proportionably lighter. In other parts of the province, I have indeed seen better ploughs, but they are in few hands, and, besides, are not quite free from these defects.

The harrows are also of a weak and poor construction; for I have more than once seen them with only wooden teeth, which however it may do for mere sand in tilth, must be very inefficacious on other soils, but the mischief of using such on one sort of land is that the slovens are always ready to extend them for cheapness to the rest. The carts and waggons are also in some parts of the province very awkward ill made things, in which the principles of mechanics are not at all considered.[3] There are however some gentlemen near Boston, who, having caught the taste of agriculture, which has for some years been remarkable in England, have introduced from thence better

[3] The tools and implements used by the colonial farmer were mostly homemade and differed very slightly from those of the European peasant of the twelfth century, or even of the Egyptian farmers in the time of Rameses II.

tools of most sorts and at the same time a much better practice of husbandry; and if they took pains to spread this about the province, it could not fail of being attended with very beneficial effects. Societies for the encouragement of agriculture seem to be the only means of bringing it to bear, by means of premiums and bounties.[4]

Another article, which I shall here mention, is that of timber, which already grows so scarce upon the south coasts, that even fire-wood in some parts is not cheap; and is forced to be brought from Sagadahock:[5] this has been owing to the planters, upon their first settling, ravaging rather than cutting down the woods: and what is a striking instance of inattention to their real interest is the new settlers going on in the same manner, although they cannot but see and know the effects of it in the parts first settled. They not only cut down timber to raise their buildings and fences, but in clearing the grounds for cultivation they destroy all that comes in their way, as if they had nothing to do but to get rid of it at all events, as fast as possible. Instead of acting in so absurd a manner, which utterly destroys woods of trees which require an hundred years to come to perfection, they ought, in the first settling and cultivating their tracts of land, to inclose and reserve portions of the best woods for the future use of themselves, and the general good of the country; points which they have hitherto seemed to have very little at heart. Indeed, this violent and unlicensed destruction of timber has been carried

[4] Societies for the promotion of agriculture did not appear in America until after the close of the Revolution. In 1785 both the Philadelphia Society for Promoting Agriculture, to which Washington and Franklin belonged, and the South Carolina Agricultural Society were formed. Cf. P. W. Bidwell and J. F. Falconer, *History of Agriculture in the Northern United States, 1620–1860* (Washington, 1925).

[5] Kennebec River.

to a degree in our colonies that calls for a preventive from the public: for it is clear to common sense that, if the legislature does not interfere in this point, the whole country will be deprived of timber, as fast as it is settled; which ought not to be the case while any attention is given to the public interests. For nothing is of more importance to this country, though a colony, than timber: the plenty which has hitherto abounded makes the planters so regardless of their essential interests as to think it a commodity of little or no value. Which must be attended with worse consequences than almost any part of the ill management which they have hitherto been attended with.

Let me, before I quit this subject, observe further that the New Englanders are also deficient in introducing those new articles of culture, which have become common in different parts of Great Britain; among others, let us instance carrots, parsnips, potatoes, Jerusalem artichokes, beets, lucerne,[6] sainfoine,[7] and particularly cabbages; these articles are many of them better adapted to the climate of New England than of Great Britain; yet they are not attended to half so much: but the farmers of this country would find their interest more in the introduction of these articles, than could ever happen to any people in the mother country, where land is so scarce that they cannot afford to make trial of any thing that they are not previously certain will answer; whereas in these colonies the case is different; land costs nothing; they have enough of various soils to try every thing, without the loss of the land bringing them into those difficulties which it must ever do in countries where a considerable rent, tythe, and

[6] Alfalfa. Cf. Jacquelin Ambler, *A Treatise on the Culture of Lucerne* (London, 1800).

[7] A perennial legume better adapted to Europe than to America.

poor's[8] taxes are paid. But this circumstance, which is such
an undoubted advantage, in fact turns out the contrary; and
for this reason, they depend on this plenty of land as a substitute for all industry and good management; neglecting the
efforts of good husbandry, which in England does more than
the cheapness of the soil does in America.

[8] Poor rates.

CHAPTER VIII

NEW ENGLAND

Comparison between the benefits resulting from agriculture in Great Britain and New England

I HAVE given in the preceding passages what I may venture to say is a fair and candid account of New England. I may be in numerous passages mistaken, but I have not purposely given a better or worse account of things than the fact has really been; this observation is necessary, in order to prepare the reader for the comparison which I am going to draw. The case is not indifferent; nor is it so strongly decisive in favour either of one or the other as to make the argument depend upon a few strong outlines, that appear clear to the reader the instant they are produced—which is the case with Canada and Nova Scotia. On the contrary, New England very much resembles, in several essential circumstances, Great Britain. For instance, it is a country which produces all the necessaries, but none of the luxuries of life. It is a country which depends as much or more upon navigation, commerce, and fisheries, than Britain does; agriculture not yielding those rich products which form the foundation in other countries of the most beneficial branches of commerce. Besides this, the face of the country in some particulars, the ranks of the people, the number of gentlemen living on their estates, the freedom of the lower classes, with various other circumstances, give an uncommon resemblance between Great Britain and

New England, which may well make it a matter of difficulty to judge between them; to which if we add that both enjoy liberty, both civil and religious, we shall find that a cool, dispassionate, and candid examination is necessary, and by no means a hasty or incautious one.

The great points in favour of New England are the enjoyments of plenty of land—a freedom from heavy taxes—from tythes—from poor rates—with an open market for all commodities raised. On the contrary, Great Britain lies under the disadvantage of having no land for new grants—is much burthened by taxes—and also by that of tythes—and poor rates: in this comparison the benefit is all on the side of New England; but in others there are points much more favourable to the mother country: *First,* the climate is more favourable than that of New England to husbandry; for though the fruits of some kind in America are far beyond what we have in Britain, yet in the articles of farming produce this advantage extends to nothing of importance. Wheat is a crop far more valuable than maize, but cannot be gained in New England upon comparable terms with what it is in Britain; nor does maize produce nearly like it in quantity, nor any thing like in value. This superiority runs through all the products of a farm, and also in the price of them: which in a comparison of the two countries should never be forgotten. The exporting price of wheat, for three or four years after the peace of Paris, in the colonies was 20s. a quarter, while in England, it was from 44s. to 50s. This principal grain regulates the rest in most parts of the world, as it does in both Britain and America; the case is the same with barley, oats, pease, beans, hay, butter, cheese, and every article the farmer carries to market. If the monstrous difference of these prices be considered, it will surely be thought a counterballance to many other advantages. I am sensible that wheat in America has of late years been at 26s. to 32s. a quarter; but then it has in England been from 50s. to 56s. so that the superiority has continued: we may safely suppose the same difference of price has run through other articles of corn; indeed we know it has, and also that, in all products which arise in whatever manner from grass lands, the superiority in the price of England is far greater; upon the whole, this difference may be reckoned at 50 per cent.

Now if a calculation is made of this superiority or even of 40 or 30 per cent I am clear it will be found to more than ballance the difference of the farmers expences in rent, tythe, and rates; and also the advantages which the New Englanders have in plenty of timber and some other articles of inferior importance.

But further, the American has in one instance an inferiority which is great and marked; it is the price and nature of the labour which he employs: he pays more than treble the rate of Great Britain, or else submits to be served in a manner which is open to an hundred inconveniencies. This is an article of such consequence as to ballance many others.[1]

[1] The American colonial farmer was always confronted with the serious problem of an inadequate labor supply. In sharp contrast to England, with its widespread unemployment and overflowing labor market, the colonies at all times lacked laborers. Wages were consequently high. As early as 1633 Winthrop, complaining of the high wages in the Massachusetts Bay colony, declared that "the scarcity of workmen had caused them to raise their wages to an excessive rate . . ." In the North, particularly in New England, the farmer depended largely upon his family for help. The few experiments with Indian labor were disappointing, for the redman proved to be neither apt nor willing. Sometimes during the planting and harvesting seasons the farmer was able to secure hired help in the neighborhood, but such help was all too frequently inefficient and undependable. More often at these busy seasons, as well as at other times, neighboring farmers "changed works"; group cooperation in some colonial communities was compulsory. Every farmer was a jack-of-all-trades: he was his own shoe-

As far therefore as the comparison concerns the substantial farmers in either country, the renters in Britain, and the renters or owners in New England that rank neither with the lower classes nor with the gentlemen, I think the advantage lies clearly in favour of the former; and no slight proof that this determination is just is the difference of wealth between these two setts of men; the farmers in Britain of the rank now under consideration are incomparable[y] richer than the similar inhabitants of New England; among whom very few are to be found that can be called men of wealth or even property: they live in a decent comfortable manner, but rarely acquire wealth.

I do not apprehend the parallel turns out the same with the lower class of farmers, for I do not think a more miserable set of men are to be found than the little farmers in Britain; they work harder, fare worse, and are in fact poorer than the day labourers they employ, whereas in New England, the little freeholders and farmers live in the midst of a plenty of all the necessaries of life; they do not acquire wealth, but they have comforts in abundance: I freely acknowledge the superiority of the colony in this article.

In that of the poor and the labourers, the comparison is equally in favour of New England: in this respect common and almost universal experience tells us that in all countries which have long been wealthy, in which a great commerce, flourishing manufactures, and established luxury are fixed,

maker, cooper, carpenter, and ironworker; he laid walls, stoned-up wells, butchered pigs and cattle, made axe handles, and brooms, and split staves and shingles. Frequently too he surveyed his own land, designed his buildings, acted as his own lawyer, and prescribed medicine for the members of his family. In a word, his home was a factory and his barn a workshop wherein he and the other members of his household produced many of the necessities of existence. Cf. P. W. Bidwell and J. F. Falconer, *History of Agriculture in the Northern United States, 1620–1860* (Washington, 1925).

that in such countries the poor are always in a state of oppression and of misery: It would be too much to say that this *must be* so, but the fact is, that it always *is* so; and, we see in the case in question of Great Britain, that the poor in general are in a state of poverty; and it is necessary they should [be], or the trade and manufactures of the country would sink, for their prosperity depends on that low price of labour which keeps the labouring poor below the proportion of the high price of every thing else.

The last circumstance of this parallel is the country gentlemen of two, three, or to five hundred pounds a year land estate; and here I must observe that the comparison turns out utterly in favour of the colony. Indeed the high prices of every thing at home, owing to the plenty of money, has almost ruined such people, so that very few will soon be found; they must either starve, or convert their estates into money, and apply it in some line of industry to make more than common interest; they must become traders or farmers if they do not suffer themselves to be eclipsed by every country grocer or woolman. But this is not the case in New England; there, four or five hundred pounds a year is a great estate—not that there is not much larger, but it is sufficient for all the comforts and conveniences of life, and for such a portion of the luxuries of it as are indulged in by any neighbour, though their estates may be larger than his. In a word, his situation is the very reverse of that of his brethren in Britain, insomuch that no change can be imagined more beneficial (in point of the expenditure of his income) than for such a country gentleman to sell his estate in England, and with the money of the sale to buy in New England; though we shall by and by come to colonies that are preferable. By such a conduct he leaves his country after making the only advantage in his power of the cheapness of money, by getting a great price for his land; and he goes immediately into another in which he finds money dear; so that he profits doubly by the change.

As to gentlemen whose fortunes are considerable enough to support them in the enjoyments of the age, they of course will remain fixed, because they can get nothing by moving which they have not at home; with the circumstance of living in the midst of the luxury and elegance of the first country in the world—luxuries which they do not behold like their little neighbours, with envious eyes, but which they enjoy in common with the rich and great.

Upon the whole there are some classes whose emigrating to New England need not surprize us, but there are others among whom it happens very irrationally.

CHAPTER IX

NEW YORK

*Climate of New York—Soil—Productions—Husbandry
—Curious accounts of a new settlement—Present state
of the inhabitants—Exports*

THE colony of New York lies between latitude 41° and
44°, which tho' partly the same parallel as New England, yet is it attended with a different climate in some respects; but in every circumstance superior, since there are
productions that will not thrive in New England, which do
admirably here; not owing to the greater heat (for New
England is as hot as New York) but to a better and more
salubrious air. The spring in New York is earlier, and the
autumn late; the summer is long and warm; indeed sometimes the heat is great, but rarely oppressive; the winter is
severe but short; it is not so sharp as in New England, and
they have in general a clear bright sky. In winter the snow
lies deep, and for two or three months; and they travel on it
in sledges both here and in New England, in the manner that
is common in the northern parts of Europe.

Sometimes indeed the cold is extraordinary great; of which
Dr. Mitchel[1] gives an instance. By the observations, says
he, made, in January 1765, by the masters of the college at
New York, Fahrenheit's thermometer fell 6 degrees below
0, which is 21 degrees below 15, the greatest cold in England.
Water then froze instantly, and even strong liquors in a very

short time. And we are told it is not uncommon there to see a glass of water set upon the table, in a warm room freeze before you can drink it, &c.*

The soil of the province is in general very good; on the coast it is sandy but backwards, they have noble tracks of rich black mold, red loam, and friable clays, with mixtures of these soils in great varieties; at some miles distance from the sea, the country swells into fine hills and ridges, which are all covered with forest trees, and the soil on many of these is rich and deep, an advantage not common in poor countries. The river Hudson which is navigable to Albany, and of such a breadth and depth as to carry large sloops, with its branches on both sides, intersect[s] the whole country, and render[s] it both pleasant and convenient. The banks of this great river have a prodigious variety; in some places there are gently swelling hills covered with plantations and farms; in others towering mountains spread over with thick forests: here you have nothing but abrupt rocks of vast magnitude, which seem shivered in two to let the river pass the immense clefts; there you see cultivated vales, bounded by hanging forests, and the distant view completed by the *Blue Mountains*[1] raising their heads above the clouds. In the midst of this variety of scenery of such grand and expressive character, the river Hudson flows, equal in many places to the Thames at London, and in some much broader. The shores of the American rivers are too often a line of swamps and marshes; that of Hudson is not without them, but in general it passes through a fine, high, dry, and bold country, which is equally beautiful and wholesome.

In general the soil of this province exceeds that of New

---

* *Present State.*

[1] Reference here is to the Catskill Mountains.

England: besides the varieties I have already mentioned, there is on Long Island sands that are made quite fertile with oyster-shells, a fish caught there in prodigious quantities: they have the effect of shell marle in Scotland. The productions of New York are the same in general as those of New England, with an exception of some fruits that will not thrive in the latter country; but almost every article is of a superior quality: this is very striking in wheat, of which they raise in New England, as I have already observed, but little that is good, whereas in New York their wheat is equal to any in America, or indeed in the world, and they export immense quantities of it; whereas New England can hardly supply her own consumption.

They sow their wheat in autumn, with better success than in spring: this custom they pursue even about Albany, in the northern parts of the province, where the winters are very severe. The ice there in the river Hudson is commonly three or four feet thick. When professor Kalm[2] was here, the inhabitants of Albany crossed in the third of April with six pair of horses. The ice commonly dissolves at that place about the end of March or the beginning of April. On the 16th of November the yachts are put up, and about the beginning or middle of April they are in motion again. If wheat will do here in autumn, where the ground is sometimes frozen four feet deep, one would apprehend it would succeed even more to the north.

Wheat in many parts of the province yields a larger produce than is common in England: upon good lands about Albany, where the climate is the coldest in the country, they

[2] Peter Kalm (1716–1769), Swedish scientist, who traveled in America and described its natural history, plantations, and agriculture in his *Travels into North America* (3 vols., London, 1770).

sow two bushels and better upon one acre, and reap from 20 to 40; the latter quantity however is not often had; but from 20 to 30 bushels are common, and this with such bad husbandry as would not yield the like in England, and much less in Scotland. This is owing to the richness and freshness of the soil. In other parts of the province, particularly adjoining to New Jersey and Pennsylvania, the culture is better and the country more generally settled. Though there are large tracts of waste land within twenty miles of the city of New York.

Rye is a common crop upon the inferior lands, and the sort they produce is pretty good, though not equal to the rye of England. The crops of it are not so great in produce as those of wheat on the better lands.

Maize is sown generally throughout the province, and they get vast crops of it. They chuse [choose] the loose, hollow loams, or sandy lands for it, not reckoning the stiff or clayey ones will do at all for it: half a bushel will seed two acres and yield an hundred bushels in return: about Albany, where they have frosts in the summer, maize suits them particularly, because tho' the shoots are damaged or even killed by the frost, yet the roots send forth fresh ones. Maize, from the greatness of the produce, may easily be supposed a rich article of culture, and especially in a province that has so fine an inland navigation through it as New York. It is also of great advantage in affording a vast produce of food for cattle in the winter, which in this country is a matter of great consequence, where they are obliged to keep all their cattle housed from November till the end of March—with exception indeed of unprovident farmers, who trust some out the chief of the winter, to their great hazard.

Barley is much sown in all the southern parts of the province; and the crops they sometimes get of it are very great, but the grain is not of a quality equal to that of Europe. They make much malt and brew large quantities of beer from it at New York, which serves the home consumption, and affords some also for exportation. Pease are a common article of culture here, and though uncertain in their produce, yet are they reckoned very profitable; and the straw is valued as winter food. Thirty bushels per acre they consider as a large crop, but sometimes they get scarcely a third of that. Oats they sow in common, and the products are generally large; sixty bushels an acre have been known on land of but moderate fertility. Buckwheat is every where sown, and few crops are supposed to pay the farmer better, at the same time that they find it does very little prejudice to the ground, in which it resembles pease.

Potatoes are not common in New England, but in New York many are planted; and upon the black, loose, fresh woodland they get very great crops, nor does any pay them better if so well, for at the city of New York there is a constant and ready market for them; I have been assured that from five to eight hundred bushels have been often gained on an acre.

There are many very rich meadows and pastures in all parts of the province; and upon the brooks and rivers, the watered ones (for they are well acquainted with that branch of husbandry) are mown twice and yield large crops of hay. In their marshes they get large crops also, but it is a coarse bad sort; not however to a degree as to make cattle refuse it; on the contrary, the farmers find it of great use in the winter support of their lean cattle, young stock, and cows.

The timber of this province consists chiefly of oak, ash, beech, chestnut, cedar, walnut, cypress, hickory, sassafras, and the pine; nor is there any preceptible difference in their value of the wood here and in New England; though it declines, for ship building, when you get further to the south; with some exceptions however, for there are other species of trees even in the most southern colonies that are equal to any for that purpose. New York not being near so much settled as New England, timber is much more plentiful, so that the planters and new settlers make great profit by their lumber. Upon most of the streams that fall into the river Hudson, there are many saw mills for the mere purpose of sawing boards, planks, and other sorts of lumber, which goes down in immense quantities to New York, from whence it is shipped for the West Indies. We shall by and by see that this is a very great article in the profit of every planter. Among all the woods of this province, are found immense numbers of vines of several species, and quite different from those of Europe, some of the grapes resembling currants rather than ours. Wine has been, and is, commonly, made of them, but of a sort too bad to become an article of export.

Hemp is cultivated in all parts of the province, but not to a greater amount than their own consumption: flax is however a great article in the exports; it succeeds extremely well, and pays the farmer a considerable profit. Linseed oil is another article of export, the seed for which is raised by the planters; but more is exported unmanufactured. Turneps also are grown in large quantities, and by some planters upon a system much improved of late years. The fruits in this province are much superior to those in New England; and they have some, as peaches and nectarines, which will not thrive there. Immense quantities of melons and water-melons are cultivated in the fields near New York, where they come to as great perfection as in Spain and Italy; nor can it well be conceived how much of these fruits and peaches, &c. all ranks of people eat here, and without receiving any ill consequence from the practice. This is an agreeableness far superior to any thing we have in England; and indeed, the same superiority runs through all their fruits, and several articles of the kitchen garden, which are here raised without trouble, and in profusion. Every planter and even the smallest farmers have all an orchard near their house of some acres, by means of which they command a great quantity of cyder, and export apples by ship-loads to the West Indies. Nor is this an improper place to observe that the rivers in this province and the sea upon the coast are richly furnished with excellent fish: oysters and lobsters are no where in greater plenty than in New York. I am of the opinion they are more plentiful than at any other place on the globe; for very many poor families have no other subsistence than oysters and bread. Nor is this the only instance of the natural plenty that distinguishes this country: the woods are full of game, and wild turkies are very plentiful; in these particulars New York much exceeds New England.

These upon the whole are circumstances which contribute much to the plenty and happiness of living in this country; and among other causes, contribute very greatly to the plenty and general welfare of all ranks of the people, nor should I here omit making some observations on the state of the settlers and other inhabitants.

To what causes it is I know not, but New York is much less populous than New England to the north, and Pennsylvania to the south:[3] there is no circumstance that results from nature, or from the government of the province that can

[3] The colony of New York was less populous perhaps because of its land system. When New York became an English colony it was required by the Peace Treaty to preserve the property rights of the Dutch settlers. The patroonship arrangement apparently appealed to the English officials for they proceeded to create large manors which rivaled their Dutch

account for this; but to whatever cause it may be owing, certain it is, that we ought to esteem it as fortunate for such persons as now chuse [choose] to settle there. There are vast tracts of unpatented land yet remaining on the river Hudson and its branches, which abound in every beneficial circumstance that can render a new country desirable to settle in.

This however, will not, in all probability last long, for the new settlements increase every day; so that in a few years there will not be many such spaces abounding in wood and navigable water unoccupied.

But there is one mistake made by most new settlers, especially on the river Hudson; they have in general an idea that the only good soils are the deep black loam, or clays; and accordingly reject all the tracts that consist of a thin reddish loam on rock; but I have been assured by some intelligent gentlemen, that experiment has proved this soil, though so thin, fertile to a great degree in most of the productions which are common in the whole province: they have mentioned particularly, barley, pease, potatoes, turneps, clover, and even wheat. And as a confirmation that this opinion was just, I was favoured with the following particular of the produce of a field of this soil, which having been rejected by several new settlers, was planted by the person to whom I am obliged for this intelligence. The piece of land contained sixteen acres, the soil a light thin loam, of a reddish colour, on a lime-stone rock.

First year

Grubbed, ploughed, and prepared for potatoes, and planted without dung: produce 11,000 bushels, which were sold at 10d. per bushel, which is 453£.

---

predecessors. Much of the best and most accessible land of the colony was thus preëmpted. Cf. C. P. Nettels, *The Roots of American Civilization* (New York, 1938), pp. 227–28.

Second year

Ploughed once, and sown with wheat, produce 512 bushels, which sold for 85£.

Third year

Planted again with potatoes, produced 8,496 bushels, which sold for 10d. a bushel, or 354£.

Fourth year

Sown with wheat again, produce 600 bushels, which sold for 120£.

Fifth year

Sown with barley, produce 730 bushels, which sold for 73£.

Sixth year

Ploughed once, and sown with pease, the produce 630 bushels, which sold for 53£.

With this crop of pease clover was sown, and left an excellent pasture, which was reckoned as profitable as any other piece of land in the whole plantation.

First year . . . . £.	453
Second do.	85
Third do.	354
Fourth do.	120
Fifth do.	73
Sixth do.	53
Total £.	1,138

Which is near £. 11 15 0 per acre per annum.

Now upon this account I have several remarks to make, which I think important, as it shews what may be done in this country, by good husbandry, even when no manure is used. The reader doubtless observes, that the *system* of management in this field ran upon the principle of an intervening crop of potatoes or pease between every two of wheat and barley. This is the husbandry which I would always recom-

mend, but which is diametrically opposite to the practice of
the New York planters; who make not the least scruple of
taking six or eight crops successively of maize, wheat, rye,
barley, or oats, without ever thinking of the least necessity
of introducing pease, buckwheat, turneps, clover, or any other
plant which in its nature or culture would prove a preparation
for corn. The idea exemplified in the preceding sketch shews
quite a different conduct.

In the next place I must observe, that the register of this
field shews strongly the importance of cultivating potatoes on
fresh woodlands; the products here reaped from them exceed
infinitely those of any other crops, which should animate the
farmers of this province to extend the culture of them; but
the importance of planting them does not only rest in the
amount of the produce, however considerable, they prepare
the ground for corn better than any other plant, of which no
bad idea can be formed from the crops which here succeeded
them. There is a notion, common in many parts, that the lands
even in New York are far inferior to those of Europe in
general, but I am apt to believe that this is very much owing
to the husbandry here being so much inferior. The instance
I have now given of a bad soil, not esteemed here, but well
managed, shews what might be done if the same attention was
given to the culture of the earth, that is common in Britain.

The same gentleman to whom I am indebted for the preceding account, gave me another of the expences and product
of a considerable plantation on the river Hudson. This I shall
insert with pleasure; for such accounts are what I have most
aimed at gaining for all the colonies, not always with success
indeed; but it is only from such that we can form a just idea
of the advantages of American husbandry. Such accounts of
agriculture in Europe are common in numerous books, while

the management and state of the agriculture of the colonies has been little attended to, for which I am clear no good reason can be assigned.

The plantations in question consisted of 1,600 acres, situated partly on the banks of the river Hudson and partly on each side of a small river that runs into it; the purchaser was not the first settler, for the land was marked out, a house built, and some offices, with a small tract of land cleared: nothing, however, was done either expensively, or with good judgment; and the place was in a state of neglect when purchased. The price was 370£.

A small saw mill, and additional offices were built on it immediately, which with some other improvements, of no great amount, came to 260£.

Eight hundred acres were grubbed, and the trees sawn and rived into plank, board, shingles, and staves: the whole expence of which was 1162£. Many of the trees were oak and elm, of great size; also some limes of extraordinary growth.

Eight new inclosures were made, the fences, posts, and rails and ditching, with all expences, came to 32£.

The stock fixed on the plantation was as follows:

Eight negroes, at 34£. . . . . £.	272
Four indented servants, at 11£. each, for 3 years	132
Two hired by the year at New York, 12£. .	72
Three German emigrants, at 9£.	81
Servants, provisions, and cloathing for negroes, besides what produced	56
Implements of husbandry, expences of, exclusive of timber	87
Salary of overseer, 3 years	110
Seed for the first crop	90
Sundry expences	113

Cattle   230
Provisions, &c. for 3 years   300
£. 1,543

The produce of the three years, in various articles, came to the following sums.

Lumber

	£.	s.	d.
17,000 feet of boards, at 5£. 2s. 6d. per 1,000	87	2	6
970 plank, at 3s. 8d.	177	16	0
220,000 shingles, at 12s. per 1,000 . .	132	0	0
60,000 staves, at 4£. 10s. per 1,000 .	270	0	0
260 pieces of timber, at 7s. 6d.	97	0	0
Sundry articles of various kinds	187	10	0
	951	8	6

Recapitulation

	£.	s.	d.
Purchase	370	0	0
Saw mill, &c.	260	0	0
Clearing, 800 acres	1,162	0	0
Eight inclosures	32	0	0
Stock	1,243	0	0
Provisions	300	0	0
Total	3,367	0	0

The annual after expence was:

	£.	s.	d.
Interest of capital	168	7	0
Repairs	12	0	0
Inclosing	10	0	0
Negroes	16	0	0
Servants wages	135	0	0
Implements	13	0	0
Sundry expences	100	0	0
	454	7	0

Produce 1st year

	£.	s.	d.
4 acres of potatoes, 260 bushels per acre, 1040 bushels at 8d.	34	13	0
82 acres Indian corn, 30 bush. per acre 240 bushels at 1s. 6d.	184	10	0
10 acres pease, failed	0	0	0
22 of wheat, 22 bushels per acre, at 3s.	72	12	0
	291	15	0

Produce 2d year

	£.	s.	d.
6 acres potatoes, 200 bushels per acre, 1,200 bushels, at 10d.	50	0	0
135 acres Indian corn, 32 bush. per acre, 4,320 bush. at 1s. 6d.	324	0	0
90 acres wheat, 20 bush. per acre 1,800 bush. at 3s.	270	0	0
40 acres pease, 15 bush. per acre 600 bush. at 1s. 3d.	37	10	0

40 acres barley ⎫
 2 do. potatoes ⎪
16 turneps   ⎬ for
35 oats   plantation   0   0   0
32 clover   ⎪
20 Indian corn ⎭

416 acres in culture.	£. 681	10	0

Produce 3d year

	£.	s.	d.
8 acres potatoes, 300 bush. per acre, 2,400 bush. at 10d.	50	0	0
170 acres of Indian corn, 35 bush. per acre, 5950 bush. at 2s.	595	0	0
60 acres wheat, 16 bush. per acre, 960 bush. at 3s.	144	0	0
80 acres pease; 40 failed, 40 at 10 bush. 400 bush. at 1s. 3d.	25	0	0

Cattle 87 10 0

150 acres clover ⎫
  2 potatoes |
 20 barley |
 20 oats   ⎬ for plantation   0   0   0
 10 Indian corn |
  2 wheat |
 38 turneps   ⎭
560 acres in culture.   £. 901 10 0

	£.	s.	d.
First year	291	15	0
Second	681	10	0
Third	901	10	0
Lumber	951	8	6
	2826	3	6

Capital 3367 0 0
Product first three years 2826 3 6

Remains 540 16 6
Three years interest 504   0 0
                            £. 1,044 16 6

800 acres were soon in culture, which were usually employed in the product of

8 acres potatoes .... £. 50
100 do. Indian corn   300
100 do. wheat   300
 40 do. pease   60
400 do. clover
 20 do. barley
 20 do. oats
 80 do. turneps
 30 do. sundries, including orchard and yield-
              ing

Cattle	200
Fruit	25
Annual lumber	60
	995
Expences	454
Profit £.	541

This profit is besides the annual improvement of waste from which the lumber is cut, and also the advantage of the surrounding wastes, which are granted as fast as the family increases, but which will not admit of calculation, because wastes are converted to profit merely in proportion to the ability, that is the money, of the planter.

The first observation I shall make on this account, is the lumber paying nearly the expence of clearing, which is an high advantage, and certainly owing to the expedition of the saw mill: in many parts of the northern provinces, where a saw mill is not used, the expence of clearing is infinitely the greatest part of a new settler's work. But it is plain from every article in this account, that the great advantage in settling is the command of a large sum of money, that the planter may go spiritedly to work and make his ground produce him something considerable immediately, which can never be done if he has not money enough to clear away the woods speedily. Half this capital I am clear would not yield a proportionable profit; on the contrary, it might not afford half such interest for the amount. It is by means of this advantage that near two thirds of the whole expenditure is repaid by the product of the three first years, which would be far enough from the case, if the sum of money at the beginning of the undertaking had been much less. If the planter's time and trouble, for three years, be not reckoned, as indeed it need not in reason be, then the sum of 1,044£. might be reckoned the original capital, which would make the annual profit on the under-taking immensely great.

But the great superiority of the account of this improve-ment, over those that can be made in the cultivated parts of Europe, is the *increase* of cultivation. The account here is stated at 800 cultivated acres, and 60£. a year from lumber; but this does not include the annual increase of the cleared land, which may be carried on as fast as the planter's money will allow. Instead of 60£. a year in lumber, it might be 2[00] or 300£. by having hands enough, and the land, when cleared, all brought into culture at the same profit as the first 800 acres; the quantity of land to be had does not stop, let him be as able and industrious as he will. This advantage I think greater even than the making the profit above stated.

For here let us consider that in the cultivated parts of Britain, or any other European country, a farmer, who is on such a farm as 3,000£. will stock, supposing him to make as great an advantage as this planter, lies under two disadvan-tages; tho' he has this neat [net] income of 541£. per annum from his business, he lives in a country where such an income is very easily spent, even by a farmer, and actually is spent by many farmers, without their making in any respect the appearance of gentlemen, which is owing to the luxury of the age, and the high prices of every thing in the country. Sec-ondly, if on the contrary he does not spend such an income, but lives frugally on a part of it, and is desirous of expending the remainder to the best advantage, he cannot throw it into an annual increase of his business, because he is on every side surrounded by the farms of his neighbours; and though he may now and then hire other farms, it is not to be depended on; and if they do not join his old one he will be better with-out them; besides the circumstance of such farms being probably either too large or too small for the money he has to spare: so that the only advantage he can, in a general way, put his savings to, is the common interest of four or five per cent.

The case of the New York planter is very different. For first he makes his income of 541£. a year in a country where money is so dear, and most things so cheap, that he may live upon a part of it in a way far more genteely, upon a comparison with all his neighbours, than he could do with twice the total in England; the consequence of which must naturally be a far greater probability of a person's saving at least a part of his income, than if he lived where the whole of it would hardly support him. Secondly, upon the supposition of his spending only a part of his income, he has the advantage of being able to throw the remainder, like a merchant, immediately into business, and to make it pay him as good interest for his money as his original stock. He has only to increase his servants, his cattle, and his works proportioned to the sum of money he has annually to lay out, which gives a proportioned increase of land under culture, and consequently an increase of crops to sell: this results from his settling in an uncultivated country, and is upon the whole, so great an advantage, that it overballances an hundred inconveniences. For by means of this circumstance, the planter is able to make a continued compound interest of all the money he can raise, at the rate of from 40 to 100 per cent. till he has enlarged his cultivation so much as to be incapable of management. The immense increase of compound interest is well known, yet ought not the reader to startle at the proposition: suppose the planter lives upon, or, more properly speaking, spends in manufactures, wine, tea, sugar, spices, and spirits, 241£. per annum, he has then 300£. per annum for improvements;

which 300£. the first year, will clear a certain portion of waste (the lumber nearly paying the expence) cultivate, stock, and convert it to saleable crops. From that time, this portion of land becomes equally profitable with the rest of the farm, and yields a proportionable advantage: this profit is the next year added to the 300£. and a still larger piece taken in, which still yielding its profit, like the rest, the accumulation continues; and the annual amount of savings grows incessantly; being, to all intents and purposes, plainly a compound interest.

But here let me observe that this prodigious advantage is not annexed to the mere settling in New York; on the contrary, the cultivated parts of the province are in this respect exactly upon a par with Britain; for fixing in a plantation, in that part of the province, would be fixing in a spot surrounded with other plantations, and consequently possessing no great part of this advantage which I have been endeavouring to explain. It is only in the back country, which is yet forest, that new settlers can find plenty enough of land to be secure of those additions to their farms, which are attended, when made, with such benefit. Nor is it only in this respect that the waste country is the most eligible to settle in; there is so much greater choice of land through such parts of the province than in the other, and the land of course so much better, that although plantations are often to be bought cheap in the cultivated parts, yet is it more adviseable for these reasons to settle in the back country; always provided there is a navigation near the farm, for all land products are, in America, too cheap to bear a land carriage.[4]

This comparison between New York and Britain is so much in favour of the former, that I think it is necessary to make

_____

[4] This is merely another way of stating that land navigation was too expensive.

some observations upon that part of the state of agriculture in Britain which gives such a superiority to America: not that I shall enter into a full calculation of this point. But at present I must observe, that the reason of this inferiority of Britain is not a want of land—for the wastes of this country including those of Scotland and Ireland, amount probably to more than a third of the whole territory; nor is it a want of fertility in those lands; but it is the mischief of being in hands that will neither cultivate them themselves, nor yet let others.[5] A man may in New York, &c. have land in fee-simple[6] for demanding it, and complying with certain reasonable conditions, which leave him absolute master of the soil for ever. In Britain he may apply for waste land, and he will be answered that he shall have a lease of 21 years, perhaps only 7 or 14; and upon such a lease he is to build, without a stick of timber, and enter into very great expences: this at once banishes the scheme in any prudent person, and makes any common husbandry more profitable. Thus is it found that when the wastes in a country are in private hands they are like to remain so, except what a few sensible active individuals do upon their

[5] Arthur Young estimated that these lands amounted to not less than 15,000,000 acres. *The Farmer's Letters to the People of England* (London, 1770), I, 5. "Shame to our monstrous land possessors—Shame to those *great men* who possess whole counties of uncultivated land! More to their glory would it be to expend part of their wealth in adding to the riches and population of their country, than to waste the whole in the career of nauseous *vanity*. Judge not of a nobleman's *greatness* by the number of footmen before his chair—but [by] the number of labourers on his estate; and never forget that there is fifty times more true lustre in the waving ears of corn which cover a formerly waste acre than in the most glittering star that shines at *Almacks*." *Ibid.*, p. 319. See also Young's *Observations on the Waste Lands of Great Britain* (London, 1773).

[6] A "fee-simple" interest in land is one which allows the owner to sell the land to any one. It can also be inherited generally. It combines all the incidents of ownership and, in the United States today, is equivalent to absolute ownership.

own estates, which bears scarcely any proportion to the quantity that remains waste. This is of most pernicious influence upon the public good, which is so intimately concerned in all wastes being cultivated. No man ought, in such a wealthy, industrious country as Britain, where every product of the earth bears such an high price, to be allowed to keep waste lands in his possession above a certain number of years; if by a given time they are not in culture, or at least a considerable part of them, and the work going on, then they ought to be forfeit and assigned in the American manner to whoever will comply with the terms of the grant. Doubtless, this will appear to the generality of the people in this country as a very wild scheme; and so it may be, but nevertheless the evil is not less real, nor does it less demand a remedy. Were the wastes of Britain to be granted away in small portions in the same manner as those of America, we should see them peopled and as well cultivated as the rest of the kingdom; notwithstanding the general want of timber on them, and their not being equal in fertility to the woodlands of America. And here I must further observe that this state of the case shews the great reasonableness, and even importance, of strenuously insisting on the new and old settlers in all parts of the continent performing their conditions of taking no more land than they people in the required proportion. Letting any persons take up more land than they can moderately people is bringing the same mischievous consequence on America that we experience in Britain; for the wastes in America that are private property are of little more use to the public than if they did not exist.

The account of a settlement given above, is not to be supposed a picture of the profit which every one makes by going to New York; I would on no account have it imagined that this is the case: this was executed by means of a large sum of money, for so 3,000£. must be reckoned in America; and not only by a sum of money, but also by the exertion of much better husbandry than is common in the colonies. So far from every settler making a profit like this, not one in forty equals the proportion of it. In general, the settlers come with a small sum of money, very many of them with none at all, depending on their labour for three, five, or seven years to gain them a sum sufficient for taking a plantation, which is the common case of the foreign emigrants of all sorts. It is common to see men demand, and have, grants of land, who have no substance to fix themselves further than cash for the fees of taking up the land; a gun, some powder and shot, a few tools, and a plough; they maintain themselves the first year, like the Indians, with their guns, and nets, and afterwards by the same means with the assistance of their lands; the labour of their farms they perform themselves, even to being their own carpenters and smiths: by this means, people who may be said to have no fortunes are enabled to live, and in a few years to maintain themselves and families comfortably. But such people are not to be supposed to make a profit in cash of many years, nor do they want, or think of it. And as to the planters who begin their undertakings with small sums of money, though they do better, and even make a considerable profit by their business, yet are they very far from equalling what I have now described; this is for want of money, for I might add that not one new settler in a thousand is possessed of a clear three thousand pounds.

The conclusion which I deduce from these particulars is that new settlements in New York are undertaken to good advantage, profit in money considered, only by those who have a good sum of money ready to expend; and by this term, I mean particularly men who have from two to five thousand pounds clear; in Britain such people cannot from the amount of their fortune get into any valuable trade or manufacture, unless it is by mere interest, or being related to persons already in trade. But it is evident that in New York they may, with such a sum of money, take, clear, stock, and plant a tract of land that shall not only amply support them in all the necessaries of life, but at the same time yield a neat profit sufficient for the acquisition of a considerable fortune.

I shall next lay before the reader the exports of this province as taken on an average of three years since the peace.*

Flour and biscuit 250,000 barrels, at 20s. £.	250,000
Wheat 70,000 qrs.	70,000
Beans, pease, oats, Indian corn and other grains	40,000
Salt beef, pork, hams, bacon, and venison	18,000
Bees wax 30,000 lb. at 1s.	1,500
Tongues, butter, and cheese	8,000
Flax-seed, 7,000 hhds. at 40s.	14,000
Horses and live stock	17,000
Product of cultivated lands	418,500
Timber planks, masts, boards, staves, and shingles	25,000
Pot ash, 7,000 hhds.	14,000
Ships built for sale, 20, at £. 700	14,000
Copper ore, and iron in bars and pigs . .	20,000
£.	526,000

* *American Traveller*, p. 73. [Alexander Cluny, *The American Traveller: or, Observations, on the Present State, Culture and Commerce of the British Colonies in America* . . ., published anonymously in London in 1769. The reference to page 73 in the original is an error: the table is on page 75. Ed.]

Let me upon this table observe that far the greater part of this export is the produce of the lands including timber; and even the metals may be reckoned in the same class; this shews us that agriculture in New York is of such importance as to support the most considerable part of the province without the assistance of either the fishery or of commerce; not that the city of New York has not traded largely, perhaps equal to Boston, but the effects of that trade have been chiefly the introduction of money by the means of barter, besides the exportation of their own products: whereas New England's exports consist five parts in six of fish, and the other products of the fishery; a strong proof that agriculture is far more profitable in one country than in the other; for settlers in colonies will never take to the sea, in a country whose agriculture yields well; but in very bad climates, and such as destroy instead of cherishing the products of the earth, any branch of industry pays better than cultivating the earth. This is a distinction that ought to be decisive with those who have a choice to make which of these colonies they will go to; for men do not usually settle themselves in countries where they are to make their livelihood by encountering a boisterous sea and leading a life of perpetual hardships and violent labour: This is very different from the employment of those who support themselves in so fine a country as New York, by agriculture.

CHAPTER X

NEW YORK

Propositions for the improvement of the husbandry of
New York—Bad management—Better system—Vines
—Winter food of cattle, &c.

THE rural management in most parts of this province is miserable: seduced by the fertility of the soil on first settling, the farmers think only of exhausting it as soon as possible, without attending to their own interest in a future day: this is a degree of blindness which in sensible people one may fairly call astonishing. The general system is to crop their fields with corn till they are absolutely exhausted; then they leave them what they call fallow, that is, to run to weeds for several years, till they think the soil has recovered somewhat of its fertility, when they begin again with corn, in succession, as long as it will bear any, leaving it afterwards to a fallow of weeds. If no spontaneous growth came, but such as cattle would freely eat, the evil would not be great, because then the land would not have more to support than it would gain by the dung, &c. of the stock supported. But the contrary is the case: an infinite quantity of rubbish comes which no beast will touch, this seeds the land in so constant a succession that the soil is never without a large crop on it. The extent to which this practice is carried would astonish any person used to better husbandry; it is owing to the plenty of land; the farmers, instead of keeping all their grounds in good order, and a due succession of valuable crops, depend on new land for every thing, and are regardless of such management as would make their old fields equal the value of the new ones.

Instead of this, the New York farmers should imitate the conduct of those of Britain: they should never *exhaust* their lands; and when they were only *out of order* they should give them what ought to be esteemed the most beneficial fallow; that is, crops which, while growing, receive great culture, at the same time that they do not much exhaust the soil; such as all sorts of roots, and pulse, and every kind of leguminous plant, with the various kinds of clovers. By introducing these in proper succession, the land is never exhausted. In the remarkable instance given of a plantation managed on this system, we find a crop of this nature introduced between every two of maize, wheat, barley, or oats; and in every round of the system, several years under clover, which is instead of the fallow of weeds of the generality of the New York farmers.

The benefit of pursuing this plan is very great; for the lands, when laid down to clovers, maintain more cattle on fifty acres than with weeds they would on four hundred; this quantity of cattle improves the ground by the summer feeding and enables the farmer to raise great store of manure in the winter, by which means his crops of corn, &c. are by much more abundant. It further keeps the whole plantation in a state of profit; whereas in the common method only a part, and that not the largest, is valuable at once, his dependance for product being only on the new broken uplands.

Another part of husbandry, in which the New York farmers are very defective, is the management of their meadows and pastures: they make it a rule to mow every acre that is possible for hay; and as long as they get a tolerable *quantity*, they are strangely inattentive to the quality; weeds, rushes, flags, and all sorts of rubbish they call good hay, and suppose their cattle have not more sense in distinguishing than themselves. This is owing also to their grasping mere extent of land, and caring but little for the good husbandry of it. Many of their meadows are marshes, which, with little trouble, might be drained, and at once improved prodigiously, yet are such undertakings very seldom set about: others of the upland sort are equally filled with various weeds, from the slovenly manner in which they are laid down, or left to clothe themselves; but the appearance of these do not at all startle men whose ideas of agriculture are so little polished.

In respect to the management of cattle, and the raising manure, the farmers of New York are equally inattentive with their neighbours of New England.

I before observed, that vines of several sorts grew spontaneously in all the woods of this province; and that wine, though bad, had been made of them: their being bad has no weight with me, since wild vines in no part of the world produce good wine; but if they would plant vineyards of them, and cultivate them with the same care as is taken in wine countries, I have no doubt but they would produce excellent wine. Some endeavours have been made in this branch, by several patriotic persons in this province;[1] but they have

[1] The first successful attempts to improve grape culture in New York State were made early in the nineteenth century when M. Parmentier, an educated Frenchman of wealth, who left France at the time of the French Revolution, planted a variety of European vines in his garden in Brooklyn. Robert Underhill of Croton-on-the-Hudson was induced to plant a vineyard of Parmentier grapes, but all died. Undiscouraged, Underhill in 1827 planted a considerable acreage of Catawbas and Isabellas which proved to be commercially successful. The pioneer grape-grower in the western part

all been on the scent of bringing vines from other countries, scarce any of which ever thrive, and some of them will not live: the frosts are so excessive cold in winter that these foreign vines, used to so different a climate, either come to nothing or produce a grape very different from what they do in their own country. The instance of the great success with which the Dutch planted French vines at the Cape of Good Hope proves nothing in this case, because the climate in general, at that Cape, is not only one of the finest in the world, but the winters are mild, and in every respect different from the peculiar climate of North America.

But good culture and a proper choice of a high dry situation, of which there are plenty in this province, and even rocky ones, would in all probability be attended with success, and make these native grapes yield a wine that would add infinitely to the value of the exports of the province. This is an object of too much importance to be left to the dilatory proceedings of the planters themselves; they are in general engaged in a plain line of husbandry, from which most of them have not the capacity or knowledge to deviate, and the rest want money for it. But the government should order a vineyard to be planted under the direction of an overseer skilled in this branch of agriculture, and also by the same means take care that it was cultivated in perfection. The expence of this would not be great.

---

of the State was Deacon Elijah Fay who planted the first vineyard in Chautauqua County in 1818. Grape-growing in this section did not become important until a quarter of a century later. The first planting of grapes in the Finger Lake region of New York was made by the Rev. William Bostwick of Hammondsport about 1830. See U. P. Hedrick, *A History of Agriculture in the State of New York* (Albany, 1933), p. 390; T. V. Munson, *Foundations of American Grape Culture* (New York, 1909).

CHAPTER XI

NEW JERSEY

Climate, soil, and productions of New Jersey—Agriculture—Defects—Improvements proposed—The people

THE climate of New Jersey much resembles that in the southern parts of New York; they have sharp frosts in the winter, though rather less so than in that province, and the heat is sometimes very great in summer; but the air is clear, dry, and pure, and much superior to the more southern sea coasts, where are many swamps; in New Jersey scarce any of these are to be found, and consequently it is much the more healthy to the inhabitants.

There is another difference in the climate of these two provinces, which has an intimate connection with husbandry, the winters being so much milder, as to allow the cattle being left out all winter. Mr. Kalm took notice of this[1] (which I before remarked was not the custom in New York). Notwithstanding, says he, it snowed several days and nights together, and the snow lay six inches high upon the grounds, yet all the cattle are obliged to stay day and night in the fields, during the whole winter. For neither the English nor the Swedes had any stables, but the Germans and the Dutch had preserved the custom of their country, and generally kept their cattle in stables during winter. Almost all the old Swedes say that on their first arrival in this country they

[1] See Peter Kalm, *Travels into North America* (3 vols., London, 1770).

made stables for their cattle, as is usual in Sweden; but as the English came and settled among them, and left their cattle in the fields all winter, as is customary in England, they left off their former custom, and adopted the English one. They owned, however, that the cattle suffered greatly in winter, when it was very cold, especially when it froze after rain; and that some cattle were killed by it in several places, in the long winter of the year 1741. About noon the cattle went into the woods, where there were yet some leaves on the young oak; but they did not eat the leaves, and only bit off the extremities of the branches, and the tops of the youngest oaks. The horses went into the maize fields, and ate the dry leaves on the few stalks which remained. The sheep ran about the woods and on the corn-fields. The chickens perched on the trees of the gardens at night, for they had no particular habitation. The hogs were likewise exposed to the roughness of the weather within a small inclosure.*

The soil in general is sandy, and upon the whole inferior in fertility to both New York and Pennsylvania; it is an error in several writers, who have treated of the agriculture, &c. of these provinces, to class them together; for the soil on the sides of the river Delaware, which parts this province from Pennsylvania, is quite different; on the New Jersey side it is all sandy, and on the other side it is loam and clay.[2]

The products are the same with those of New York, both in corn, and roots, and fruit, excepting the pease are found to thrive much better in the latter; and the peaches of New Jersey are of a finer flavour than those of New York.

On the most sandy parts of the province, and which to appearance are very poor, they cultivate maize to advantage;

---

* Kalm's *Travels into North America*, II, 51.

[2] This is not true of upper New Jersey.

and on this sand it grows eight feet high; but in the cultivation of it they are very inattentive to its nature; sowing
rye broad-cast between the rows, which precludes that weeding and hoeing which is so necessary to this plant. The aspara-
gus plant is a common weed in maize plantations here, which,
sowing rye, prevents the farmer from eradicating. Others,
yet more slovenly, mark out the hillock for sowing the maize
and leave the intervals of five or six feet untouched. About
New Brunswic[k], Amboy, &c. and many tracts on the river
Rareton [Raritan], the soil is much richer, and the maize is
finer: about this part the country is in general beautifully
variegated, and almost entirely cultivated.

Buckwheat is very generally cultivated in New Jersey,
they find it pays them even as well as wheat, by its superior
produce: they never give any other preparation to the land
for it than one or two ploughings, and harrow in the feed,
about a bushel and half to the acre, which yields them, if
the season is wet, for dry years do not suit it, from 30 or 40
bushels on good land, and very seldom less than 28. They
make bread, or more properly speaking, cakes of it, which are
eaten by every body, but its principal uses here, as in Europe,
are for fattening poultry and hogs.

Rye is a common crop in New Jersey, which is rather surprising, for wheat yields as good products. What is extraordinary, the farmers in this country sow less seed rye than
in England, where two bushels are the common quantity for
an acre, but here they sow only one; they commonly receive
twenty in return. Barley is cultivated in common over the
whole province; they sow two bushels an acre, and receive
from 30 to 50 bushels; this seems to be the grain which thrives
better in the province than any of the European ones.

All the bread-corn of this country yields sufficient, in the very worst seasons, to feed the inhabitants; and not only to feed them, but at a reasonable and equable price: the bread eat by the lowest ranks, whether of maize, wheat, or of rye, is of the finest sort that can be gained from the grain; nor is the crop in general ever known so scanty as materially to affect the market price, which is greatly owing to the constant and regular exportation which always goes forward.

Cabbages are lately cultivated here by almost every planter in the province, the sort is the great white winter cabbage; it is not found only in gardens, but whole fields of it are common; it is eat in large quantities in every family, but the cows get no slight portion of the crop; for hogs also they are much esteemed. There are no tracts of good land in this province without having portions assigned to the culture of hemp; which does extraordinary well here. To the north of New Jersey, the pieces sown with this plant are but small, but here, large fields of it are everywhere to be seen, which is a prospect that ought not a little to endear us to this country, for no staple produced in America, not even sugar, is more valuable.[3] Unfortunately they nowhere produce more than is sufficient for home consumption; but this, I apprehend, is owing to a want of sufficient encouragement; no object can demand it more, or pay us better for it, yet has not the legislature hit upon the proper effective means for

[3] The British government was very anxious to secure hemp, lumber, pitch and tar, so necessary for British shipyards, from Colonial America rather than from countries with which England might at any time be involved in war. It was for this reason that the British government repealed the import duties in so far as the colonies were concerned, and offered bounties on such goods as should be shipped to the British Isles. The bounty on hemp was made £6 per ton as early as 1702. Deep, rich soil and plenty of moisture were essential to its successful production. Cf. G. L. Beer, *The Commercial Policy of England toward the American Colonies* (New York, 1922), pp. 398–420.

extending the culture, so as the mother country, as well as
the navigation of New York and Philadelphia, may profit
by it: an object which one cannot apprehend so difficult as
this negligence might make us believe.

In the most southern parts of the province, saffron is commonly planted;[4] but the drug produced is not reckoned so
good as that which is the product of England: this is not to
be attributed to either soil or climate, for both suit it in an
extraordinary degree; but they are not careful enough in
the culture, nor in the manufacture of the commodity after
it is produced: they do not weed the crops with that assiduous
care which the planters of Cambridgeshire and Flanders exert,
and which seems to be essential to the success: nor are they
equally attentive to curing, drying, and caking of it.

They have, in various parts of New Jersey, many tracts of
meadow land, much of which is marshy; they mow them
twice a year, about the latter end of May, and the end of
August or beginning of September; they get large crops of
hay, some yield three tons an acre at the two mowings, but
it is of a coarse sort: however, the produce is of great value
in a country where the general fault is the not laying in store
of winter provision for cattle. But there is a general fault
here in the management of all grass lands, which is letting
poor and indifferent sorts of grass occupy ground that would
yield much better sorts: the marshes produce nothing but
the *Carex*.[5] Another circumstance which should not be forgotten is the planters neglecting the artificial grasses, which

---

[4] Saffron, the autumn-flowering species of crocus, has been cultivated
since ancient times. The orange-yellow powder obtained from the stigmas
was used medicinally or for perfume. In some parts of the world it is
highly esteemed as a spice for food. That grown in England at the eve of
the American Revolution was esteemed the best in the world.

[5] A genus of herbs belonging to the sedge family.

they might have upon their uplands, from their dependance upon these marshes; this has another bad consequence in making the farmers adopt a worse system than they otherwise would; for such farmers as have some marsh land have no notion of sowing the clovers upon their arable fields, by way of a fallow; which one would suppose they must do, rather than leave them to rest without any other crop than weeds. This dependance on marsh land, however, by no means proves answerable to their cattle, for in no province are all the four-footed animals worse treated.

Every farm in New Jersey has a large orchard belonging to it, some of them of a size far surpassing any thing in England. The common fruits are apples and peaches, with some cherries and pears; the peaches are of a fine flavour, and in such amazing plenty that the whole stock of hogs on a farm eats as many as they will, and yet the quantity that rot under the trees is astonishing. Apples are not suffered to go to such waste as they make cyder in vast quantities, and also export them by ship-loads to the West Indies. This favourable climate to fruit is a circumstance of great importance to all ranks of people, especially the lower ones that settle there; since it gives them a plenty of one article of food, very wholesome in this climate, without the least expence or trouble. Water-melons also are in such plenty that there is not a farmer or even a cottager without a piece of ground planted with them: in some parts of the province they have whole fields of these and gourds. The country people eat them as they do in Naples and the Ecclesiastical State,[6] at all times of the day while they are at their labour, when thirsty; in the same manner as a labourer in England would drink ale or small beer; with this difference, that

[6] Papal lands of Central Italy.

the fruit never intoxicates, and if taken with any tolerable moderation is perfectly wholesome.

In a word, I must observe that the plenty of all the productions of nature which contribute to the food of mankind, which abounds in this province, is equal to what can be expected or wished for by any one: this is owing to the regularity of the summer season; the summer frosts are of no account, they have no cold nights, the rains are not excessive, nor are they hardly ever troubled with a drought; these important circumstances are of such effect, that the farmers are reaping or gathering some crop or other in every month from May to November.

In respect of timber, their woods yield them all the trees that are found to the northward, with the circumstance of being plentifully stored with some of the most valuable sorts; among these the white cedar figures particularly, being the most useful of all their trees. They use it in building preferably to oak, from its lasting longer, and the shingles made of it surpass all others; they are more durable at the same time that they are lighter, circumstances invaluable in shingles, where they have scarcely any other covering to their houses. All the churches, and the houses of the principal people have no other roofs. Of this tree is also made the best rails for fencing; nor are the posts of it bad, as it long resists putrefaction; great numbers of hoops are also made of it, and likewise staves. But considering the value of this tree, the people of New Jersey are very deficient in their care of it; the farmers and settlers seem to make little account of it, but destroy all with the same relentless severity that is common throughout all our colonies. The sassafras is much less valuable, yet they leave that standing singly about their cleared fields.

Having thus particularized the principal products of the country, I shall, in the next place, offer a few remarks on the defects in the management of the farmers which are most striking; since it is only by properly attending to these, that future improvements are to be expected. First I shall observe that their culture of maize deserves much reprehension: so luxuriant a vegetable demands great attention in the management while growing, particularly in the articles of keeping the plants quite clean from weeds, and ploughing the spaces between the rows often enough to keep them fine and well pulverized; instead of which, I have before observed, that they sow rye in them, or else leave them to a crop of weeds; this is miserable management, and such as tends strongly to keep the ground in that bad state which is a general enemy to all improvement; maize is of itself a very exhausting plant, and requires all the nourishment that can be given to it; this nourishment is not manure only but the hoeings and ploughings which surround the plant that keep the land loose, and kill all the weeds, and for this purpose there is no article of culture that is better adapted than one which will admit being planted at the distance of six or eight feet *square;* for if the rows only were so far asunder, and the plants thicker together, they then could receive only the common horse-hoeing, which would not be near so efficacious: it was certainly with this intention that good farmers first used this method of planting, nor could there well be a greater perversion of the method than keeping to the distances, and instead of ploughing, cropping them with rye.

I need not observe here that in all countries one great principle of husbandry is the procuring and using as much dung and manure as possible. The farmers of New Jersey cannot raise hemp for exportation in large quantities for want of more manure; yet do they give in to one practice which is very negligent: they leave the straw of most [of] the buck-wheat they cultivate about their fields in heaps; they find their cattle will not eat it and so think there is no other use for it; but surely these men might reflect on the importance of *litter*, as well as *food* for cattle; in the consumption of their hay and other straw they might certainly use far more than they have, or perhaps can have; but to possess it on their own farms without using it is unpardonable; nor is it a universal practice which keeps the whole country in counte-nance, for there are some planters who have better ideas, use all their straw carefully for litter; and the advantage which these men reap from the practice ought surely to make the rest follow their example. There is no error in husbandry of worse consequence than not being sufficiently solicitous about manure; it is this error that makes the planters in New Jersey and our other colonies seem to have but one object, which is ploughing up fresh land. The case is, they exhaust the old as fast as possible till it will bear nothing more, and then, not having manure to replenish it, nothing remains but taking new land to serve in the same manner. Whereas would they be properly attentive, raising as much manure as possible at the same time that they introduced their crops in a proper system so as to keep the land clean and in heart, in this case they would find no such necessity of changing the soil: and by the use of clovers in the manner they are sown in Britain, all their lands would be in profit, and perhaps equally profitable; instead of which they have now only a part under the plough that pays them any thing, and the rest are over-run with weeds and trumpery. One would imagine that the error of such a conduct would soon be discovered and rectified of itself; but the American planters and farmers are in general the greatest slovens in christendom; plenty of land ruins their husbandry in every respect of general conduct—neatness—good management—spirited attempts, &c. Kalm confirms these observations, and carries the cause back to the first coming of the settlers; he says,

After the inhabitants have converted a tract of land into fields which had been a forest for many centuries together, and which consequently had a very fine soil, they use it as such, as long as it will bear any corn; and when it ceases to bear any, they turn it into pasture for the cattle (*that is, leave it to whatever spontaneous growth of weeds comes*) and take new corn-fields in another place where a fine soil can be met with, and where it has never been made use of for this purpose. This kind of agriculture will do for some time; but it will afterwards have bad consequences, as every one may clearly see. The depth and richness of the soil they found here who came over from England (as they were preparing land for ploughing which had been covered with woods from times immemorial) misled even the English, and made them careless husbandmen. It is well known that the Indians lived in this country for several centuries before the Europeans came into it; but it is likewise known that they lived chiefly by hunting and fishing and had hardly any fields. They planted maize, and some species of beans and gourds, and at the same time, it is certain that a plantation of such vegetables as serve an Indian family during one year, take up no more ground than a farmer in our country (*Sweden*) takes to plant cabbage for his family upon, at least a farmer's cabbage and turnep ground taken together is always as extensive, if not more so than the corn-fields and kitchen gardens of an Indian family. Therefore the Indians could hardly subsist for one month upon the produce of their gardens and fields. Commonly, the little villages of the Indians are about twelve or eighteen miles distant from each other. From

hence one may judge how little ground was formerly employed
for corn-fields, and the rest was over grown with thick and tall
trees; and though they cleared, as it is usual, new ground as soon
as the old one had quite lost its fertility, yet such little pieces as
they made use of were very inconsiderable when compared with
the vast forests which remained. Thus the upper fertile soil increased considerably, for centuries together; and the Europeans,
coming to America, found a rich and fine soil before them, lying
as loose between the trees as the best bed in a garden. They had
nothing to do but to cut down the wood, put it up in heaps, and
to clear the dead leaves away. They could then immediately proceed to ploughing, which in such loose ground is very easy; and
having sown their corn, they got a most plentiful harvest. This
easy method of getting a rich crop has spoiled the English and
other European inhabitants, and induced them to adopt the same
method of agriculture which the Indians make use of; that is, to
sow uncultivated grounds as long as they will produce a crop
without manuring, but to turn them into pastures as soon as they
can bear no more, and to take in hand new spots of ground
covered since time immemorial with woods, which have been
spared by the fire or the hatchet ever since the creation. This is
likewise the reason why agriculture and the knowledge of this
useful branch is so imperfect here that one can learn nothing on
a large tract of land, neither of the English nor of the Swedes,
Germans, Dutch, and French, except that, from their gross mistakes and carelessness for futurity, one finds opportunity every day
of making all sorts of observations, and of growing wise at the
expence of other people. In a word, the corn-fields, the meadows,
the cattle, &c. are treated with equal carelessness, and the English
nation so well skilled in these branches of husbandry is with difficulty found out here. We can hardly be more lavish of our woods
in Sweden and Finland than they are here: their eyes are fixed
upon the present gain, and they are blind to futurity. Every day
their cattle are harassed by labour, and each generation decreases
in goodness and size by being kept short of food as I have before
mentioned. On my travels in this country, I observed several
plants which the horses and cows preferred to all others: they

were wild in this country, and likewise grew well on the driest
and poorest ground, and where no other plants would succeed.
But the inhabitants did not know how to turn this to their advantage, owing to the little account made of natural history, that
science being here (as in other parts of the world) looked upon
as a mere trifle, and the pastime of fools. I am certain, and my
certainty is founded upon experience, that by means of these
plants, in the space of a few years, I have been able to turn the
poorest ground, which would hardly afford food for a cow, into
the richest and most fertile meadow, where great flocks of cattle
have found superfluous food, and are grown fat upon. I own
that these useful plants were not to be found on the grounds of
every planter; but with a small share of natural knowledge, a
man would easily collect them in the places where they were to
be got. I was astonished when I heard the country people complaining of the badness of the pastures; but I likewise perceived
their negligence, and often saw excellent plants growing on their
grounds which only required a little more attention and assistance
from their unexperienced owners.

The principal improvements wanting in the agriculture of
this province, are the introduction of such general good management upon the common crops of the farmers, as to enable
them to raise a staple on some parts of each farm—suppose
hemp and flax: at present their conduct is in general so bad,
that very many planters cannot raise an acre of hemp, &c.
this is owing to the neglects which prevail so much throughout their management; and especially to the badness of their
systems: on the contrary, they should adopt the best British
husbandry of introducing crops which yield both winter and
summer food for cattle, between such as are found most to
exhaust the land; an idea, which would in the execution,
bring with it a remedy for almost all the inconveniencies they
feel at present, suppose they proceed in some such system
as this:

1. Maize.
2. Roots for winter food of cattle, or cabbage.
3. Barley or oats.
4. Clovers.
5. Wheat.
6. Buckwheat.
7. Barley or oats.
8. Roots.
9. Roots.
10. Hemp.

[these crops to be] varied in different fields, so that the total quantities of each article might be proportioned to the size of the plantation. Two crops of roots, both well manured, would be a preparation that would bring hemp on all the good and tolerable land in New Jersey. In this system dung would not be wanting, because there is so much food for cattle cultivated that great stocks might be kept, which with a due management of litter would enable the planter to keep his fields always in heart; instead of the seventh crop of barley, perhaps maize might be thrown in again: it is true, it is a great exhauster, but then it yields such an immense quantity of excellent fodder, that, with a proper attention to cattle and dung, I don't know whether it may not more than make amends for that quality. The reader will observe that if this system is changed for such as are common in Jersey, of corn in succession till a piece of land is worn out, so far from being able to have a portion in hemp, they cannot plainly do well even by their corn, since only the first crops on a piece of new land enjoy a tolerable preparation. Nothing but such an improvement in the general management of common husbandry in our old colonies can ever make hemp an article of exportation in them: and a circumstance which is continually acting even against that is the vast increase of people, which has of late years so raised the price of grain among them, as to make the culture of it much more profitable than formerly; this perhaps may rise higher still, and if that is the case, it may come to be more profitable than even hemp; which is not so rich a product to the farmer as those may think, who consider only the many hundred thousand pounds that are paid by England for it. Hemp is not near equal to tobacco in profit.

The inhabitants of this province consist almost entirely of planters; and though there are many considerable estates for that country among them, yet in general they are little freeholds, cultivated by the owners; they have no town of any note, New York and Philadelphia being their places of export and import, Perth Amboy not being yet considerable; this circumstance keeps them very much at home and pretty free from luxury, that is from the pleasures of a capital: they live in a very plentiful manner, which indeed they could hardly fail of doing in so plentiful a country; for no where on the coast are the necessaries of life in greater plenty. Fish, flesh, fowl, and fruits, every little farmer has at his table in a degree of profusion; and the lower classes, such as servants and labourers, artizans, and mechanics in the villages are all very well cloathed and fed; better than the same people in Britain. Tea, coffee, and chocolate, among the lowest ranks, are almost as common as tea in England; they are universal articles in every farmer's house, and even among the poor.

CHAPTER XII

PENNSYLVANIA

Climate of Pennsylvania—Soil—Productions—Agricul-ture—Defects—Improvements

THE climate of Pennsylvania has a strong distinction between the maritime and back parts; the former, for near a hundred miles, is much like New Jersey, or rather hotter; but the latter is more temperate and pleasant, neither so cold in winter, nor so hot in summer, being in all respects as agreeable and healthy a climate as can any where be found in America. The heat in this province is not sufficient for rice, nor is there that plenty of swamp land (happily for the inhabitants) that is found more to the south; tobacco grows well in many parts of it, yet did it never become a staple, not however owing to the climate, for in Canada they have some tobacco. But for wheat and all kinds of plants, cultivated in Europe, with fruits, few parts of America exceed the back country of Pennsylvania; that is to say, the hilly (not the mountainous) tracts. The air is very clear and healthy; the sky serene; and in general the climate agrees perfectly well with European constitutions. In the worst parts of the province, the winters, though severe, considering the latitude, do not generally last above two months, that is, the season of frost and snow. In summer, the heats here are great, and almost without intermission; but in the hilly parts these heats are, as I before observed, much moderated: it is owing to this warm sun, that melons, water-melons, pump-ions,[1] and other fruits which here require hot-beds, and some that cannot be raised with them, grow abroad, and in the common fields in a plenty and of a flavour much superior to what is found more to the northwards; and though no better treated than turneps, they are ripe so early as July. Cherries are ripe by the twenty-fifth of May, and wheat is commonly reaped before the end of June. The months of September, part of October, April, May, and the first half of June, are the fine and agreeable months in this country.

A considerable part of the soil of this province is a sand, or light sandy loam; these prevail chiefly in the maritime parts; with variations however, for in some large tracts it is a strong loam, and in others clay. In the back parts of the province there are immense tracts of a black mould and rich loam; and in general the new forest land has several inches, whatever may be the soil, of a light black mould, which is certainly formed in long process of time by the putrefaction of vegetable substances. The finest parts of the province are the level tracts that join upon the Alleg[h]any mountains.

The productions of this country, in corn, timber, and fruits, are nearly the same as those of the Jerseys; only exceeding them in quality and plenty. Vines are in greater abundance, and mulberry trees among the most common in the province. The fruits are finer, and if any thing in greater plenty; hogs are frequently fattened with peaches; for in the orchards they fall in such quantities, that great numbers are left to rot upon the ground.

Wood grows very scarce near Philadelphia, however plentiful it may be in the remoter parts of Pennsylvania: the first

[1] Pumpkins.

settlers, with the usual foresight of the Americans, destroyed the timber, as if it was impossible they should ever want any; which, with the continued consumption ever since, for building, firing, and by iron works, have so lessened it that wood is almost as dear at Philadelphia as it is in some parts of Britain; indeed in winter, firing is one of the most expensive articles of housekeeping in that capital. The best fuel here is the hickory, a species of the walnut; then they prefer the white and black oaks. Notwithstanding the want of wood here, there are not far from Philadelphia some very considerable woods; but being the private property of people of fortune, they were reserved for many years in expectation of that high price which the commodity now fetches. Within these ten years much has been felled, but there yet remains large tracts full of very fine timber, which is every day cutting [being cut] down.

In the productions commonly cultivated, wheat is the grand article of the province. They sow immense quantities, about the latter end of September generally; rising from two to three bushels of seed an acre, which on good lands yield from 25 to 32 bushels per acre; on fields of inferior quality, or such as are almost exhausted by yielding corn, they get from 15 to 25 bushels, and sometimes not so much as 15, but this never happens without its being owing to previous bad management. Some few planters have summer fallow for wheat, in the English manner, but the common preparation is the ground lying what they call fallow, which is the same management as that of Jersey and New York; viz. leaving the land, after it is exhausted by yielding corn, to recover itself under a crop of spontaneous growth, weeds or whatever trumpery comes: or else they sow it in succession, after wheat or other corn. It is owing to this general bad management that they get not greater crops; for in the back parts of the province are as fine lands for yielding this grain as any in the world; but soil alone will not do, good culture is no less requisite.

Nor is it to be forgotten here, for one should not praise or condemn in wholesale, that some planters have introduced the English way of sowing wheat on clover lays, which has been found one of the greatest improvements that ever were introduced; for by this husbandry, the lands, at a smaller expence than usual, are made to yield much better crops. I may also remark that this most beneficial practice increases in Pennsylvania. It is to be attributed to more enlightened knowledge spreading in the province, from the voyages to Britain being more frequent, and from books of husbandry being more read in proportion to the increase of wealth and luxury: the same causes will doubtless by and by operate, however gradually, in introducing other practices which in Europe have been found beneficial. I have been informed that a gentleman in the back parts of this province has introduced the culture of wheat by the drill plough, which was invented by Mr. Tull,[2] an English writer, and since perfected in France by M. du Hamel:[3] it answered greatly;

[2] See *supra*, p. 38.

[3] Henri Louis Duhamel Du Monceau (1700–1782), eminent economist and botanist, was one of the most remarkable French savants of the eighteenth century. His discovery of the parasitical fungus which was destroying the roots of the saffron plant won him admission to the French Academy of Sciences in 1728. Thereafter he wrote more than sixty memoirs, nearly all on important subjects. Along with the naturalist Buffon he made numerous experiments on the growth and strength of wood. He experimented also on the growth of the mistletoe, on layer planting, and on smut on corn. He was probably the first to distinguish clearly between the alkalis, potash, and soda. His *Treatise on the Culture of Land* (Paris, 1751), a *Treatise on the Trees and Shrubs which grow in France in the Open Ground* (Paris, 1755), and *De la Physique des arbres* (Paris, 1758), are regarded as his most important works.

but the culture of maize is the completest horse-hoeing husbandry of all others.

They sow large quantities of rye on their sandy lands, and
on other fields when they are exhausted with wheat; rye is
reckoned to pay them in some parts of the province, as well
as wheat.

Barley is also a common grain in this country, though not
so general as in Britain, where it yields the universal drink
of all ranks of people; whereas in Pennsylvania, the quantities of cyder made is prodigious, and rum is consumed in
great quantities; not however that beer is unknown, on the
contrary they make much, and cultivate hops also with success. Of barley they sow four or five bushels on an English
acre, generally in April, and it is ripe the end of July. Oats
are managed in the same manner: the preparation for both
these grains is common with that of wheat, save their giving
wheat the preference in soil, and earliness in the system.
They sow them on the American fallow of weeds; after one
another, and very often after wheat and maize. Barley yields,
on good land, from 30 to 40 bushels, and on bad from 20
to 25 [bushels]. Near the Alleg[h]any mountains, on some
fresh land, from 50 to 65 bushels of barley have been known;
a crop often exceeded in England, where good management
more than ballances the advantages of soil and climate; 35
bushels of oats are reckoned a very good crop.

Maize is not cultivated in such quantities in some parts
of Pennsylvania as in more northern colonies, where wheat
is not so common. Here is a field of it near every farm house,
but small in proportion to what is found in New Jersey,
New York, &c. for the plain reason that they cannot raise
wheat to equal advantage. But in some parts of this province,
particularly the sandy ones, there are large quantities; they

cultivate it nearly on the same principles as in New Jersey, that is, in a most incomplete manner: for even rye is sometimes sown in the intervals, which is such a piece of bad husbandry as ought to be banished by every man who would pride himself on having ideas of modern culture. Wheat thriving so well in Pennsylvania, makes them neglect maize; which is a much less valuable grain: this is a distinction which should always be made; it is not that maize is not a profitable crop in itself, but their lands will yield one which is much more beneficial. This will be the better understood when I add that Indian corn yields but 2s. 7d. a bushel, when wheat is at 7s. 6d. both Pennsylvania currency; a difference that at once accounts for the preference in a country that will yield wheat.

Much greater quantities of hemp and flax are raised in this colony than in any to the northward: this is owing to a more favourable climate, and to a better soil; for in the parts of Pennsylvania adjoining to the Alleg[h]any mountains are very large tracts of land, which are as favourable to the production of these plants as can be wished: it is not want of good land in certain quantities, nor of climate, that prevents the export of hemp, but the demand for it at Philadelphia, which exceeds, for home consumption, what the province can raise. Improvements might be made, of which more hereafter, that would enable Pennsylvania to export hemp; but without a change in certain branches of rural economy, they never will raise this commodity for exportation. A people increasing at such an amazing rate makes the necessaries of life so dear that no other husbandry answers so well, that is, they possess not a staple that will pay them for a neglect of wheat and common provisions. Hemp and flax would be as proper ones as could be proposed to this colony, but they do not pay well enough to make them such objects as tobacco is in Virginia; and while that is the case, we may be certain it will never be planted. Of flax-seed there goes annually to Ireland large quantities.

And here I should remark that they have in this province a native flax, which promises to be a treasure. It is a sort of *dogs-bane*.[4] The country people use it instead of flax, for various domestic purposes; preparing the stalks of it in the same manner as we prepare flax or hemp. They spin and weave several kinds of stuffs of it: it was of this plant that the Indians made a kind of linen bags, fishing net twine, and other manufactures, long before the Europeans settled on this continent. It is an idea which ought to be pursued; what is at present used is nothing but the quantity gathered wild as a weed; why not take the hint, and make it an article of culture? I have not a doubt but it would succeed well, and answer all the purposes of the real flax, with this infinite advantage, that it is congenial to the climate and consequently would thrive far better than flax, which has been imported here from Europe. Nothing can argue less attention to the agriculture of these colonies than overlooking the natural productions of the continent in favour of the transplanted ones, which it would be folly to suppose could thrive so well; for the climate of North America is quite peculiar: even in the southern latitude of Philadelphia, which in Europe hardly knows what a frost is, the cold is so severe that ships cannot stir from that port for at least one month of the winter. Let us compare this with the same parallel in Europe and we shall find the amazing difference of the two hemispheres. This ought to teach them the value of those productions, which are

---

[4] A family of herbs having a milky juice poisonous to dogs; sometimes called Indian hemp. Dogsbane is also known as apocyuum.

indigenous in the country: hemp, flax, and vines are all instances, and striking ones.

Cabbages and turneps are commonly cultivated in Pennsylvania, partly for the table, and partly for cattle, but by no means for the latter in the quantities they ought to be: they raise both of an immense size, and without any very extraordinary culture, though they seldom attempt them without dung. One reason why they are bad husbandmen, in this respect, is the favourableness of the climate, which is such as to allow cattle to be out all winter and to pick up their living in the woods; such a circumstance must necessarily render the farmers negligent in raising winter food for cattle, which for so many reasons is a point in husbandry so necessary in all sorts of countries, since none I ever yet heard of, is, from heat of climate alone, so rich as to dispense with the want of dung. Another great disadvantage of this neglect of turneps and cabbages is the want of them among the successive crops of corn which the Pennsylvania farmers crowd upon their land in much too quick a succession.

Mulberry trees are among the most common productions of the province of Pennsylvania; indeed, they are so plentiful that silk might be made in any quantities, provided the country was populous enough; but agriculture answers so much better in a country where land is had almost for nothing that people cannot make profit by silk worms; at least they think so: yet for curiosity, some families have kept them, and wound off large quantities of silk, more than sufficient to shew that any quantities might be made, if the people could or would find time for the business. Nor do I think that any employment of their time would pay them better; especially considering that six weeks in a year is all that is required for making silk.

Buckwheat is not so commonly cultivated in Pennsylvania as more to the northward; what the reason for this is I know not, since it agrees perfectly well with the climate, and produces larger crops than in New York: perhaps they find wheat so much more profitable than any other product, that they cultivate it on land which more to the northward would be differently employed. They sow about a bushel and half to the acre, which yields sometimes more than forty bushels, but generally from 30 to 36.

In several parts of Pennsylvania, they are very well acquainted with the husbandry of watering meadow lands by conducting brooks over them; which they do in a very artificial manner, bringing the water in little streams along the sides of the hills, and letting it into the meadows at command. By this management, which agrees wonderfully in so hot a climate, they mow three crops a year, whereas without water they would mow them but once, and at that mowing not get so much as by the worst of the present three. This is an improvement well known in many parts of Europe, particularly on the Thames in England, in Flanders, in Lombardy, and in several of the provinces of Spain, but it is no where practiced to more advantage than in Pennsylvania; which is surprising, considering the very low state in which most other parts of husbandry is found.

Many of the planters, especially in the back parts of the province, where the wild tracts are adjoining, keep great stocks of cattle: some of them have from forty to sixty horses; and four or five hundred head of horned cattle, oxen, cows, bulls, calves, and young cattle; they let them run through the woods, not only in summer, but also in winter; which is a circumstance that makes them very inattentive to the providing winter food: sheep also they have in great numbers, and tho' the wool does not equal the best in England or Spain, yet is it much better than is produced in many of our counties, and makes cloth that answers exceedingly well for the general wear of the province, fine as well as coarse cloths; and accordingly, almost all the farmers, and their servants, with the lower classes of other sorts, are clad in it; they have no lands in the whole province but what do excellently for feeding sheep, even the very worst tracts maintain great numbers. Sheep are kept in such numbers that wool might be a valuable article of exportation unwrought, and by a proper policy in the mother country, wool might become as good an import from the colonies as any other.

The farmers make their fences like those to the northward, of planks and posts; but in those parts of the province which have been long settled, wood is too scarce for this method, and they have substituted live hedges, not however with judgment, for they have taken the privet for this purpose, which badly answers it for want of spines; they have plenty of hawthorn, but have not yet sagacity to use it. They are in general, throughout the province, very careless of their fences, which is the consequence of having such plenty of land; considerable plantations, that are not yet all under culture, have no other ring fence than marks set upon the trees, so that the cattle turned into the woods may wander into those of other men, and others cattle make equal trespasses; and if the farm joins the wild country, it is the same. Some men are even so careless that when they take in a new field for corn, they will plough, sow, and, sometimes, reap it before they go about [making] the inclosure, submitting to the depredations of cattle rather than have the trouble of fencing it. There is nothing can give a man that only travels through a country so bad an opinion of the husbandry of it, as to see two circumstances; first, the fences in bad order; and, secondly, the corn full of weeds. In many parts of Pennsylvania, a country in which nature has done so much, a man will do so little that both these are almost every where to be seen by every traveller.

Pennsylvania is not without negroe slaves for cultivation, though the number bears no proportion to the white servants; it may also be proper to remark, that there are in this province, and it is the same in others, a difference in the white servants; they have, throughout the province, the same sort of servants that perform work in England, that is, hired by the year, in which case, they are washed, lodged, and boarded, but find their own cloaths; an able bodied man, in husbandry, will get from 10£. to 16£. a year sterling. Maids will get so high as 5£. to 7£. Another sort of white servants, which are unknown in Britain, are the new settlers that are poor. Very many of these cannot even pay their passage from Europe, which amounts to 10£. sterling, and agree therefore with the captain of the ship, that he shall sell them for a certain number of years to be servants, in which case the farmers buy them, that is, pay their freight, &c. and this usually puts something also in the captain's pocket, beyond what he would otherwise have. If the passenger has some money, but not enough, he is then sold for a shorter time to make up the sum. There are laws in the province to regulate this kind of servitude, which seems very strange to us; the master is bound to feed, clothe, and use the servant as well as others. Others that have money enough to pay for their passage, especially Germans, yet will not pay, but choose to be sold in order to have time to gain a knowledge of the language and the manner of living in the country. Both these sorts of servants are greatly preferred to the common hiring method; for the wages do not amount to much more than half the other, and at the same time there is a security of keeping them, which with common servants is not the case; nor are these near so industrious. These distinctions in servitude are met with in other colonies, but they do not occur so often, because for one new comer in them, there are twenty in Philadelphia.

The agriculture of the province is not equal to what the preceding productions would admit of; and to which they might be encouraged by soil, climate, and getting labour more plentifully than many other colonies. I have in two or three instances mentioned bad management, and shall in speaking of their general conduct shew others.

Their system which is a point of so much importance is like that I have mentioned more than once to the northward. They sow a piece of land with wheat till it will bear wheat no longer, and perhaps after that they will do the same by various crops of oats, buckwheat, pease, &c. The following is the system that was pursued in a large new field in a plantation near Durham about fifty miles to the north of Philadelphia, the account was given me, among several others concerning the same plantation, by a person on whose accuracy I can depend.

1. Wheat.	8. Barley.
2. Wheat.	9. Oats.
3. Maize.	10. Barley.
4. Wheat.	11. Buckwheat.
5. Wheat.	12. Barley.
6. Barley.	13. Oats.
7. Barley.	14. Pease.

This is not only a proof of the planter's bad husbandry; it is also a proof of what excellent land it must be to yield such a succession of crops in plenty, enough to induce a man to sow them. After this system for fourteen years, it was left what they call a fallow for seven years more; that is, the land unploughed for whatever spontaneous growth comes; for some years there is nothing but weeds, but there afterwards appears some grasses thinly scattered which cattle eat, many sorts of shrubs and trees also spring up, which the cattle feed on also, and if the land was so to be left for twenty or thirty years longer it would become a forest.

This absurd way of having an eye to nothing but exhausting the land as quick as possible by constant crops of corn, is pernicious to their interests: it is owing as I before said, to plenty of land, for new settlers always take up as much as they possible[y] can, and far more than they know how to stock or cultivate: they can afford no care for manuring, nor yet to clear two pieces of ground for corn as long as one will bear it. They clear a field and have not strength of ploughs and cattle and men to crop more than that; they therefore stick to it as long as they can get any corn, and when the land will no longer bear it, they clear another piece and serve that in the same manner, till they have run through their whole ground, and then they go back again to the piece they cleared first, which by that time is half forest and half weeds and grass; this they clear again and sow it as before with corn as long as it will yield any. It is very evident that this must necessarily be the system while the settlers spend half their fortune in buying the land, that is, in paying the province fees for it: if a man has a hundred pounds in his pocket, and was able with it to cultivate properly forty or fifty acres, and he takes three or four hundred, which in patent fees costs him half his fortune, he then plainly lessens his ability to cultivate, while his cultivation ought to increase greatly. The writers on the subject of husbandry give very numerous instances of this in England, where farmers are too apt to hire much more land than they have money to stock well and manage properly; no wonder therefore, that in America we should see the same error, where all sorts of people turn farmers—where no mechanic or artizan—sailor—soldier—servant, &c. but what, if they get money, take land, and turn farmers.

There are very few defects in rural economy but many instances are here to be produced; and many of which flow from the same cause as their bad system, viz. taking too much land for their money; among which we are to rank their neglect of the native products of the country, which might be turned to profit, such as flax, vines, mulberries, &c. The extreme carelessness every where seen in the whole management of cattle, their slovenly fences, their utter inattention to raising manures, with other circumstances, not of equal importance.

In this condemnation however, there is a tract of country around Philadelphia which is to be exempted: land here is of such value that they think it worth cultivating with some care. There are several estates in that neighbourhood, which are let for twenty shillings an acre; and which even at that rent have been sold at twenty-five years purchase. But all this is the neighbourhood of that flourishing and wealthy city:[5] it does not hold to any great distance from that place. I must also exempt the lands of certain gentlemen who are fond of improvements, and who manage them in a manner

---

[5] At the eve of the American Revolution, Philadelphia with a population of about 25,000, ranked first as the greatest emporium of British America. Boston stood second with a population of slightly over 20,000, and New York in population was close on the heels of its New England rival. See H. J. Carman, *Social and Economic History of the United States*, Vol. I (Boston, 1930), p. 169.

superior to the generality of farmers, to whom it is a great reflection that they do not copy such better methods. These instances however are not so common as one could wish.

Duly considering the state of husbandry in this colony, I shall venture to propose some improvements which I think would greatly further the interests of the inhabitants.

Their system is the first thing that demands attention, because a thousand evils flow from this alone: instead of exhausting their lands with perpetual corn crops, as long as it will bear them, they certainly ought to throw in corn with such moderation as never to exhaust the soil; to inter-mix crops of pease, buckwheat, turneps, cabbages, potatoes, clover, and lucerne among those of maize, wheat, barley, oats, and flax; this would keep the land clean and in heart; and when they had kept it in a system of corn as long as they wanted it, throw in the artificial grasses, that they might have at once a good meadow, instead of that miserable management which they call a fallow. The land, in their system, after it is done with corn, is of no more value than the sky to them, for some years at least; but in the system now proposed, they would get meadows that would feed large herds of cattle, or yield at least a ton or a ton and half of hay per acre immediately. The great advantage of pursuing a system of this nature, even upon their own principles, would be that it admits their spreading their culture for fresh land in the manner they do at present; it only obviates the mischief arising from exhausting it, and leaving it of no value.

In this proposition I mentioned lucerne, a grass which I am confident would answer with them to a great degree, and for several reasons. They know not how to raise dung, from the circumstance of their cattle running abroad all the winter; for where cattle are not confined, no dung can be made. The want of dung makes them solicitous for such land, and at the same time much confines their culture; with plenty of it, all their crops would be far more considerable: another point to be mentioned, is the heat of the climate, in a great measure, burning up the pasture, (except the watered ones) in all the maritime half of the province: now to remedy all these inconveniencies, I propose lucerne. In that climate, the common broad cast culture would do for it, and perhaps best. They should use it for soiling (as the British farmers call the operation) their horses, cows, and other cattle, under cover all summer through, keeping them well and regularly littered with straw; and if they formed composts of the dung thus raised, with marle or loam, in the manner it is practiced in the West Indies, it would be so much the better.

In this conduct they would, on a small quantity of land, be able to keep a large stock of cattle, which is alone a circumstance of great consequence in any country, and the quantity of dung they would be able to raise, if they used litter plentifully would be of the highest importance in the management of their farms.

A union of this method with the improvement of their system, mentioned above, would not only vastly increase their products of corn, making one acre yield as much as two or three, but would also enable them at the same time to raise staples for exportation in a greater plenty than they do at present, flax-seed being the only one which they raise in their fields; both flax and hemp might then be valuable articles with them.

In the next place let me observe that their inattention to vines is very inexcusable. In the back country they have hilly, and even rocky dry tracts of ground, that would in all probability answer perfectly well for them; their argument,

that the wine made from these grapes at present is bad, is
not a conclusive one: when planted in vineyards, and properly
trained and dressed, with the intervals between the rows,
cultivated as in Europe, the produce might and probably
would be of a different flavour from the uncultured grapes
now found under the drip of forest trees. It is at least a
point that should be tried; for though the reasoning of the
Pennsylvania farmers will never convince the world, fair
experiment would; the importance of the object loudly speaks
the expediency, not to say necessity, of the trial. Another
objection made here is the want of hands; but that is obviat-
ing every day by extreme increase of population: nor do we
know, with any accuracy, that the vineyard culture in America
would not answer the present price of labour; it is to be remembered that they do not require attendance during the
whole year, but only at an inconsiderable part of it.

Another improvement which might be made, is the introduction of silk: mulberries are in great plenty throughout
the province, and silk has been wound off there, equal to
the finest that comes from India or Italy. The people do
not in the least pretend that the climate is improper, their
only argument is that the price of labour is too high. But
this is as mistaken as any thing that could be urged, for
servants are in no countries hired to make silk; it is a work
executed at a certain season of the year, which lasts only for
six weeks, by the females of the family, by the young, and
aged, that cannot perform laborious work: this is the course
of the business in the silk countries of Europe. Silk is a
commodity that is never to be adopted as the principal means
of supporting a people, the time requisite for it is too short,
as it leaves a sufficiency for other articles. Nothing can therefore be more absurd than to urge the high price of labour

as a reason why silk cannot be made in this province. Labour is yet dearer in Georgia, but silk is there made in large quantities.

The native flax is another article which ought to be attended to by sensible planters in this province. It is amazing to think that more experiments have not been made on it: it is certainly an article that promises great advantages: but trials [are needed] of a nature more accurate and scientific than what is to be expected from the planters and farmers of this country. Persons should, by government, be appointed to examine into this matter, and to try what a proper cultivation will do in improving this production.

These and other articles of improvement, for the province of Pennsylvania, deserve much more attention than they have hitherto met with. Why cannot the gentlemen of Philadelphia, and its neighbourhood, who are lovers of agriculture, form themselves into a society for the encouragement of that noble art? They might, in monthly meetings, be able to settle a plan of operations, which would, in a few years, by means of an annual subscription given in bounties and premiums, alter the face of things. They might reduce these doubtful points to certainty; they might introduce a better system of rural economy, and be in a few years of infinite service to their country.

Before I conclude this chapter, I shall insert a table of the exports of the province.

Biscuit flour, 350,000 barrels, at 20s. ...... £.	350,000
Wheat, 100,000 qrs. at 20s.	100,000
Beans, pease, oats, Indian corn, and other grain	12,000
Salt beef, pork, hams, bacon, and venison ...	45,000
Bees wax 20,000 lb. at 1s.	1,000
Tongues, butter, and cheese	10,000

Deer, and sundry other sorts of skins	50,000
Live stock and horses	20,000
Flax-seed, 15,000 hhds. at 40s.	30,000
Timber plank, masts, boards, staves, and shingles	35,000
Ships built for sale, 25, at £. 700	17,500
Copper ore, and iron in pigs and bars	35,000
Total £.	705,500

Upon this account I must observe that far the greatest part is the cultivated produce of the lands; which is the very contrary to New England, whose lands yield nothing to export. In proportion to this circumstance, is the value of a colony, for it is the nature of colonization that the people ought, on first principles, to support themselves by agriculture alone. Wheat appears to be the grand export of this province: that, and other articles of food, amount to above half a million, which is a vast sum of money to export regularly, besides feeding every rank of people in the utmost plenty; but of late years this has risen to much more, for wheat, instead of being at 20s. a quarter, is at above 30s. No circumstance in the world can be more strong, in proof of the temperature, moderation, and healthiness of the climate, than this of exporting such quantities of wheat, which, throughout the globe, thrives no where in climates insalubrious to mankind: though nearly a universal grower, yet it is an article of export only in good and wholesome climates: consider our European experience, the exports of wheat are from England and Poland to the coast of Africa. All the intermediate countries, from extremity to extremity, are temperate and fine climates. Barbary, though hot, is one of the best in the world; provided (as in all cases of climate) you fix in the tracts that lie properly with respect to other circumstances, such as a freedom from low marshy coasts, which in all countries, especially hot ones, are the most unwholesome in the world: hilly and mountainous tracts are generally wholesome and temperate.

This export of more than seven hundred thousand pounds worth of products shews of what vast importance this colony is of to Britain; but I must observe, that in a national light it is much to be regretted that a larger portion of this sum is not in what are commonly called *staples;* that is, products which cannot be raised in proper quantities in the mother country; or which she is forced to buy of foreigners, such are copper, iron, naval stores, flax seed, &c. The Pennsylvania export of these is,

Skins .... £.	50,000
Flax seed	30,000
Timber	35,000
Ships	17,500
Copper and iron	35,000
£.	167,500

As to wheat and provision, that part of them which goes to the West Indies is in the light of a staple, but all that comes to Europe rivals the exports of Britain, and are to be considered differently. This is a fresh proof of the necessity of regulating the husbandry of Pennsylvania so as to enable the farmers to raise more of these valuable products, which are of so great account to the mother country. This is a distinction which is very essential, and which good management may make as much for the advantage of Britain as of the colony.*

* For understanding the importance of staples well, consult [Arthur Young's] *Political Essays concerning the Present State of the British Empire* [London, 1772].

CHAPTER XIII

PENNSYLVANIA

The inhabitants of Pennsylvania—Method of living— New settlers—Mode of settling waste tracts—Planta- tions—Comparison between the husbandry of Britain and Pennsylvania

THIS country is peopled by as happy and free a set of men as any in America: out of trade there is not much wealth to be found, but at the same time there is very little poverty, and hardly such a thing as a beggar in the province. This is not only a consequence of the plenty of the land, and the rate of labour, but also of the principles of the Quakers, who have a considerable share in the gov- ernment of the country. It is much to the honour of this sect that they support their own poor in all countries, in a man- ner much more respectable than known in any other religion.[1]

There are some country gentlemen in Pennsylvania who live on their estates in a genteel and expensive manner, but the number is but small; many are found, who make much such a figure as gentlemen in England of three or four hun- dred pounds a year, but without such a rental; for money is scarce in this country, and all the necessaries and conveniencies of life cheap, except labour. But in general the province is

---

[1] Consult August Jorns, *The Quakers as Pioneers in Social Work* (New York, 1931), chap. i; see also R. M. Jones, *The Quakers in the American Colonies* (London, 1911), chap. xi.

inhabited by small freeholders, who live upon a par with great farmers in England; and many little ones who have the necessaries of life and nothing more.

In the settled parts of the colony, there are few situations to be found that are without such a neighbourhood as would satisfy country gentlemen of small estates, or country parsons in Britain. There are, besides Philadelphia, many small towns in which are found societies that render the country agreeable; and the country itself is scattered with gentlemen at moderate distances, who have a social intercourse with each other, besides occasional parties to Philadelphia.

The most considerable of the freeholders that do not however rank with gentlemen, are a set of very sensible, intelligent, and hospitable people, whose company, in one that is mixed, improves rather than lessens the agreeableness of it; a circumstance owing to many of them being foreigners, which even gives something of a polish to the manners when we find ourselves in the midst of a country principally inhabited by another people. The little freeholders (there are not many farmers, except near Philadelphia) are in ease and circumstances much superior to the little farmers in England.

The method of living in Pennsylvania in country gentlemen's families, is nearly like that of England: the only business is to ride about the plantation now and then, to see that the overseers are attentive to it; all the rest of the time is filled up with entertaining themselves; country sports, in the parts of the province not fully settled, are in great perfection; they have hunting, but their horses are unequal to those of England; shooting and fishing are much more followed, and are in greater perfection than in England, though every man is allowed both to shoot and fish throughout the province, except the latter in cultivated grounds. They have partridges, pheasants, bustards, wild turkies, wild geese, ducks, and other water fowl, wood pigeons, &c. And the rivers are most of them very full of fish, especially in the back country, to which parties are made in boats with nets; in which excursions, shooting is joined: the fish they take are brought home alive in well-boats, and put into their stores: every planter has his pond at least, but generally a chain of them, on a brook, which always supplies fresh water; in these stores, as they call them, are kept the products of their river-fishing, ready at all times for the table.

Their meals are three times a day, and served quite in the English taste: coffee, tea, and chocolate are of the best sorts, cheap enough to be commanded in plenty by every planter, especially coffee and chocolate; sugar also is cheaper than in England; these, with good bread and good butter, give a breakfast superior to what gentlemen of small estates usually make in England. For dinner and supper they are much better supplied, as may easily be supposed, when the plenty is considered that abounds in an American plantation: game, variety of fish, venison almost every where, poultry in prodigious plenty and variety, meat of all kinds, very good, and killed on every plantation of any size; several sorts of fruits, in a plenty surpassing any thing known in the best climates of Europe, such as melons, water-melons, and cucumbers, in the open field; apples, pears, cherries, peaches, nectarines, gooseberries, currants, strawberries, and raspberries, gathering some every month, from May till October. Their grapes, though plentiful to excess, are inferior. These are circumstances that make it neither difficult nor expensive to keep an excellent table. The wine commonly drank is Madeira, at not more than half the price of England; freight is cheaper, and there is none [not any], or a very trifling, duty. French and Spanish wines are also drank; rum is very cheap; and good beer is brewed by those who are attentive to the operation.

From hence it is sufficiently clear, that the time passed at the table need not be a barren entertainment. To this we must add reading, which fills up some hours very agreeably; great numbers of books, including all the new publications, are imported from London at Philadelphia; besides which, that city, which has a college and a literary society itself,[2] employs several printers, and sends forth news-papers every day. If to this we add, that there are many families in which music is well understood—that Philadelphia abounds with schools of all sorts, and has a college—that the roads for communication are good—the post regular—and carriers numerous, it will upon the whole be thought that gentlemen of education and ideas may, without any violence on themselves, pass their time on a plantation in Pennsylvania, not only in plenty, but agreeably. It must be at once apparent, that a given income would go much further here than in Britain; this is so strongly a truth, that an income of four or five hundred pounds a year, and a plantation, can hardly be spent without extravagance, or indulging some peculiar expence; whereas that income from an estate in Britain will hardly give a man the appearance of a gentleman.

[2] College of Philadelphia and the American Philosophical Society. See Michael Kraus, *Intercolonial Aspects of Culture on the Eve of the Revolution* (New York, 1928). The American Philosophical Society was formed by Benjamin Franklin, Cadwallader Colden, and others in 1743. Franklin suggested that such a society should be "formed of the *Virtuosi* or ingeneous men residing in the several colonies, to be established in the City of Philadelphia as the most central place" in the colonies. Although the Society languished for a time, its membership included men from the colonies of New York, New Jersey, Pennsylvania, Maryland, Carolina, and New England. See J. T. Adams, *Provincial Society, 1690–1763* (New York, 1927).

The new settlers upon the uncultivated parts of the province are either such as go backward to the waste country and take up what land they please, paying the fixed fees to the proprietors, or such as buy uncultivated spots of other planters, who have more than they want, or chuse to sell: in this case, they make as good a bargain as they can; but the land is dearer than that which is had of the proprietors. It is remarkable to see the small tracts that men will buy with a view to support a whole family.

The progress of their work is this; they fix upon the spot where they intend to build the house, and before they begin it, get ready a field for an orchard, planting it immediately with apples chiefly, and some pears, cherries, and peaches. This they secure by an inclosure, then they plant a piece for a garden; and as soon as these works are done, they begin their house: some are built by the countrymen without any assistance, but these are generally very bad hovels; the common way is to agree with a carpenter and mason for so many days work, and the countryman to serve them as a labourer, which, with a few irons and other articles he cannot make, is the whole expence: many a house is built for less than twenty pounds. As soon as this work is over, which may be in a month or six weeks, he falls to work on a field of corn, doing all the hand labour of it, and, from not yet being able to buy horses, pays a neighbour for ploughing it; perhaps he may be worth only a calf or two and a couple of young colts, bought for cheapness; and he struggles with difficulties till these are grown; but when he has horses to work, and cows that give milk and calves, he is then made, and in the road to plenty. It is surprising with how small a sum of money they will venture upon this course of settling; and it proves at the first mention how population must increase in a country where there are such means of a poor man's supporting his family: and in which, the larger the family, the easier is his undertaking.

When a settler is possessed of a tolerable sum of money, as from one hundred to two hundred pounds, or such as begin with from two to six or seven hundred, they reap equal advantages from this plenty of land and the necessaries of life, for their money goes so much farther; and they are able to live much better, and in all respects more comfortably than upon equal sums in Europe; that this is the case will be seen from the following account of a new settlement formed on the river Scoolkuyl [Schuylkill], between 30 and 40 miles beyond Reading near the Kittalanny mountains,[3] in one of the most healthy and beautiful countries in the province. The tract of land was 5,000 acres, which, being part of a large grant not settled, were purchased. The person who settled here went from the West of England, his whole fortune being twelve hundred pounds: it was some years after the event that this account was taken; but though it may not be minutely accurate, yet is it sufficiently so to explain the expences of forming a settlement, and also the advantages of laying out such a sum of money.

Freight and expences of three persons from Bristol £.   57
Expences of a residence at Philadelphia for about
    half a year   25
Purchase of 5,000 acres   267
    N.B. A part of it unprofitable waste.
Building a very neat house fit for a small family;
    the expression,[4] such as in England, would let
    for 20£. a year   96

[3] The Kittalanny (Kittatinny) Mountains are about 2,000 feet high and form one of the ranges extending across Pennsylvania and New Jersey.

[4] Expression as here used refers to the "neat house" in first part of the sentence and means similar to or comparable.

Furniture 90
Barn, stables, and other offices 22
Two negroes 56
Wages for five years, of six German servants
    bought 120
Cloathing and expences one year 32
Implements of husbandry 70
A boat 10
Arms, ammunition and sundries 9
A year's housekeeping and family expences 112
Live stock
    8 horses, at 4£. . . . . £. 32
    10 cows, at 3£. 30
    30 young cattle, at 20s. 30
    70 swine 16
    50 sheep 10
       Poultry 5   123
Cash reserved for feeding the land, orchards, gar-
    dens, and incidental expences 111

                                     £. 1,200

The annual expences of the family, &c. were afterwards:

	£.	s.	d.
Labour, in cloathing negroes, wages paid be- sides the six Germans and labourers . . .	27	10	0
Housekeeping and family expences	60	0	0
Repairs of implements and new ones bought	16	10	0
Expences in building and additions to furni- ture, &c.	20	0	0
Province taxes, &c.	11	11	0
Sundry expences	20	0	0
£.	155	11	0
To which should be added interest of 1,200£. at 5 per cent	60	0	0
Total	215	11	0

The product was extremely various, but for several years it ran nearly as follows, none being reckoned but what was sold off the plantation, the increase of cattle was all the time considerable, besides the family living off the land; the 60£. for housekeeping being only for manufactures, India goods, rum, &c.

	£.	s.	d.
220 quarters of wheat	·220	0	0
40 quarters of Indian corn	14	0	0
100 qrs. of barley, pease, and beans	46	0	0
Product of cattle sold	34	0	0
Fruit and cyder	10	0	0
Sundry sorts of lumber	13	0	0
	337	0	0
Expences	215	0	0
Neat [net] profit .... £.	122	0	0

Which with the 5 per cent. is 182£. which on 1200£. is 15 per cent. This appears to me to be very considerable, for besides this amount of profit there is to be reckoned the increasing value of the estate, from buildings, fruit trees, improvements, and the stock of cattle which on all American farms presently quadruple their numbers. What these articles amounted to cannot be said, but must certainly be considerable; this circumstance with that of living in so plentiful and agreeable a manner, are the greatest advantages of this country: one point is however to be attended to, which is the ability of employing the profit made in increasing the business, hiring more servants and breaking up more land, which would presently increase the profit considerably.

I am of opinion that 15 per cent. is much exceeded by many farmers in England, upon a capital of 1200£., but they do not besides, live in the manner of the Pennsylvanian planter, who has at least the advantages in housekeeping that are enjoyed in England by a country gentlemen of four hundred pounds a year: this makes a vast difference; and the British farmer lies under the disadvantage like all his brethren of not being able to increase his business; but what an amazing advantage compared with this is the cultivated spot being in the midst of 5,000 acres all belonging to the planter, who enlarges his improvements gradually as suits him! This can no where be had in a country that is all parcelled out into estates, except a purchase is made of a tract of waste land; which is of a very different price in Britain and America.

Another account I gained of a new settled plantation, was one on a much smaller scale. It was of 300 acres of waste.

			£.	s.	d.
Patent fees on the grant			30	0	0
Buildings			45	0	0
Implements			17	10	0
Two servants bought			26	0	0
Housekeeping, &c.			36	0	0
Furniture			25	0	0
Orchard and feed			13	10	0
	£.	s.	d.		
2 horses, at 3£. 10s. ...	7	0	0		
4 cows, at 2£. 10s.	10	0	0		
10 swine, at 5s.	2	10	0		
Poultry	0	10	0	20	0	0
			£. 213	0	0

The annual expences were reckoned:

	£.	s.	d.
Taxes and repairs	3	0	0
Implements	5	10	0
Wages and cloathing	16	0	0
Housekeeping, &c.	27	0	0
	51	10	0

The products annually sold in corn and lumber amounted to about 127£. This is very considerable, but the planter and a son both worked almost as hard as his servants. In a few years he got almost the whole grant into culture; purchased more land, had near a dozen servants, and above 200 head of cattle. Such a rise is not to be experienced in cultivated countries.

In no territory in the world, I apprehend, can a man with two or three hundred pounds enter into husbandry with such a prospect of making a small fortune: in England, the sum is nothing; but where there is such a plenty of fresh land to be taken up, the case is different; a man's expences are few, he is enabled to save something every year, and every shilling he saves he can throw into an increase of culture, which is the greatest inducement to industry in the world.

My enquiries into the domestic economy of this province has brought[5] me acquainted with another instance which I shall lay before the reader. Such accounts form but very unentertaining reading for people who look for amusement alone; but I cannot help esteeming them as the only means of gaining that sort of intelligence which is truly useful. The following instance was of a person who left Scotland a few years ago in order to settle in this province.

	£.	s.	d.
Freight from Glasgow to Philadelphia . .	25	0	0
Patent, fees, &c. of 1,000 acres	37	10	0
Building a house, a barn, a stable, a cow-shed, a fruit house, a cyder apparatus, a poultry building, a hog-yard, and a boat-house	136	0	0
Inclosing 86 acres with posts and planks in three divisions	16	0	0

[5] Here "brought" undoubtedly means "made."

	£	s.	d.
Inclosing 111 acres with live hedge and bank in three divisions	21	0	0
Planting an orchard of 16 acres, containing 16,000 apple trees, 2,000 pears, 3,000 cherries and 3,000 peach-trees ..	22	10	0
Expence of the garden	11	10	0
Six negroes	185	0	0
Cloathing and food of ditto for a year ...	22	0	0
One servant, a foreigner, bought for three years, at 4£. 10s.	13	10	0
Two ditto for 4 years, at 3£. 5s.	26	5	0
Cloathing, a year	14	10	0
Furniture	36	0	0
Arms	6	13	6
Ammunition	2	17	0
A schooner	15	0	0
A boat	6	5	0
Implements of planting	38	0	0
A year's housekeeping	36	0	0
	659	5	0

Live stock

			£	s.	d.
10 cows, at 3£. .... £. 30					
10 horses 50					
60 sheep 18					
Swine 14					
Poultry, &c. 2			114	0	0
Sundries			30	0	0
		£.	803	5	0

Product of the first year

	£.	s.	d.
15 acres of wheat, at 2½ qrs. per acre, 37½ qrs. at 20s.	37	10	0
60 acres Indian corn, 40 bushels per acre, 2,400, at 1s.	120	0	0
Cattle	15	0	0
Lumber	10	10	0
£.	183	0	0

Product of the second year

	£.	s.	d.
20 acres of wheat, 2 qrs. per acre, 40 qrs.	40	0	0
40 acres Indian corn, 30 bushels per acre, 1,200 bushels, at 1s. 3d.	75	0	0
10 acres of barley, 3 qrs. per acre, 30 qrs. at 8s.	12	0	0
15 acres of pease and beans, 3 qrs. per acre, 45 qrs. at 10s.	22	10	0
Fruit and cyder	10	0	0
Lumber	15	0	0
Cattle	20	0	0
£.	194	10	0

Lest any persons should be misled by these accounts of produce, the first and second years, I must observe that many planters receive very little produce the first and second and some even the third years, which is owing to the ground being a thick wood: these and others, who soon make a considerable product, are such as get a tract of meadow, or rather upland pasture in their grant, which for profit they plough up immediately and sow with corn. But at the same time I should observe that in this province the expence of clearing even the thickest woods is not great, it is more than repaid in good management, by the lumber which arises on the land; but for this several hands are requisite, which cannot be procured by people who settle with only small sums of money. It is much to be regretted that the preceding account is not more complete, particularly in the common annual expence and produce: however, it is evident from it, that the profit of the plantation was very soon considerable.

It is worthy of remark on these accounts, that the product seems to be made by the common husbandry of the province,

which is so far from being perfect. May we not conclude
that the benefit would have been much greater had a more
correct agriculture been practiced? There is the greatest reason to suppose that a man well acquainted with the true
principles of husbandry settling in this province would be able
to advance the profit of a plantation much beyond this account.

Having now laid before the reader, upon the best authority
I have been able to gain, a state of the husbandry of this
province, it remains for me to compare it with that of Great
Britain; which is one of the most important articles of this
work, and indeed of as great consequence as any intelligence
that can be laid before the reader, concerning American affairs; for, unless this comparison is well understood, it is
impossible to know the principles upon which America acts
on the population of Britain. To find a man equally skilled in
the husbandry of both countries is hardly to be expected; but
though I cannot give accounts of which I have such certainty
of knowing to be accurate, in the case of Britain, as in that of
Pennsylvania, yet as there are some late writers concerning
English agriculture, who are acknowledged to be of undoubted authority, I shall be able, by means of their works,
to draw up such an account of the profit of husbandry in England, as shall have no material errors in it, in order to form
the contrast to that of Pennsylvania. Upon these authorities,
suppose a man, with a certain sum of money, to enter into husbandry in England, with a view to make the best interest he
is able of his money—I shall suppose with 1,200£. as that sum
has been calculated in the instance of this province. From the
accounts we have of British husbandry, we are to suppose
that the greatest profit is made by the culture of the best
land.

Stock of a farm of 250 acres of rich land

	£.	s.	d.
Rent, tythe, and parish taxes, of 250 acres at 27s.	337	10	0
Housekeeping, &c. for one year	80	0	0
Eight horses for the culture of 150 acres arable land, at 15£.	120	0	0

Live stock for 100 acres of grass

	£.	s.	d.
15 cows at 7£.	105	0	0
10 oxen at 5£.	50	0	0
20 young cattle at 30s.	30	0	0
10 swine at 10s.	5	0	0
300 sheep at 10s.	150	0	0
Poultry	3	0	0
Two men, one maid, and a boy, wages	27	0	0
Pay of four labourers a year, at 20£.	80	0	0
Implements of husbandry and harness	130	0	0
Seed for the first crop	40	0	0
Contingent expences, and cash in hand, for advantage of markets, purchase of manure, &c.	42	10	0
£.	1,200	0	0

The annual expences

	£.	s.	d.
Rent, &c.	337	10	0
Housekeeping	60	0	0
Labour	107	0	0
Repair of implements	50	0	0
Ten oxen	50	0	0
Sundry expences	30	0	0
	634	10	0
Interest of 1,200£. at five per cent	60	0	0
Total £.	694	10	0

Annual produce

	£.	s.	d.
The system in which the arable fields are thrown is supposed to be 1. Turneps 2. Barley or oats 3. Clover 4. Wheat which we are told is the best husbandry of Britain; upon this system the 37 acres of corn, sown in spring, is to be divided into 30 to sell or barley, and 7 for the teams of oats; 30 at 4 quarters an acre, 120 quarters at 24s.	144	0	0
37 acres of wheat, 3½ quarters an acre 129 quarters at 50s.	322	10	0
Profit of 15 cows at 5£.	75	0	0
Product of 10 oxen	100	0	0
Profit on young cattle	30	0	0
Do. on swine	35	0	0
Do. on sheep	130	0	0
Hay fold	20	0	0
Profit by poultry	10	0	0
Sale of wood	10	0	0
Total £.	876	10	0
Expences as above	694	10	0
Profit £.	182	0	0

This profit, with the interest before deducted, is 141£. which from 1,200£. is 20 per cent. This calculation is upon the supposition of 100 acres out 250 being grass land; supposing the whole arable, which some writers esteem the most profitable, the account may then be stated as follows (though I should premise, that not many tracts in England are to be found without grass, and landlords are tenacious of having it ploughed up):

	£.	s.	d.
Rent, tythe, and parish taxes, of 250 acres at 27s.	337	10	0
Housekeeping, &c. one year	80	0	0
Twelve horses at 15£.	180	0	0
Live stock for 60 acres of clover, and 10 of grass, and 60 of turneps (exclusive of maintaining the 12 horses)			
5 cows at 7£.	35	0	0
5 young cattle at 30s.	7	10	0
200 sheep at 10s.	100	0	0
Swine	10	0	0
10 oxen for turneps	50	0	0
Poultry	3	0	0
Four men, one maid, and two boys wages	50	0	0
Pay of five labourers at 20£.	100	0	0
Implements of culture of all sorts	250	0	0
Seed	55	0	0
Total £.	1,258	0	0

The annual expence

	£.	s.	d.
Rent, &c.	337	10	0
Housekeeping	100	0	0
Wages and labour	150	0	0
Repairs of implements	80	0	0
Ten oxen	50	0	0
Contingent expences	40	0	0
Interest of 1,258£.	62	18	0
£.	820	8	0

The annual produce

	£.	s.	d.

The system of this farm, like that of the former, is supposed to be
  60 acres turneps
  60 —— barley
  60 —— clover
  60 —— wheat
  10 —— grass
60 acres wheat, 3½ qrs. per acre, 210 qrs. at 50s. ....
	525	0	0

48 acres of barley, 4 qrs. an acre, 192 qrs. at 24s.*	230	8	0
Profit on 5 cows	25	0	0
Do. on young cattle	8	0	0
Do. on sheep	90	0	0
Do. on swine	30	0	0
Do. on poultry	15	0	0
Sale of wood	10	0	0
Sale of 10 oxen	100	0	0
Total .... £.	1,033	8	0
Expence	820	8	0
Profit £.	213	0	0

Which, with 62£. 18s. interest, is 275£. 18s. and that on 1,258£. is about 21½ per cent.

It appears from these accounts, that in England, on the best land, and with excellent husbandry, about 20 per cent is made by employing 1,200£. on 250 acres. The circumstance of the husbandry being excellent, is not to be forgotten; for not all parts of this kingdom practice so good a system as,

1. Turneps,   3. Clover,
2. Barley,   4. Wheat,

* The feed for the land in the next year, saved, besides these crops in both instances.

which the writers on husbandry justly enough reckon to be excellent: nor will perhaps half the kingdom admit of such a system, from being too heavy and wet to yield turneps; in which case, the profit is not to be supposed nearly to equal the turnep culture, which excludes the barren expence of a fallow: but the number of farmers, even in this enlightened age and country, that practice the above culture is very small; on the contrary they, like the planters of America, are too apt to take several crops of corn running, instead of introducing turneps and clover.

It appeared above, that the profit on 1,200£. employed on a plantation of 5,000 acres in Pennsylvania, in a few years after settling it, was 15 per cent., whereas in England that sum yields 20 or 21 per cent. But then there are other circumstances to be considered, which I am afraid will more than ballance this difference. The produce from the American farm was gained by the common management of the province, which is as bad and unprofitable a system as can well be imagined; consequently it would admit of great improvements, without introducing any other crops: but the 20 per cent. in England is gained from the most capital management which common crops will admit, and on the most favorable soil that is to be found plentifully in Britain. In one case you are open to an immense improvement, in the other none can be imagined without deviating from common husbandry. *Secondly*, The American has the fee-simple of 5,000 acres into his bargain, with all the timber on it; this, however plentiful land may be, is a very different affair from *renting* 250 [acres]. Of the same superiority is the house and offices, orchards and gardens, made and to be enjoyed for ever, with nothing in the opposite scale to ballance them. The American lives upon his own freehold; if the Englishman would do the same, he must buy it, in which case his 250£. a year would, at 28 years purchase, cost 7,000£. and upon 7,000£. of it he would make perhaps 2½ per cent. *Thirdly*, and which is the most important of all, the Pennsylvanian can by an annual increase of culture, expend all his savings at the same advantage of 15 per cent. or rather at 20 or 25; for when the buildings are raised, the estate bought and stocked, additions to culture will certainly pay better interest than the original sum, out of which were such expences, together with freight, &c. all which may, in respect of the profit, be called barren. On the contrary, the English farmer can do nothing better than put out his profits at the common interest of five per cent. or perhaps only four; for he can very rarely increase his land, as he grows rich, without leaving one farm and moving into a larger, which is quite another affair from the gradual increase of the American. *Fourthly*, Both the farmers are supposed to live partly off their farms, a sum of money being allowed in either case for buying such articles as their lands do not produce. But what an amazing difference is there between them in this respect. With the sum charged to the English farmer, he will not be able to live much better than a day-labourer—and not to live at all if he is not saving to a degree. But on the other hand, the Pennsylvanian lives, in point of table and sports, to the full equal with a country gentleman in England of four or five hundred pounds a year; and, in several instances, far superior to one of 1,000£. a year.

In all these articles, the freeholder in Pennsylvania is so much superior, that the comparison will scarcely bear mentioning; nor is it less in all those circumstances of convenience and agreeableness, which result from living upon your own land—your own manor: the farmer gets a long lease with difficulty, and at the end of it must pay perhaps more than the land is worth, or quit his farm: and during the whole lease [he is] plagued possibly either by his landlord or steward; he must not kill a hare or a partridge without being liable to a prosecution—he must not—but the comparison in all these respects will not bear an idea of equality.

But here it should be observed that to gentlemen or any persons of enlarged ideas, agriculture in Britain is probably far more profitable than in the preceding sketch; for if plants not commonly cultivated are introduced on the farm, the advantage will be far more than 20 per cent. of this, carrots, potatoes, cabbages, hops, madder, &c. are instances. To give some idea of this, it will be proper to lay before the reader a calculation of this point, upon the data given by writers of husbandry that can be depended upon. I shall begin with carrots.

Expences per acre

	£.	s.	d.
Ploughing and other tillage	0	15	3
Manuring	1	0	3
Seed and sowing	0	5	9
Hand-hoeing	1	9	0
Digging up	1	10	0
Carting, clearing, &c.	1	7	0
Rent, tythe, &c.	0	17	0
£.	7	4	3

Produce

560 bushels, at 1s. 1d.	30	6	8
Expences	7	4	3
Profit £.	23	2	5

This a single crop; but the average of several expence per acre, 6£. 4s. 5d.

	£.	s.	d.
Product	27	14	1
Profit	21	3	5*

This is 350 per cent but then we are sensible that deductions must be made for general expences on the farm, which have no place here, as some labour, fences, housekeeping, &c. &c.

In madder a gentleman has expended 206£. 14s. on 10 acres, the produce was 540£. and the profit 33£. 6s.† This is 161 per cent. With cabbages another person has made the following advantage upon an average.

Expences

	£.	s.	d.
Rent	1	10	0
Ploughing	1	11	6
Planting	0	4	6
Horse-hoeing and weeding	0	9	6
£.	3	15	6

Produce

	£.	s.	d.
By feeding cattle	16	16	4
Expences	3	15	6
Profit £.‡	13	0	10

This is 347 per cent. In all these cases, we know upon a whole farm, such crops are not in general to be gained: and that ex-

* *Course of Experimental Agriculture*, II, 190. [This two-volume work prepared by Arthur Young was originally published in 1770. Its sub-title really explained its purpose: *Containing an Exact Register of all the Business Transacted during Five Years on near Three Hundred Acres of various Soils; the whole stated in near Two Thousand Original Experiments.* Ed.]

† Farmer's Tour Through England, II, 299. [This reference is to Arthur Young's, *The Farmer's Tour through the East of England* (London, 1771). Ed.]

‡ *Six Months Tour*, II, 121. [This reference is to Arthur Young's, *A Six Months' Tour Through the North of England* (London, 1770). Ed.]

pences so reckoned would run much higher; but it is evident that the introduction of such crops would be far more profitable than common ones. Hops are found, in trials, to yield about 100 per cent. but potatoes exceed them all, yielding sometimes crops from 50£. to 100£. an acre, from an expenditure of from 20£. to 30£.

If a farm was to be cultivated in England upon the principle of cultivating crops only which would yield such large products, in that case, the profit of husbandry would turn out over a whole farm much more than 20 per cent. probably 40 or 50 per cent. Whether Pennsylvania by adopting the same improvements would equal it, is not to be decided here, the trial never having been made; but certainly a man that could make 40 per cent. by husbandry in England, would act very imprudently to change his situation without much stronger proofs of superior advantages elsewhere, than he can have at present.

Settling upon a plantation in this colony seems to be of superior benefit to people who can pay their freight to America, and then have money enough left to buy a small plantation, build a house, &c.—Also to those who with a sum of money from 500£. to 2,000£. would in *common husbandry* apply it to the greatest advantage.—Also to country gentlemen of small fortunes, to whom the extreme dearness of Britain is very burthensome—but to men who will adopt the profitable modern improvements of husbandry, Britain is more beneficial than America.—And to such whose fortunes bear a proportion to the luxury of the age, England certainly is the first country in the universe. These distinctions are never to be forgotten; general assertions for or against any country are always erroneous: nothing can be plainer than the fact that those whose incomes are too small to maintain them in

England, may live in a far superior sti[y]le in Pennsylvania, but with other classes the contrary is the case: every one must know that in order to reap advantage from this circumstance they must quit all connections in their native country; they must give up both friends and relations, and all those endearing circumstances which renders a native country so agreeable. They must cross an immense ocean, and fix in a new hemisphere, where the people and climate are equally new: they must submit to a much hotter sun than that of England, and also to greater cold; and they must run the hazard of being destroyed or wounded by poisonous serpents that abound far more than in Britain: in return for these circumstances, they will enjoy the advantages specified above; great most certainly, but of value only to those whose fortunes are so small that they cannot live like their forefathers, whose money in cheaper times went so much farther. When a man lives [in] the ridicule and contempt of his neighbours, because his mean circumstances force him to strict frugality, he had better fly to vipers and rattle-snakes than into the company of his neighbours: and when even his penury will scarce keep him from starving, it is of little consequence to know that the inhospitable clime he lives in is his native one: there are a thousand comforts in a competency which may make amends for the loss of such friends as poverty brings. And as to crossing an ocean, and living in another hemisphere, they are what are done by others even in wealthy situations at home; there is nothing terrible in it to people of sense.

CHAPTER XIV

VIRGINIA AND MARYLAND

Climate of Virginia and Maryland—Soil—Productions—
Face of the country

THESE two provinces lie between latitude 31½° and
40°, being in extent about 250 miles from north to south,
and the same breadth from east to west, that is from the sea
to the Alleg[h]any mountains. The parallel is the same as
Morocco, Fez, the coast of Barbary, Syria, Lesser Asia,
Greece, Sicily, Naples, and the southern provinces of Spain,
that is perhaps, without exception, the countries of all the
world that enjoy the finest climate.

That of Virginia and Maryland has its objections, but is
notwithstanding fine: in summer the heats would be insupportable on the coast, were it not for the sea breezes which
refresh them greatly. In the back country, among the mountains, this heat is much less violent than in the low country;
for there they enjoy one of the most temperate climates in
the world: the weather is changeable, and the changes are
sudden: in winter, frosts come on with very little warning,
and after a warm day; and in summer the tempests of thunder and lightning are extremely violent and sudden, but do
no more harm than in much more temperate climates. Their
rains at certain seasons of the year are very heavy, but not of
long duration, and the frosts of winter are sooner: in general,

throughout the year the sky is clear, and air is pure and wholesome.

The soil of the country varies much; all the sea coast, for above one hundred miles, is a low, flat, sandy beach, so low, that the country is not descried from on ship-board till you are in the rivers, out of which the trees seem to rise: the low lands on the banks of them are a rich, black mould, more than a foot deep, of a fertility exceeding every thing in Pennsylvania or to the northward: the higher lands are sandy, but not therefore barren or of little value; there is a moisture in it that is sufficient even for tobacco, which will do on the most luxuriant soils in the world. When you get from one hundred to one hundred fifty miles from the coast, the country rises, and increases in inequality for another hundred miles, till you come to the Alleg[h]any mountains. This line of country is far superior to the coast in climate, healthiness, and agreeableness, and in general the soil much exceeds it.*

The products of Virginia and Maryland differ considerably from those of Pennsylvania, from their nearer neighbourhood to the sun. As to timber and wood, they have all the sorts

* "The whole sea coast of North America, says Dr. Mitchel(1), from the bay of New York to the gulph of Mexico is a low, flat, sandy beach; the soil for a great distance from it is sandy and barren, the climate is very rainy, and as these rains have no drains from the land, but stagnate all over a low flat country, they form innumerable swamps and marshes, which render it very unhealthful. It is a common opinion that all this part of the continent, which stretches into the ocean at a considerable distance from the rest, has been recovered from the sea, and that it is nothing but a drained marsh or sand bank, which indeed it very much resembles, and in nothing more than its pernicious influence on mankind. Accordingly in all this space nothing is to be found either on the surface or in the bowels of the earth, but beds of sea shells, in place of stones, metals, and other minerals, and the earth is as barren in these as in other productions." *Present State*, p. 184. This is in general true of the coast, but the same writer acknowledges all the merit of the back country.

that are found upon the Continent: many sorts of oaks, cedars, firs, cypress, elm, ash, and walnut;[1] some of their oaks are said to measure two feet square and sixty feet in height. They have also beech, poplar, hazel, besides sassafras, sarsaparilla, and other dy[e]ing woods. The unsettled country is all a forest of these trees, without underwood, and not standing so close but they may any where be rode through. Near the coast the low lands are all swamps, from which grow cedars, pines, and cypresses. This plenty of wood is of great advantage here, as in all the colonies more to the north, in affording lumber for the West Indies, which forms a considerable article in the exports of the province.

As to fruit trees, they have all those which are known to us in Europe or Pennsylvania; particularly apples, pears, cherries, quinces, plums, grapes, peaches, and nectarines, in the same plenty as in Pennsylvania, so as to be applied to the same use of feeding hogs as there. All other fruits are produced here, as may from the climate be supposed.

Besides tobacco, which is the staple of these colonies, and of which I shall speak more by and by, wheat and all our other kinds of grain and pulse thrive here equally, if not in a superior degree, to any of our other colonies; a circumstance in which the country resembles those in the same parallel in Europe and Africa, Sicily, Spain, and Barbary, which produce the best wheat that is known in the world; and in these articles of common husbandry the planters have increased much more than in tobacco, for reasons which I shall explain hereafter.

No part of America, or indeed of the world, boasts more plentiful or more general production of all sorts of garden

[1] He omits chestnut which, at the time, grew in both Virginia and Maryland.

vegetables; and in a state of excellence that is proportioned to the heat of the climate. The same remark may also be made of their fish and fowl, having every sort that is found in Pennsylvania, with others that are peculiar to the country; being in all respects of food as plentiful as any territory in the world.

The face of the country varies in different parts of the provinces: for about one hundred or one hundred and fifty miles from the sea it is generally low and flat, much spread with marshes and swamps: these in Carolina are applied to the culture of rice, but Virginia and Maryland are not hot enough for that production, which by the way is a proof how much better their climate is. This part of the country is intersected with immense rivers and bays of the sea, so as to afford a greater inland navigation than is known in any other country in the world. As the land recedes from the coast it gradually rises, until at the distance above-mentioned it begins to grow hilly, which in as many miles more ends in the Alleg[h]any mountains. In all this part of the provinces, the face of the country is as beautiful as can well be imagined: there are not many level tracts, and those are rich meadows, not swamps or marshes. In the vales streams of clear water are every where to be found, and even navigable rivers enter among the mountains: the hills hang to the eye in a great variety of forms, and spread with forests that give an amazing magnificence to the scenery. Spots are here frequently found that possess every picturesque beauty which in England our nobility are so emulous to create in their parks; and all this back country possesses a climate free from the extreme heats which oppress the inhabitants of the coast. At the same time that it enjoys so many advantages of health and agreeableness, it is likewise fertile in an high degree, and in most parts of it capable of producing fine crops of tobacco, to which it is in most parts applied, where navigation is at a convenient distance. From all these circumstances it is evident that no part of our American colonies is more desirable in most respects.

CHAPTER XV

VIRGINIA AND MARYLAND

Description of tobacco—The culture—Remarks—Full account of a plantation

THIS plant [tobacco] is cultivated in all parts of North America, from Quebec to Carolina, and even the West Indies; but, except in Maryland, Virginia, and North Carolina, they plant no more than for private use, making it an object of exportation only in these provinces, where it is of such immense consequence.

It was planted in large quantities by the Indians, when we first came to America, and its use from them brought into Europe; but what their method of culture was is now no longer known, as they plant none, but buy what they want of the English.[1] Tobacco is raised from the seed, which is sown in spring upon a bed of rich mould; when about the height of four or five inches, the planter takes the opportunity of rainy weather to transplant them. The ground

---

[1] Tobacco is closely related to the potato and the egg-plant. In pre-Columbian time the Indians of different regions used it in different ways which the white man adopted. Tobacco smoking was observed by Columbus, and in the sixteenth century tobacco was introduced into Spain and later into other European countries. The use of tobacco in Europe and the Orient became general in the seventeenth century. By 1617 the cultivation had become the chief occupation of the colonists in Virginia where tobacco was used for money. Tobacco is now grown in many parts of the world. See G. M. Jacobstein, *The Tobacco Industry in the United States* (New York, 1907).

which is prepared to receive it, is, if it can be got, a rich
black mould; fresh woodlands are best: sometimes it is so
badly cleared from the stumps of trees, that they cannot give
it any ploughings; but in old cultivated lands they plough it
several times, and spread on it what manure they can raise.
The negroes then hill it; that is, with hoes and shovels they
form hillocks, which lie in the manner of Indian corn, only
they are larger, and more carefully raked up: the hills are
made in squares, from six to nine feet distance, according to
the land; the richer it is the further they are put asunder, as
the plants grow higher and spread proportionally. The plants
in about a month are a foot high, when they prune and top
them; operations, in which they seem to be very wild, and to
execute them upon no rational principles; experiments are
much wanting on these points, for the planters never go out
of the beaten road, but do just as their fathers did, resembling
therein the British farmers their brethren. They prune off
all the bottom leaves, leaving only seven or eight on a stalk,
thinking that such as they leave will be the larger, which is
contrary to nature in every instance throughout all vegetation.
In six weeks more the tobacco is at its full growth, being then
from four and a half to seven feet high: during all this time,
the negroes are employed twice a week in pruning off the
suckers, clearing the hillocks from weeds, and attending to
the worms, which are a great enemy to the plant; when the
tobacco changes its colour, turning brown, it is ripe and they
then cut it down, and lay it close in heaps in the field to sweat
one night: the next day they are carried in bunches by the
negroes to a building called the tobacco house, where every
plant is hung up separate to dry, which takes a month or five
weeks; this house excludes the rain, but is designed for the

admission of as much air as possible. They are then laid close in heaps in the tobacco houses for a week or a fortnight to sweat again, after which it is sorted and packed up in hogs-heads; all the operations after the plants are dried must be done in moist or wet weather, which prevents its crumbling to dust.

There are among many inferior distinctions of sorts, two [of which are] generally attended to, *Oroonoko,* and *sweet scented;* the latter is of the finest flavour and most valued, growing chiefly in the lower parts of Virginia, viz. on James river and York river, and likewise on the Rappanhannock and the south side of the Potomack: the Oroonoko is principally in use on Chesepeak [Chesapeake] bay, and the back settlements on all the rivers. It is strong and hot; the principal markets for it are Germany and the North.

One of the greatest advantages attending the culture of to-bacco is the quick, easy, and certain method of sale. This was effected by the inspection law, which took place in Virginia in the year 1730, but not in Maryland till 1748.[2] The planter, by virtue of this, may go to any place and sell his tobacco, without carrying a sample of it along with him, and the merchant may buy it, though lying a hundred miles, or at any distance from his store, and yet be morally sure both with respect to quantity and quality. For this purpose, upon all the rivers and bays of both provinces, at the distance of about twelve or fourteen miles from each other, are erected ware-houses, to which all the tobacco in the country must be brought and there lodged, before the planters can offer it to sale; and inspectors are appointed to examine all the tobacco brought

[2] Cf. L. C. Gray, *History of Agriculture in the Southern United States to 1860* (Washington, 1933), I, 225–31.

in, receive such as is good and merchantable, condemn and burn what appears damnified or insufficient. The greatest part of the tobacco is prized, or put up into hogsheads by the planters themselves, before it is carried to the warehouses. Each hogshead, by an act of assembly, must be 950 lb. neat [net] or upwards; some of them weigh 14 cwt. and even 18 cwt. and the heavier they are the merchants like them the better; because four hogsheads, whatsoever their weight be, are esteemed a tun, and pay the same freight. The inspectors give notes of receipt for the tobacco, and the merchants take them in payment for their goods, passing current indeed over the whole colonies;[3] a most admirable invention, which operates so greatly that in Virginia they have no paper currency.*

The merchants generally purchase the tobacco in the country, by sending persons to open *stores* for them; that is, warehouses in which they lay in a great assortment of British commodities and manufactures; to these, as to shops, the planters resort, and supply themselves with what they want, paying, in inspection receipts, or taking on credit according to what will be given them; and as they are in general a very luxurious set of people, they buy too much upon credit; the consequence of which is, their getting in debt to the London merchants, who take mortgages on their plantations, ruinous

* *Mair's Bookkeeping*, p. 333.

[3] The system of barter or payment in kind developed in Virginia and other English colonies in default of an adequate supply of coin. In 1730 the Virginia Assembly provided for the establishment of warehouses for the storage of tobacco, the owners receiving transferable notes similar to present-day silver certificates, which might be used to satisfy debts, public and private, in the county or district wherein they were issued. The ingenuity of the colony was taxed, however, to preserve this currency at a uniform standard, since the market value of tobacco fluctuated widely. See D. R. Dewey, *Financial History of the United States* (New York, 1928); and C. J. Bullock, *Essays on the Monetary History of the United States* (New York, 1900), Part I, chaps. i–iii.

enough, with the usury of eight per cent.[4] But this is apparently the effect of their imprudence in living upon trust.

Respecting the product of tobacco, they know very little of it themselves by the acre, as they never calculate in that manner, and not many tobacco grounds were ever measured: all their ideas run in the proportion per working hand. Some are hired labourers, but in general they are negroe slaves; and the product, from the best information I have gained, varies from an hogshead and a half to three and an half per head. The hogshead used to be of the value of 5£. but of late years it is 8£. per head, according to the goodness of the lands and other circumstances. But [as for] the planters, none of them depend on tobacco alone, and this is more and more the case since corn has yielded a high price, and since their grounds have begun to be worn out. They all raise corn and provisions enough to support the family and plantation, besides exporting considerable quantities; no wheat in the world exceeds in quality that of Virginia and Maryland. Lumber they also send largely to the West Indies. The whole culture of tobacco is over in the summer months; in the winter the

---

[4] By the eve of the American Revolution the vast majority of the great landed proprietors of the colonial tidewater region were heavily in debt to British merchants, a condition which arose primarily from their wasteful system of marketing. Thomas Jefferson estimated that the Virginia planters owed at least £2,000,000 and that "these debts had become hereditary from father to son for many generations, so that the planters were a species of property annexed to certain mercantile houses in London." In 1791 a group of British merchants submitted a statement to their government listing the debts due them from American customers in 1775. The total principal and interest amounted to £4,930,656 and of this £4,137,944 —over five-sixths—was due from States south of Pennsylvania. See H. J. Carman, *Social and Economic History of the United States* (Boston, 1930), I, 284–85; J. S. Bassett, "Relation Between the Virginia Planter and the London Merchant," in *Annual Report of the American Historical Association* (Washington, 1901), I, 551–75.

negroes are employed in sawing and butting timber, threshing corn, clearing new land, and preparing for tobacco; so
that it is plain, they make a product per head, besides that
of tobacco.

Suppose each negroe makes two hogsheads of tobacco, or
16£. and 4£. in corn, provisions, and lumber, besides supporting the plantation, this is a moderate supposition; and if true,
the planter's profit may be easily calculated: the negroe costs
him 50£. his cloathing, tools, and sundries, 3£.; in this case,
the expence of the slave is only the interest of his cost, 2£. 10s.
and the total only makes 5£. 10s. a year. To this we must add
the interest of the planter's capital, province taxes, &c. which
will make some addition, perhaps thirty or forty shillings
per head more, there will then remain 12£. 10s. a head profit
to the planter; which is more than cent. per cent. profit: but
this being a point of considerable importance, shall be further
examined.

There is no plant in the world that requires richer land,
or more manure than tobacco; it will grow on poorer fields,
but not to yield crops that are sufficiently profitable to pay
the expences of negroes, &c. The land they found to answer
best is fresh woodlands, where many ages have formed a
stratum of rich black mould. Such land will, after clearing,
bear tobacco many years, without any change, prove more
profitable to the planter than the power of dung can do on
worse lands: this makes the tobacco planters more solicitous
for new land than any other people in America, they wanting
it much more. Many of them have very handsome houses,
gardens, and improvements about them, which fixes them to
one spot; but others, when they have exhausted their grounds,
will sell them to new settlers for corn-fields, and move backwards with their negroes, cattle, and tools, to take up fresh

land for tobacco; this is common, and will continue so as long as good land is to be had upon navigable rivers: this is the system of business which made some, so long ago as 1750, move over the Alleg[h]any mountains, and settle not far from the Ohio, where their tobacco was to be carried by land some distance, which is a heavy burthen on so bulky a commodity, but answered by the superior crops they gained:[5] the French encroachments drove these people all back again; but upon the peace, many more went, and the number increasing, became the occasion of the new colony which has been settled in that country.

A very considerable tract of land is necessary for a tobacco plantation; first, that the planter may have a sure prospect of increasing his culture on fresh land; secondly, that the lumber may be a winter employment for his slaves and afford casks for his crops. Thirdly, that he may be able to keep vast stocks of cattle for raising provisions in plenty, by ranging in the woods; and where the lands are not fresh, the necessity is yet greater, as they must yield much manure for replenishing the worn-out fields. This want of land is such, that they reckon a planter should have 50 acres of land for every working hand; with less than this they will find themselves distressed for want of room.

But I must observe that great improvements might be made in the culture of this crop; the attention of the planters is to keep their negroes employed on the plants and the small space that the hillocks occupy, being very apt to neglect the intervals; the expence of hoeing them is considerable, and consequently they are apt to be remiss in this work. Here they ought to substitute the horse-hoeing management, which would cost much less, and be an hundred times more effectual.

[5] The author here refers to the early Kentucky settlements.

The roots of the tobacco are powerful; they spread far beyond the hillocks, which ought to convince the planters that they should seed them there by good culture, but this is little considered. A few men once got into the use of a plough, they invented in the back parts of Virginia, for opening a trench in the intervals, to kill weeds, loosen the earth, and carry the water of hasty rains off; but, from the carelessness of servants, the scheme came to nothing, though it promised better ideas in future.

I would propose to them the use of such a machine as in Kent is applied to cultivating the intervals of the hop-grounds, which consists of several flat triangular shares, which work near each other, being let into a beam from which it is drawn; they call it, if I mistake not, a nidget;[6] this would keep the tobacco intervals in a fine pulverized state, and prepare them to be thrown against the hillock, for the nourishment of the roots, by a machine made upon the principles of that I have just mentioned, but upon an improved construction. In one of the *Tours through England*,[7] there is a draft of one, which, with a little alteration for breadth, would do admirably for this purpose. Would the planters enter into these ideas, they would soon find their expences lessen, at the same time that their products increased. This culture, upon the Tullian system, would so improve the intervals, as to prepare them for the plants in the following year, and they would not so soon come to the complaint of their lands being exhausted.

Let us calculate what the culture of tobacco would cost per acre, if labour was the same price as in England; this is not difficult to do.

[6] The nidget, correctly described by the author, was in reality a crude type of cultivator.

[7] See Arthur Young, *A Six Months' Tour through the North of England* (London, 1770), diagram following p. 106.

	£.	s.	d.
Seed, sowing, and preparation of a seed bed, the share of an acre	0	1	6
Three ploughings of the plantation	0	3	6
Harrowing	0	0	6
Measuring out the spaces for the hillocks, and marking them by setting up sticks . .	0	1	2
Hilling with hoes and shovels	0	2	6
Planting	0	1	2
Topping and pruning the plants at ¼ a plant, at six feet asunder, there are 1,210 upon an acre	1	5	0
Pruning ten times more, at 3s. 6d. an acre	1	15	0
Worming ten times, at 2s.	1	0	0
Hoeing the hillocks four times during the season, at 1s. 6d.	0	6	0
Hoeing the intervals, suppose once	0	5	0
Cutting down, and laying into heaps	0	2	0
Carrying to tobacco-house, and hanging up	0	8	10
Taking down, and laying in heaps	0	3	6
Sorting	0	2	6
Packing in hogsheads	0	3	6
£.	6	1	8

Suppose a man earns, on an average 1s. 4d. a day, the year round, it amounts in a year to 20£. 16s. At 6£. 1s. 8d. an acre, therefore he would be able to cultivate something better than 3½ [acres]. The same proportion probably holds for the negroes, for as their annual expence is only 7 or 8£. a year, the separate charges per acre would be proportioned, and the quantity of land to be managed by one hand the same: this calculation is upon supposition that the ground is fresh, and requires no manure; if that is to be carried on, the account would be different; and perhaps three acres would prove the quantity. The product we found was from one hogshead and an half to three and an half per working hand, or from 12 to

28£. The average is about two hhds. or 16£. which divided by three, the number of acres, gives the produce per acre of 5£. 6s. 8d. when tobacco is at 8£. a hhd.; according to the rate of labour in the dear parts of England, it costs more than this in mere labour to cultivate, which shews, if any thing can shew it, how much cheaper the labour of negroes is, being certainly as about three to one.

Having ascertained these points as nearly as I am able, I shall in the next place calculate the settling a tobacco plantation. I am sorry I cannot give a real account, but though I applied to many for it, it is what I could not procure; from the similar accounts before given in other colonies, I shall be able to come near the truth. I shall suppose the planter to go from England as in former cases.

Freight and expences of two persons from London .... £.	50
Ditto of two others	25
Two ditto women	100
20 negroes at 50£.	1,000
An overseer	40
Patent fees and expences on taking up 2,000 acres	40
House	100
Offices and tobacco-house	100
Furniture	100
Implements of culture	50
A sloop and canoe	50
Arms, ammunition, and sundries	10
Expences of negroes	60
Extra expences* on ditto	10
Housekeeping and family expences	100
House servants wages	20

* Their first year's work is clearing some ground and the garden and orchard: after that the getting lumber and the negroes' spare time from the crop will clear land as fast as it is wanted.

Live stock

10 horses, at 4£.	£.	40	
40 cows, at 3£.		120	
50 young cattle		50	
100 swine		25	
100 sheep		25	
Poultry		5	265
Expences on orchard and garden			20
Incidental expences			80
			£. 2,210

The annual expence

	£.	s.	d.
Province taxes	20	0	0
Expence of negroes	60	0	0
Repairs of implements	15	0	0
Housekeeping, &c.	60	0	0
Building and furniture	20	0	0
Overseer	30	0	0
House servants wages	20	0	0
Incidents	20	0	0
	245	0	0
Interest of 2200£.	110	0	0
£.	355	0	0

Annual produce

	£.	s.	d.
44 hogsheads of tobacco, at 8£.	352	0	0
4£. a head in corn, provisions, and lumber	88	0	0
Product of cattle	80	0	0
Fruit and cyder	10	0	0
	530	0	0
Expences	355	0	0
	175	0	0
Add the interest before charged	110	0	0
£.	285	0	0

Which from 1,885£. is 13 per cent. but [for] housekeeping 60£. might be added, as it is expended in products extra from the plantation. The receipts would then be 345£. and the interest 15 per cent. The 175£. is the sum the planter might annually lay out in negroes and other labour: here lies his great advantages, if he chooses to make use of them; for having land [in] plenty and [being] able at any time to get more, the money he lays out in labour and the small additions of tools, &c. is expended at compound interest, at the rate he makes per cent. by his negroes. Suppose the negroe (which is much more than truth with good management) and attendant charges costs him 8£. a year, the produce is 20£. and all other contingent charges would not reduce it so far but the profit would be immense, and soon accumulate into considerable fortune.

On the other hand it is said, fortunes are rarely made by tobacco planters, and that it is much more common to see their estates eat out by mortgages; but this proves nothing; it deserves, however, a due examination.

The tobacco planters live more like country gentlemen of fortune than any other settlers in America; all of them are spread about the country, their labour being mostly by slaves, who are left to overseers; and the masters live in a state of emulation with one another in buildings (many of their houses would make no slight figure in the English counties), furniture, wines, dress, diversions, &c. and this to such a degree, that it is rather amazing they should be able to go on with their plantations at all, than they should not make additions to them: such a country life as they lead, in the midst of a profusion of rural sports and diversions, with little to do themselves, and in a climate that seems to create rather than check pleasure, must almost naturally have a strong effect in bringing them to be just such planters as foxhunters in England make farmers. To live within compass, and to lay out

their savings in an annual addition to their culture, requires
in the conduct a fixed and settled economy, and a firm determination not to depart from it, at least till a handsome fortune
was made. This would not be long, as a slight calculation will
shew.

First year of increase	£.	s.	d.
Saving of the last	175	0	0
Four negroes at 50£.	200	0	0
Implements	10	0	0
Expences on negroes	12	0	0
Addition to buildings	20	0	0
Sundries	8	0	0
Produce 20£. a head	80	0	0
Annual saving	175	0	0
£.	255	0	0

Second year			
Six negroes at 50£.	300	0	0
Implements	20	0	0
Negroe expences	30	0	0
Sundries	10	0	0
£.	360	0	0
Produce 10 at 20£.	200	0	0
Annual saving	175	0	0
£.	375	0	0

Third year			
Eight negroes at 50£.	400	0	0
Expences on 18, at 3£.	54	0	0
Implements bought, and additional repairs	30	0	0
Sundries	16	0	0
Building	10	0	0
£.	510	0	0
Produce 18 at 20£.	360	0	0
Annual savings	175	0	0
£.	535	0	0

Fourth year

Ten negroes at 50£.		500	0	0
Expences, &c. 28 at 3£.		84	0	0
Implements		40	0	0
Building		30	0	0
Sundries		20	0	0
Clearing land		26	0	0
	£.	600	0	0
Produce 28 at 20£.		560	0	0
Annual saving		175	0	0
	£.	735	0	0

Fifth year

2,000 acres more land patent fees		40	0	0
Another overseer		40	0	0
Buildings		50	0	0
Clearing land		100	0	0
Implements		50	0	0
Sundries		30	0	0
8 negroes at 50£.		400	0	0
Expences on them		102	0	0
Allow the planter		48	0	0
	£.	860	0	0
Produce 34 at 20£.		680	0	0
Annual saving		175	0	0
	£.	855	0	0

Sixth year

Overseer	40	0	0
Clearing land	50	0	0
Implements	50	0	0
Sundries	40	0	0
15 negroes at 50£.	750	0	0
Expences, &c. 49, at 3£.	147	0	0
Allow the planter	28	0	0
	1,095	0	0

Produce 49 at 20£.	980	0	0
Annual savings	190	0	0
£.	1,170	0	0

Seventh year

Account of the whole plantation

Province taxes	40	0	0
Expences on 72 negroes at 3£.	216	0	0
Repairs of implements	50	0	0
Housekeeping	300	0	0
Building and furniture	50	0	0
Overseers	80	0	0
House servants	30	0	0
Incidents	50	0	0
Interest	94	5	0
	910	5	0

Produce

72 negroes at 20£.	1,440	0	0
Cattle	150	0	0
Fruit and sundries	50	0	0
	1,640	0	0
Expences	910	5	0
£.	729	15	0

Hence it appears that he can either continue the increase of culture, with a view to grow rich as soon as possible; or he may stop, and at the same time that he spends 300£. a year in manufactures, and foreign luxuries, may lay up 729£. 15s. a year: or else he may here begin a second system of increase; taking the annual sum of 729£. for the foundation in the manner before explained, which would soon accumulate into a great income.

To all accounts of that sort, there may be many objections made, in all countries, and in all branches of culture—and it would be the same if the account had been actually realized by a planter; but slight variations should not be attended to: and the greatness of this profit will admit of deductions, according to more accurate ideas, and yet the remainder be far more than sufficient to prove that the poverty of the planters is not necessary to their condition, but merely owing to their extravagant way of living. In most articles of life, a great Virginia planter makes a greater show and lives more luxuriously than a country gentleman in England, on an estate of three or four thousand pounds a year. The great object I labour to prove, is, that this branch of agriculture, under its present circumstances, of price of negroes, and price of product, is such as will admit of great profit—to the capability of making a considerable fortune; and this advantage to be gained while the planter shall live in the midst of all the conveniencies of life, and most of its agreeableness!

I must own I am very solicitous to have this point well understood, for upon it much of this country's interest depends. Tobacco is one of the most valuable commodities that is produced by our colonies, perhaps the most so; and therefore the great advantages of selling in these parts should be well known. Settlers are always going to America, but those who go to the north of these provinces can raise no commodities that are of consequence to Britain: all the corn and provisions that [the] West Indies wants can be more than raised in the tracts from New York to Florida; and lumber is had in plenty in the southern ones, as well as in the northern; new settlers, therefore, going to colonies that have not a staple, is going where they can be of little use to Britain, and their making a choice so disadvantageous to the mother country, can only arise from a want of knowledge of the real state and improvements of the tobacco colonies; since in the back parts of these they will find that healthy and agreeable country which attracts them in Pennsylvania; as to the more southern colonies we are not to expect many to go to them because the heat is too great to be agreeable to British constitutions. Since, therefore, tobacco culture is that which suits the central country, which is free from the intense cold of the northern colonies and the oppressive heats of the southern ones, and at the same time is in possession of a staple highly valuable to Britain and profitable to cultivate, they are [it is] necessarily the country which should be so well known as to induce settlers to make it their choice. The poverty of the planters here, many of them at least, is much talked of, and from thence there has arisen a notion that their husbandry is not profitable: this false idea I have endeavoured to obviate, and to shew that the cause of it has little or no reference to their culture, but to the general luxury and extravagant way of living which obtains among the planters—a circumstance which ought rather to occasion a contrary conclusion—a supposition that their agriculture was very valuable; for men without some rich article of product cannot afford, even with the assistance of credit, to live in such a manner: it must be upon the face of it a profitable culture, that will support such luxury, and pay eight per cent. interest on their debts. What common culture in Europe will do this?

The observation I made on settlements in Pennsylvania are applicable in the present instance. It is not so much the profit which the farmer makes on his land as the ability he has of extending his culture in proportion to the money he makes. This cannot be done in Britain, nor in any cultivated country, but is the glory of America. If a man makes twenty per cent. on his agriculture in England, and lays by 500£. a year, he can get only four or five per cent. for that saving of 500£. He cannot lay it out in an increase of culture. But let him do the same in America, and he is able every year to increase his husbandry in whatever proportion his money will allow: this is making compound interest of his savings, and will, under a thousand disadvantages, accumulate presently into a considerable fortune, in comparison with the sum the planter first began with. This is a point which should never be forgotten, and in which consists the great superiority of America. It is not sufficiently considered by those who decry the profit of the Virginia planters, because they are not rich. They enjoy advantages which would make any set of men rich; but if instead of applying their money in making use of those advantages, he [the planter] spends it in temporal enjoyments of living, dress, and equipage, he, nor the by-stander cannot, with any degree of propriety, charge that to the agriculture of the province, which is in fact owing to the private expences of individuals.

Before I quit these observations on this part of the husbandry of Virginia and Maryland, I should remark that to make a due profit on tobacco, a man should be able to begin with twenty slaves at least, because so many will pay for an overseer: none, or at least very few, can be kept without an overseer, and if fewer than twenty be the number, the expence of the overseer will be too high; for they are seldom to be gained under 25£. a year, and generally from 30 to 50£. But it does not follow from hence, that settlers are precluded from these colonies who cannot buy twenty negroes; every day's experience tells us the contrary of this; the only difference is, that they begin in small; and either have no slaves at all, or no more than what they will submit to take care of themselves; in this case, they may begin with only one or two, and make a profit proportioned to that of the greater number, without the expence of an overseer. This is exactly similar to the conduct of English husbandry; a great farmer will employ a bailiff at the expence of 40 or 60£. a year; but this is far enough from preventing others from farming, who occupy no more than they can cultivate with their own hands, or with the assistance of only one man. Settlers of all kinds fix in these colonies, with advantages as great, if not greater, than any others. The culture of corn and other provisions is as profitable here as any where else; and plantations are every day left by tobacco planters, who quit and sell them at low prices, in order to retire backwards for fresh land, to cultivate tobacco to advantage; besides which, the new country is to be had here, equally with any other province, and upon terms as advantageous.

It is no slight benefit to be able to mix tobacco planting with common husbandry; this is as easily done as can be wished, and is indeed the practice of the greatest planters. A man may be a farmer for corn and provisions, and yet employ a few hands on tobacco, according as his land or manure will allow him. This makes a small business very profitable, and at the same time easy to be attained, nor is any thing more common throughout both Maryland and Virginia.

CHAPTER XVI

VIRGINIA AND MARYLAND

Observations on the waste lands of Great Britain—Not applicable to the same profit as those of Virginia— Reasons—Are superior in the hands of their owners— Remarks

I AM sensible that an objection may be made to the preceding recommendations of settling in Virginia, &c. upon the principles of the superior, or at least equal advantages of settling on the waste lands of Britain; the great benefit of the American wastes is the capability of enlarging the husbandry at pleasure proportioned to the money which the farmer has annually to lay out: agriculture in the cultivated parts of Britain has nothing equal to this advantage, but the identical circumstance is to be found in the moors and other wastes of Britain; this therefore is a case in direct opposition to that of the colonies, and consequently deserves examination here.

In the plantations every man, however low his condition and rank in life, can obtain on demand, and [by] paying the settled fees, whatever land he pleases, provided he engages to settle on it in ten years a certain number of white persons;[1] and when he has got his grant, it is a freehold to him and his

---

[1] The headright system, to which the author here refers, had been worked out under the régime of the Virginia Company. See L. C. Gray, *History of Agriculture in the Southern United States to 1860* (Washington, 1933).

posterity for ever. In this circumstance nothing can be more different, or in more direct opposition than the two cases. The wastes in Britain are all private property, generally belonging to men of fortune, who, so far from being ready to make presents of them to whoever demands them, will scarce be prevailed on to let them on long leases: but suppose they gave leases at a trifling rent, they would not build and inclose them, and that is too great an expence here for a new settler, who could build a handsome house in Virginia for less than a beggarly cottage would cost in England. Thus therefore there are many essential reasons for men's preferring the wilds of America to the wastes of Britain, in relation to the state of the land; and the ease and plenty of living makes another object highly advantageous in Virginia, but by no means so in Britain.

The pleasures of being a land owner are so great, and in America the real advantages so numerous, that it is not to be wondered at that men are so eager to enjoy [them], that they cross the Atlantic ocean in order to possess them; nor is it judicious to draw comparisons between our British wastes and these, between which there is no analogy in those essential circumstances that are the foundation of the great population of America; and at the same time that this is the case with our waste lands, it is the same with our cultivated ones which are equally different.

It is true that many of the good farmers in Britain will make more per cent. for their money than is done in America; but this singly is not the enquiry: in all the articles of living while the money is made, the state of the farmer and planter is very different: the one lives penuriously and with difficulty, the other on comparison riots in plenty; the poorest villager in some of our colonies lives better than a farmer of 200£.

a year in Britain, that is frugal enough to save money. Besides this, what a difference there is between living in one case on their own freehold, and in the other on the grounds of a landlord! But the great point is the advantageous disposition of the savings or other money which a Virginia planter can apply annually to an increase of culture; this is a point deserving the highest attention.

At the same time that I have been so clear in stating the superiority of Virginia in these cases, I must form an exception which is that of the landlords farming their own wastes in Britain: in this case they enter at once into most of the advantages of America, and with a power of making yet greater profit; for they may improve them in any quantities, and by building farmhouses, let them in farms very soon after the breaking up, which rotation they will make a profit of many more per cent. than is commonly made any where in America; especially if he proceeds in the work of improvement upon the plan of taking in land enough to form a farm every year, and to let one every year. In this manner from 3,147£. capital, 62,066£. may be made in eleven years on moors.* From 9,558£. capital, 142,294£. may be made in eight years.† From 1,781£. the lowest sum that can be thus employed, 12,000£. may be made in fifteen years.‡ This writer seems to think such a work might be as well executed by a renter as by a landlord: but this does not by any means appear; for the latter I think the reasoning clear, but not for the former, since difficulties may be found at setting out, in procuring the land; it is not every landlord would let his

* So stated in the *Farm. Lett.* II, 189. [This reference is to Arthur Young's *The Farmer's Letters to the People of England* (2 vols., London, 1770). Ed.]

† Page 224.

‡ Page 263.

wastes on *long* leases, at rents *low* enough. Other sorts of wastes are calculated in the same book to yield an equal and superior profit.

This immense profit to be made by improving British wastes turns on the very circumstance which makes husbandry so advantageous in America; the plenty of land enabling the farmer to extend himself annually: this is the great object that will be found uniformly profitable through every part of the world; and as wastes in Britain are plentiful enough, there is no reason for general assertions that land is plentiful in America but dear in Britain, since it is plain this is applicable only to those who want to buy or hire; but to those who are already the possessors, many have in Britain as much as they could have in America, and far more than they know what to do with.

Before I conclude this chapter I shall remark that the quick population of the American wastes, and the desolate state of the British ones, form a contrast which deserve attention in the legislature of this island: I have shewn that the reason of one country peopling and improving so quick, and the other being quite at a stand, is lands being given away in America—or next to it—and not to be had at all in Britain; for very few will be induced to sell land absolutely waste, the price it brings being too small, and vanity of possessing many acres (however wild) great in every one. Thus there being plenty of land in Britain as waste as that of America is no object, unless those who are desirous of possessing it in the latter country could get it equally easily in the former one.

But as the improvement of the wastes of a kingdom is ever an object of the highest consequence, particularly to population, the legislature might easily devise a method if not to cure the whole evil, at least to do much good: and this would

be to appoint an office to buy up all the waste land that acci-
dentally came to market in the three kingdoms, and to settle
large families on little farms in them, giving them as freeholds for ever, with a reservation of a quitrent,[2]—not sufficient
to pay the interest of the purchase, but to lessen the expence
if it was too great; but as long as it was kept moderate, no
quitrent at all should be taken, since the object of peopling
great tracts of waste land, in the heart of a country, is of
much more consequence than any moderate sum would be.
Without some plan of this sort being executed, we may be
certain the moors and wastes will never be improved, and
consequently our political writers should cease declaiming on
the impropriety of peopling American wastes instead of British ones; the one can be done, the other cannot; and therefore if the peopling [of] America is an advantage to this
kingdom, as it certainly is, it ought, beyond a doubt, to be
promoted, notwithstanding the inability of peopling our own
wastes.

[2] In some degree this proposal was prophetic of future British land
legislation. See N. S. B. Gras, *A History of Agriculture in Europe and
America* (New York, 1925), chap. xi.

CHAPTER XVII

VIRGINIA AND MARYLAND

Exports of Virginia and Maryland—Observations—General husbandry—Defects—Improvements proposed

TO SHEW the vast importance of these colonies to Great Britain, it will be necessary to lay before the reader the last accounts of their exports, from which we shall also see what proportion their common husbandry bears to their tobacco.

Tobacco, 96,000 hogsheads, at 8£. . . . . . . £.		768,000
Indian corn, beans, pease, &c.		30,000
Wheat, 40,000 quarters, at 20s.		40,000
Deer and other skins		25,000
Iron in bars and pigs		35,000
Sassafras, snake-root, ginseng, &c.		7,000
Masts, plank, staves, turpentine, and tar . . .		55,000
Flax-seed, 7000 hogsheads, at 40s.		14,000
Pickled pork, beef, hams, and bacon		15,000
Ships built for sale, 30 at 1000£.		30,000
Hemp 1000 tons at 21£. (besides 4000 tons more and 2000 of flax worked up for their own use)		21,000
Total		1,040,000

Upon this table I must observe once more, how extremely important these colonies are to the mother country: to raise [in raising] above a million sterling, the greatest part of which are true staples, and the rest necessary for the West

Indies, with no fish, whalebone, oil, &c.—commodities which some of the colonies have run away with from Britain, by rivalling her in her fishery—possessing no manufactures, even to such a degree that all attempts to bring the people into towns have proved vain. By manufactures, I mean those for sale; for as to private families working wool, hemp, and flax for their own use, it is what many do all over America, and are necessitated to do, for want of money and commodities to buy them. A colony so truly important, I say, deserves every attention from the mother country, and every encouragement to induce settlers to fix in it.

But in this list of exports one article appears which demands particular attention, I mean hemp. To the north of these colonies, none is exported; on the contrary, they import from Britain the hemp which we import from Russia, which is brought from the Ukraine, paying this immense freight, a proof strong enough that they cannot raise it. In Virginia and Maryland the soil is much better than to the northward, and will yield it, which we find it does in large quantities, even to the amount of 100,000£. an amount that is near a seventh of their tobacco, besides flax. This is the commodity of all others which we most want from our colonies, for it is so necessary for our navy that we ought certainly to have it more within our own command than it is at present; and the purchase carries away immense sums of money annually: to raise it therefore in America, and purchase it with our manufactures, is an object of the greatest importance. It is evident that if we are to expect hemp, it must be from this part of that continent; and consequently here we should give our great attention. It is also a matter of great importance to settlers to know that the climate and soil of the country will do for so valuable a product as hemp as well as tobacco; and their management is such, that both may be cultivated to advantage on the same plantation; and it is well known, that in America the profit on hemp, when land is found that will produce it, is as great as that on tobacco.

The latter plant thrives best on a rich, deep, black mould that is dry, and upland: but hemp loves the same soil in low lands that have a good degree of moisture in them. Very many tracts of land are yet to be had in the back parts of Virginia, which contain both sorts in plenty, and would consequently do well for the cultivation of both these products. A situation for hemp requires water-carriage as well as tobacco, being a bulky commodity.

	£.	s.	d.
Hemp, per ton	21	0	0
Tobacco	16	0	0
Wheat, at 30s. a quarter	7	10	0
Indian corn, barley, pease, beans, &c. at 16s. a quarter	4	8	0
Indigo, at 2s. 6d. a lb.	280	0	0
Ditto at 5s.	560	0	0
Silk, at 20s. a lb.	2,240	0	0
Wine	20	0	0

Such a scale of value per ton should always be attended to by new settlers: from hence it is apparent that indigo may be cultivated without water-carriage; or at least will bear a considerable land-carriage to get at water, because the expence of moving it will bear very little proportion to the value: but the Indian corn, pease, &c. being worth but 4£. 8s. a ton, the carriage must necessarily be that of water alone, as the value is too small to bear an expensive carriage: even wheat is in the same predicament; at 30s. a quarter I should not suppose it would ever bear a land-carriage of above ten or twelve miles in order to get at water. Hemp and tobacco will pay it much better, and will allow of being brought much farther by land. The writers on American affairs have, respecting navigations, confined themselves to the circumstance of the bulkiness of hemp and tobacco; but the value per ton is the only object that deserves attention; and we find that upon comparison with any sort of corn, hemp and tobacco is of a value that will bear some carriage, though not a very long one. In Virginia the planters are many of them able to ship their tobacco at their doors: this great advantage, which is of equal importance in all other productions as well as tobacco —in silk, indigo, &c. it is the same—this advantage has made it supposed a necessity; but there are many plantations in which they think a navigable river for sloops and boats of great importance to them; and not a few have not even this.

The culture of hemp in several circumstances of expence and produce has a resemblance with tobacco. In the richest soils of England it takes from three and a half to four acres and a half to produce a ton, which is worth from 28£. to 35£. And the labour upon an acre amounts to from 3£. 10s. to 5£. This is less than what I supposed tobacco would cost in England; consequently we may determine that hemp is cultivated in Virginia by negroes at an expence something less per acre than tobacco. One negroe manages three acres of tobacco, and would therefore do the same or better in hemp, which, to produce the same as in England, would be near a ton, or 21£. —the price in America; this exceeds tobacco. That this calculation does not exceed the truth we may find by an expression of Dr. Mitchell's, speaking of the lands on the Ohio and Mississippi, "Every labourer," says he, "might cultivate TWO ACRES or more in hemp, and ONE OR TWO in indigo, the pro-

duce of which would be worth from 30 to 40£. a year.* Now
if they could manage two in hemp, and one or two in indigo,
we may fairly conclude they might cultivate three in hemp:
and this makes hemp more profitable to the planter than
tobacco: but supposing them only on a par, it is an object of
no slight importance to know that those lands which are
not perfectly adapted to tobacco, may be made equally profitable under hemp.

The wheat and other corn which is among these exports,
are raised principally on old tobacco plantations that are worn
out for that plant without the assistance of much manure.
This is a point which deserves attention: exhaust the lands
in these colonies as much as you will with tobacco, you will
leave it in order for grain, which is a matter of great consequence to the settlers; since corn is there a very profitable
article of culture, and upon the rich lands of this country will
(even after tobacco) yield large crops with very little assistance from manure.

The usual course of the business has been the planters exhausting the land first with tobacco, and then retiring backwards with their negroes in quest of fresh land for tobacco,
sell[ing] their old plantations to new comers who have not
money enough to go largely into tobacco with negroes and
therefore confine themselves to common husbandry: and this
is upon the whole very advantageous. Planters who meet
with very rich fresh woodland, employ themselves so eagerly
on tobacco, as scarcely to raise corn enough for their families,
in which case their little neighbours are very useful to them
in selling it. This does not however seem to be good manage-

* Present State, p. 248. [John Mitchell, The Present State of Great
Britain and North America, with Regard to Agriculture, Population, Trade
and Manufactures (London, 1767). Ed.]

ment, as tobacco employs the negroes only in summer: indeed they may occupy the winter entirely in clearing fresh land.

Tobacco and hemp, I have already given as good an account of as my intelligence will allow: but the common husbandry of these provinces demands the same attention. Wheat they sow as we do in England in October; about two bushels to an acre, which produces seldom less than twenty-five; sometimes thirty-five and forty. Rye they do not cultivate much, as their lands are in general good enough to give them great crops of wheat. Barley produces from twenty-five to forty bushels: oats from 30 to 60: pease from 10 to 60: Indian corn seldom less than 50 and sometimes 80. Turneps and cabbages thrive in the greatest luxuriance, and produce crops far beyond any thing we know in Britain. Potatoes also, with good management, yield, without any dung, crops much greater than can in these islands be gained by the force of manuring: yet are the farmers of these colonies most inexcusably negligent in not giving these crops due justice, in properly preparing their land, and keeping them during their growth free from weeds. If the fertility of the soil and climate was well seconded by the knowledge and industry of the planters, the crops would be much greater than they are, and husbandry would prove the most profitable business in the known world. But the planters, who have the power of being good cultivators of their fields, abandon them to the overseers of their negroes, and pursue only their own pleasures—and others, who may have more knowledge, have not the substance to make improvements: it is the same in Britain, and probably in every other part of the world. The foregoing account of the products of the crops of common husbandry is sufficient to shew the immense profit which might be made by agriculture in this country, if it was followed with understanding and spirit: for want of these necessary ingredients, twice the land is run over to produce that which half of it would be more than sufficient for, under scientific management.

In the systems of crops generally pursued here, the farmers go upon the bad ideas of their brethren to the northwards; they take successive crops of corn, till the land will produce no more, then they leave it fallow for some years, and serve fresh ground in the same manner: all the inconveniences which I have mentioned in preceding articles result from this, but the plenty of land seduces the planters to act thus contrary to their own interests. The summers in Virginia and Maryland being hotter than in Pennsylvania, this method must be still worse than there, because the land they leave in this manner fallow must be [left] the longer before it acquires a turf to support cattle: this shews the necessity, if the farmer would make the most of his grounds, of leaving the land in tolerable heart; and with the last crop of corn sowing grass seeds that are adapted to the climate. Good meadows are very scarce except where water can be thrown over them, a husbandry not practiced near so much as it ought [to be].

In the management of their woods, they have shewn the same inattention to futurity with their neighbours; so that in the old settled parts of the provinces, they begin to fear a want of that useful commodity, and would have felt it long ago, had they not such an immense inland navigation to supply them. The woods upon a tobacco plantation must be in great plenty for the winter employment of the slaves, or else the planter's profit will not equal that of his neighbours.

Their fences are extremely incomplete, and kept in very bad order: all their attention is to secure the tobacco-field, but the rest of the plantation is never in this respect kept in the order that it ought to be: this is another evil occasioned by plenty of land; they will grasp at more than they have money to cultivate, even upon the tobacco system, which requires plenty; and then they are forced to manage it in a slovenly manner.

Cattle might be made an article of great profit in these provinces: the planters are obliged, on account of manure, to keep great stock; but they are little attentive to make the most advantage of them, either in the raising manure, or in the management of the beasts themselves. The breed they think little of improving; and their treatment of their horses and oxen, for draft, is such as would move the ridicule of the smallest farmers in England. These are points which they mistakenly think of little importance, giving all their attention to the tobacco; but with better management these objects would prove so profitable as to shew that they demanded no less conduct than their principal crop. In the article of raising manure, particularly, they might make five times their present quantity, which would be attended with a corresponding increase of their staple in some of their fields; but for want of knowledge in this essential part of their business they lose much.

There are some improvements in the rural economy of these provinces which demand particular attention, for they would admit of more and greater [profit] than any of our other plantations. Under the article tobacco, I remarked several alterations which would render that culture much more beneficial; of which the effect of general good management, enabling them to keep more land under that staple, is an essential article, which would make a vast difference in the interest of Britain. No object in the American department is of such consequence; and this should induce the administration to take whatever measures that could be desired, in order to improve the agriculture of these provinces. Means might be invented which would introduce by degrees better ideas.

Among the articles of improvement, which are the most obvious, there is nothing which demands greater attention than the culture of silk. None of our colonies enjoy a climate so well adapted to the purpose: mulberry trees are found every where in profusion, and the work of winding the silk and attending the worms might be carried on without any material interruption of their tobacco culture; but the advantage of making silk is its being in a great measure proper for uniting with almost any business, since women, old, infirm persons, and even children, make as good a figure in it as the most robust men, a point of vast consequence. The common objection is the want of hands; but that seems to be made by persons who are not acquainted with the business: five or six weeks in a year would be sufficient for the work, and a family of a moderate number might, it is very well known, make 40 or 50£. a year, which would at once be 40 or 50£. sterling a year to them, an object of equal consequence with any that could be found. It is supposed that the number of people in the tobacco colonies does not fall short of 800,000; if silk was well understood among them, it would be no difficult matter to have from them as many pounds of silk, without any deduction from their tobacco; but if only 500,-000£. were made, it would add exceedingly to the wealth of both Britain and the colony.

In a country newly settling or settled, people really cannot spare either the time or attention, small as it is, for making silk; but the case is very different in Maryland and Virginia, which are in a great measure well peopled countries, compared to several of our colonies. The people are numerous enough to make it an object of consequence, and are in general sufficiently at their ease to render the undertaking as profitable as it is in Italy or China. I cannot but attribute the remissness shewn in this article, [not] to a want of people, or of time, but merely to that of attention and knowledge. They are unacquainted with the conduct of the worms, and the winding of the silk, and probably think it a more troublesome business than it is, and one which is of much longer duration. But this ignorance might soon be banished, if persons skilled in the culture were sent from Europe to instruct them; a few, moving through these provinces, and shewing the women the management (which is a matter of entertainment rather than of labour) would in a few years make it familiar to abundance of families. The importance of silk from our colonies is an object that well deserves some expence, it will pay excellently for it; since there is great difference between paying for our raw silk with money and buying it with our manufactures.

Another article to be mentioned here is the culture of vines, for which the back parts of Virginia are as well if not better adapted than those of Pennsylvania: wine is another commodity which the nation is in as great want of from the colonies as any other, for the sums paid by this kingdom to France, Spain, and Portugal, for this production of their lands, are immense. There is the greatest reason to suppose that vineyards would thrive here advantageously, from the uncommon plenty of wild vines found in the woods thro' all the back country. The planters know not what would be the effect of culture on these vines, though the grapes at present will not make good wine, yet is there no reason to think that cultivation, upon approved principles, would not render them of a quality sufficiently excellent? The richest vineyards of Champaigne and Burgundy, left wild, would, it is well known, produce a wine far enough from the flavour of those celebrated ones: it is ploughing between the rows, dressing, and pruning, that gives the flavour to the grapes; and why should not the same causes have the same effect in America? But the trial upon a large scale, and executed with the requisite skill and spirit, would prove this: for attaining so excellent a purpose, it would be necessary to plant a large vineyard in a proper situation respecting aspect and soil, and to cultivate it by hands brought from the vine-countries of Europe. At the same time, divisions should be allotted to setts of European and Madeira vines, of various sorts; by which means it would be found with certainty what the soil and climate would yield in this article of husbandry. Probably the native vine would, with culture, produce the best wine, from its agreeing with the peculiar climate of North America.

In all colonies, government should be at the expence of a large plantation,[1] for the valuable purpose of making experiments on those products which are desired to be produced. Thus in the back parts of Virginia, in such a plantation, should be cultivated vines among other articles: by such a conduct, that certainty would be gained which we want at present. The Society for the Encouragement of Arts, Manufactures and Commerce have offered some very sensible and patriotic

---

[1] In making this statement the author anticipated the establishment of government experiment stations for agricultural purposes.

premiums for planting the largest quantity of setts in various districts:[2] such endeavours can never be too much commended; but at the same time it wants not much sagacity to foresee that the effect must be very trifling: such premiums may be easily gained without the knowledge that is desired; for suppose a certain number of setts planted (not amounting to any thing like a sufficiency for one tenth of a vineyard), this is but of little consequence if the succeeding management is not duly and spiritedly performed, and by persons skilled in the vineyard culture; points which it is not to be supposed will be attended to by the accidental persons that may be candidates for such premiums. And how is the society or any persons in England to know whether the person who plants the greatest number of setts is situated in the most favourable spots—or possesses a soil equally proper with many other tracts in the province? All such experiments should certainly be encouraged, but there is very little reason to believe that they can be attended with any great effect.

The want of people is urged in this case, as well in that of silk; and I own with much more reason, since population is more necessary for the management of vineyards than for that of silk-worms; but in answer to this, I should propose the employment of negroes. Why should not they be instructed in pruning and dressing vines, as well as pruning and picking tobacco, or the operose[3] performances they execute in the culture of sugar, in the manufacture of which

---

[2] The Society for the "Encouragement of Arts, Manufactures and Commerce" was instituted in London in 1754. Few English counties in the eighteenth century were without an organization for the promotion of agricultural improvement. See The Right Honorable Lord Ernle, *English Farming, Past and Present* (5th ed., London, 1912), pp. 209–10.

[3] In other words, laborious or requiring labor.

there is very great dexterity requisite, so that negroe boilers, &c. have been sold for above three hundred pounds apiece, when experienced in the work. There can be no doubt but they might be employed in the culture of vines equally well, and perhaps to great advantage; this is a point of importance which should be well attended to, for the vineyard culture requires many hands, of some kind or other; and as the colonies have not the common population (except in certain districts) sufficient for the purpose, vine planters would be under a necessity of depending for at least much of the work on slaves, the number of which can be multiplied at pleasure to any amount. In the article of cooperage the Virginians would have great advantage over the vine countries of Europe; their woods would yield them staves, hoops, and heading upon the spot, instead of sending those articles to the West Indies. The length of freight from America to England might easily be remedied, by favouring the import at the custom-house; perhaps it would be proper to exempt them for some time from all duties.

I have in several parts of this work mentioned the great importance of raising hemp in our colonies, and at the same [time] shewn the difficulties which have prevented any export of it, except [from] the tobacco colonies; these are principally the want of good land, or plenty of manure. But they have a native hemp in Virginia, which they call silk-grass, which might probably be made to answer many purposes of the highest use, if not exceed the common hemp, since the threads of it are stronger; some most excellent fabrics have been made in private families of this grass, which shew it to be perfectly well adapted to a manufacture, yet has it been quite neglected: besides this silk-grass, they have three or four sorts of native hemp, which thrive well on their poorest lands, and which have been found to answer well in culture on a small scale.*

It is impossible to know what the merit of the plants indigenous in these colonies is, unless there was a plantation established at the public expence, under the direction of a skillful botanist, and one perfectly well acquainted with the practice, as well as the theory of agriculture. In such a plantation, improvements might be made in the culture of tobacco: vineyards might be planted and cultivated, both of the native vines, and also of foreign ones. Experiments might be made on the culture of silk. All the native plants, like those I have just mentioned, which promised anything of utility, might be brought into culture, and trials made of their worth as materials for manufacture. Such a plantation well supported would be attended with some, if not all [of], those excellent consequences which flowed from the gardens of the Dutch East India Company, at the Cape of Good Hope.[4] Such objections may be made to the proposal I have now offered as were doubtless made to the establishment of those famous gardens; but the company wisely rejected objections, when they did not amount to a proof that the measure was wrong; and it has accordingly turned out one of the finest monuments of the spirit of that celebrated body of merchants. Objections may certainly be made to the proposal, and the expence mentioned as a reason for not adopting a design which could not fail of being most highly beneficial; but the expence is a

---

* Mitchel[1]'s *Present State*, p. 261.

[4] Despite this statement, South Africa made slow headway agriculturally under the Dutch East India Company. Wine, grain, and cattle were the principal products. For gardens as well as other features of Cape of Good Hope economic life under the Dutch see C. P. Lucas, *A Historical Geography of the British Colonies* (Oxford, 1897), Vol. IV, chap. iii; and J. H. Hofmeyr, *South Africa* (New York, 1931), chap. iii.

very poor reason against measures of this nature, unless it was urged by ministers who shewed, in all their other actions, the same spirit of economy which seemed to dictate such a refusal.

On another occasion I remarked that the heat of the climate of Pennsylvania burnt up the grasses of the pastures, except the low tracts over which water was thrown; this is yet stronger with Virginia and Maryland, which are hotter than Pennsylvania; for this reason the culture of lucerne[5] would, in these provinces, be attended with yet greater advantages: their tobacco and hemp demand far more manure than they can at present raise, no object therefore can be of greater importance than an increase of it. This is only to be brought about by keeping their cattle confined; if they were folded in yards, fed in the soiling way, on lucerne, they would raise greater quantities of dung than in any other method could be effected. This observation is also applicable to the winter food of cattle; the climate of these colonies is so mild that the cattle run out all winter; which, though an amazing advantage to the planter in many respects, is yet a preventive of raising manure, for it is the confinement alone of cattle which affords that. Upon this principle the planters here ought to attend to cabbages, turneps, potatoes, &c. as well as their brethren in the more northern settlements.

[5] Alfalfa.

CHAPTER XVIII

THE OHIO

*Description of the countries adjacent to the Ohio—
Staples—New colony—Principles on which it is
founded—Remarks*

THIS immense country, which in our maps is laid down
as a part of Virginia, reaches from the eastward of lake
Erie, on the frontiers of New York in the latitude 43°, to its
junction with the Mississippi in latitude 36½°; the length of
this tract, in a strai[gh]t line, is not less than 800 miles.
For 300 miles it bounds on the mountains, which are the
limits of Pennsylvania, from which to lake Erie is an oblong
of 200 miles long, by about 100 broad, which space is one
of the finest parts of North America. But the territory which
is here principally to be considered is to the south of this,
from the neighbourhood of Fort Pitt[1] to the Cherokee river[2]
—which falls into the Ohio near the Mississippi, to the south
of the former river; most of the country to the north of it
belonging to the Six Nations,[3] partly inhabited by them, and
part their hunting ground.

[1] Fort Pitt, formerly Fort Duquesne, and now the site of the city of
Pittsburgh, was located at the junction of the Allegheny and Monongahela
rivers.

[2] Now the Tennessee.

[3] The Six Nations were a group of confederated and related tribes of
North American Indians (Iroquois). The Iroquois Confederacy, or Iroquois League, consisted originally of Five Nations: Seneca, Cayuga, Onon-
daga, Oneida, and Mohawk. These tribes banded together about fifty years

The want of fresh land in Virginia, for the tobacco planters to spread themselves over, occasioned many settlers to pass the Alleg[h]any mountains and fix themselves on the rivers that fall into the Ohio; this was so early as from 1750 to 1755; the French had in 1748 and 1749 partly usurped and secured all this tract of back country by their forts; a plan which they afterwards brought fully into execution; and when they were informed of the step taken by the British settlers, they warned them from what they called their master's territories, and soon after by force drove them back. This was the origin of the late war; the events of which relating to this country need no recapitulation here.[4]

Upon the conquest of Fort Duquesne,[5] the back settlers of Virginia and Pennsylvania renewed their emigration and

---

before the Dutch arrived in New Netherland (New York). The Five Nations had one of the highest material cultures of the Eastern Indians. They were semi-sedentary and practiced considerable agriculture, raising corn, squash, tobacco, pumpkins, lima beans, and other vegetables. Their "long houses" of bark, in which numerous families lived, were a distinctive mark of their culture. They were expert basket-makers and their pottery was of good grade. In the early eighteenth century the Five Nations became the Six Nations when the Tuscarora, an Iroquoian Confederacy of North Carolina, came North and in 1714 was admitted to the Iroquois Confederacy of New York. As allies of the British the Iroquois were of great assistance in blocking the French during the French and Indian War. See L. H. Morgan, *League of the Hodé-no-sau-Nea or Iroquois* (New York, 1904).

[4] The Seven Years' War in Europe or the French and Indian War as it was known in America. See Francis Parkman, *Montcalm and Wolfe* (Boston, 1884).

[5] By the middle of the Eighteenth century Great Britain and France were pitted against each other for the mastery of the North American continent. A place of great strategic importance to both contestants was the present site of Pittsburgh. Here the English were in process of building a fort when they were driven out by the French under Captain Coutrecoeur who completed the fortification and named it Fort Duquesne as a compliment to the captain-general of Canada. In 1758 Fort Duquesne was captured by the British and renamed Fort Pitt. See Edward Channing, *A History of the United States*, Vol. III (New York, 1912).

in great numbers once more passed the mountains and settled themselves on the Ohio and its branches. Here they cleared grounds, and began their plantations; but in the latter end of 1763, a proclamation appeared, which forbid all settlements beyond the rivers which fall into the Atlantic Ocean.[6] But the people who had fixed themselves on the fertile lands of the Ohio, were too well pleased with their situation to obey this proclamation, while others continued daily to join them.

The territory in which they planted themselves being without the bounds of the provinces of Virginia and Pennsylvania, the people who had settled there became soon a lawless sett,

---

[6] The principal objects of the famous Royal Proclamation of 1763 were to provide for the government of the British possessions in America which had been acquired by the Treaty of Paris (1763); to define certain interior boundaries; and to regulate trade and intercourse with the Indians. Formulated by Lord Shelburne, president of the British Board of Trade, it provided that all territory between the crest of the Alleghenies and the Mississippi from Florida to 50° north latitude was, for the time being at least, closed to settlers and land speculators. The sale of Indian lands except to the Crown was prohibited, and all those who had settled in the reserved region were ordered to withdraw. Henceforth no person could carry on trade with the Indians unless he was licensed. Fugitives from justice taking refuge in the reserved territory were to be apprehended and returned. The colonists, especially ambitious pioneers, colony promoters, and venturous speculators who had either already secured claims to thousands of acres along the Ohio and its tributaries, or who planned to obtain domains beyond the mountains, were vexed. Veterans of the Seven Years' War and members of the Ohio and Mississippi land companies voiced their opposition in no uncertain terms. Six of the older colonies questioned its validity on the ground that it involved territory over which they had prior claim. Of all the acts of the imperial government which in any way contributed to the disruption of the Empire, none perhaps was of greater importance than this proclamation. See Carl Becker, *The Eve of the Revolution* (New Haven, 1918); H. E. Egerton, *The Causes and Character of the American Revolution* (London, 1923); C. H. Van Tyne, *The Causes of the War of Independence* (Boston, 1922); and especially C. W. Alvord, *The Mississippi Valley in British Politics* (Cleveland, 1917), I, 199 ff.

among whom a licentious spirit prevailed; living without government, they had continued quarrels with the Indians, and the whole aspect of their affairs foreboded no good. The country in which they settled belonged to the Six Nations, who complained repeatedly of this invasion of their property, offering to the governor of Virginia to sell their right in all the country to the south of the river Ohio.

Their remonstrances were too much slighted, for it was several years before any measures were taken to give them satisfaction; from remonstrating they proceeded to threaten in terms severe, though not departing from respect. Then it was that a conference was held with the chiefs of these nations, and a bargain was struck: for the sum of something more than ten thousand pounds paid by [the] government to the Six Nations, they made over all their right to the tracts of country to the south of the Ohio.[7]

This purchase was made, not with a view to encourage any settlements beyond the mountains, but only to satisfy the Indians; the tenor of the proclamation of 1763 was ad-

[7] This reference is undoubtedly to the Transylvania Company of Judge Richard Henderson. In 1764 Daniel Boone, a North Carolina frontiersman, had undertaken contrary to the Proclamation of 1763 an exploring expedition into Kentucky in behalf of a group formed by Judge Henderson, a scion of an aristocratic Virginia family which had come to North Carolina for its rich and cheap lands. Ten years later, following the clash between the Indians and the whites known as Lord Dunmore's War, Henderson established the Transylvania Company and for the sum of £10,000 and goods bought from the Cherokee Indians the region bounded by the Ohio, Kentucky, and Cumberland rivers. Here he planned to form a proprietary colony under the Crown. But the royal governors of Virginia and North Carolina issued proclamations denouncing his enterprise, and when the Virginians took their government into their own hands they promptly annulled Henderson's title. See Archibald Henderson, *Conquest of the Old Southwest* (New York, 1920); T. R. Roosevelt, *Winning of the West* (New York, 1889), Vol. I; and Allan Nevins, *The American States during and after the Revolution, 1775–1789* (New York, 1924), chap. xiv.

hered to, and the governor of Virginia ordered to admit of no colonization within the specified limits. But such orders could not be obeyed; for the country was found so fertile and pleasant that fresh numbers every day thronged thither; and the expediency of establishing a government over them was found daily greater.

In this situation of affairs it was that an association of gentlemen, principally of America, formed the plan of establishing a new colony in the lands thus purchased of the Indians; they brought into the idea some respectable merchants of London, at the head of whom was a member of the House of Commons, Mr. Walpole.[8] They petitioned the treasury for leave to execute their plan, offering to pay to [the] government the ten thousand pounds the whole country had cost, for the property of only a part of it, and to be at the whole expence of the civil government of the new province.

This petition was referred from the treasury to the board of trade, which board made a report upon the petition, in which they strongly condemned the project, offering the reasons on which they founded their opinion; reasons which were by no means satisfactory to the understanding of those who were well acquainted with the state of the colonies.

The affair then came before the privy council, in which it was debated, and a difference of opinion found, which occa-

[8] The proposal of the Walpole Company, an English organization including Lord Camden and the Earl of Hertford, and sponsored by George Grenville, that the home government hand the Ohio and Kentucky country over to the Old World company instead of granting it to colonial land companies, greatly angered and alarmed the colonists. See I. S. Harrell, *Loyalism in Virginia* (New York, 1926); H. J. Carman, *Social and Economic History of the United States* (Boston, 1930), I, 256–57; C. P. Nettels, *Roots of American Civilization* (New York, 1938).

sioned a debate; it ended in the petition being granted; after which Mr. Walpole and his associates took such measures as they thought necessary for the establishment of their new colony.

This is the history of the transaction brought down to the present time;* the latter part is too recent to know upon what terms the proprietors portion out the lands, nor yet are the exact limits known: but the accounts we have had of the country before it was thought of establishing a colony in it are such as will enable us to form a pretty clear idea of it. In the observations on the report of the board of trade on the petition of Mr. Walpole and his associates, the following circumstances are drawn up.

First, The lands in question are excellent, the climate temperate, the native grapes, silk worms, and mulberry trees are every where; hemp grows spontaneously in the vallies and low grounds; iron ore is plenty in the hills, and no soil is better adapted for the culture of tobacco, flax, and cotton, than that of the Ohio.

Second, The country is well watered by several navigable rivers, communicating with each other; and by which and a short land-carriage of *only forty miles,* the produce of the lands of the Ohio can, even *now,* be sent cheaper to the seaport town of Alexandria, on the river Potomack, (where general Braddock's transports landed his troops) than any kind of merchandize is at this time sent *from Northampton to London.*

Third, The river Ohio is at *all* seasons of the year navigable for large boats like the west country barges, rowed only by four or five men; and from the month of January

* Since this was written, it has been reported that some interruption has happened in the grant.

to the month of April large ships may be built on the Ohio, and sent laden with *hemp, flax, silk,* &c. to this kingdom.

Fourth, Flour, corn, beef, ship-plank, and other necessaries can be sent down the stream of the Ohio to West Florida, and from thence to the islands, much cheaper and in better order, than from New York or Philadelphia.

Fifth, Hemp, tobacco, iron, and such bulky articles, can also be sent *down* the *stream* of the Ohio to the *sea,* at least 50 per cent. cheaper than these articles were ever carried by a land-carriage of only sixty miles in Pennsylvania—where *waggonage* is cheaper than in any other part of North America.

Sixth, The expence of transporting British manufactures from the sea to the Ohio colony will *not* be so much as is now paid, and must ever be paid to a great part of the countries of Pennsylvania, Virginia, and Maryland.

That we may more particularly elucidate this important point, we shall take the freedom of observing that it is *not* disputed, but even acknowledged, by the very report now under consideration, that the climate and soil of the Ohio are as favourable as we have described them; and as to the native silk-worms, it is a truth that above 10,000 weight of cocoons was, in August 1771, sold at the public filature in Philadelphia, and that the silk produced from the *native* worm is of a good quality and has been much approved of in this city. As to hemp, we are ready to make it appear that it grows, as we have represented, spontaneously, and of a good texture on the Ohio. In the report itself it is urged— "every advantage derived from an established government would naturally tend to draw the stream of population; fertility of soil, and temperature of climate offering superior incitements to settlers, who, exposed to few hardships, and struggling with few difficulties, could with little labour earn an abundance for their own wants." This is the state of the intelligence which is to be gained from the parties concerned; from those who petitioned, and from those who wanted the petition to be rejected, both agree as to the fertility and healthiness of the territory. But I remarked before, that the same accounts were current before a colony was thought of.

Upon occasion of the last war Dr. Mitchel[1][9] was employed by the ministry to take an accurate survey of all the back countries of North America, most of them being then but little known except to the French, who were in possession of a line of forts through all North America. No person could have been more properly appointed, for he was not only able to lay down the country with exactness, but being well acquainted with practical agriculture in Virginia and Pennsylvania, he was able to understand the nature and value of those countries he should traverse. This was the origin of his map of North America, the best general one we have had; at the time it was published, it was accompanied by a bulky pamphlet, written by the Doctor and entitled, *The Contest in America*,[10] in which he enters into a full elucidation of the importance of the back countries, and of the fatal effects which must flow from leaving the French in possession of their encroachments. Among others he considers particularly the territory of the Ohio, and shews of how much

[9] John Mitchell emigrated from England and settled in the little village of Urbanna on the Rappahannock in Virginia about 1700. A distinguished botanist and a correspondent of Linnaeus, he achieved some distinction as a collector of plant specimens in America and as the discoverer of several new species. He was also a physician and his treatise on yellow fever was used by Dr. Benjamin Rush during the outbreak of that disease.

[10] This report appeared in book form in London in 1757 under the title *The Contest in America between Great Britain and France, with Its Consequences and Importance.*

importance it is to the planters of Virginia; he there mentions the want of fresh lands for planting tobacco, and the necessity of their being able to extend themselves for that purpose beyond the mountains. The country is described as one of the finest and most fruitful in all America, and abounding greatly in deer, wild cows, and wild oxen; and at the same time situated in one of the finest and most healthy climates in all that country.

This account agrees also with another which was given near an hundred years ago by La Honton,[11] who, speaking of the country to the south of lake Erie, mentions its being one of the finest on the globe, both in respect of climate and soil; it is a tract, he observes, of vast meadows, full of wild bees and deer, and the woods of vines and wild turkies.

Dr. Mitchel[1], in another work published in 1767 (*The Present State*), gives other particulars concerning this territory, which deserve attention; and especially in the point of affording that fresh land which is so much wanted in the tobacco colonies, where their plantations (as was shewn in the article of Virginia) are exhausted by continual crops of that product: "they will," says he, "be in a short time worn

---

[11] Baron Louis Armand de la Hontan or Lahontan (1666–c. 1713) was a French explorer in America. He entered the Army and came to New France in 1683 as captain of a regiment. He fought against the Iroquois in two expeditions. A close student of Indian life, he was sent West in 1687 with Duluth to command the new Fort St. Joseph on the St. Clair River. This post he abandoned, and traveling westward by the Fox-Wisconsin portage he reached the upper Mississippi. His elaborate description of the physical features and tribes of the region in his famous book *Nouveaux Voyages de Mr. le Baron de Lahontan dans l'Amerique Septentrionale*, although not accurate in some respects, forms one of the first extended accounts of the West and its life which we possess. See F. C. B. Crompton, *Glimpses of Early Canadians: Lahontan* (New York, 1925); L. P. Kellogg, *The French Régime in Wisconsin and the Northwest* (Madison, 1925); J. B. Brebner, *The Explorers of North America, 1492–1806* (New York, 1933), chap. xx.

out, and when that happens, there must be an end of the tobacco trade, without a supply of fresh lands fit to produce that exhausting weed as well as to maintain cattle to manure them, with convenient ports and an inland navigation to ship off such a gross and bulky commodity; of which [fresh lands] there are none in all the British dominions in North America, but the rich lands on the Mississippi and the Ohio: whoever are possessed of these must soon command the tobacco trade, the only considerable branch of trade in all North America, and the only one that this nation has left." In other passages the same writer describes these lands as being of considerable depth and fertility, having a natural moisture in them, and being excellently adapted for hemp, flax, and tobacco; also that no country can promise better for silk, wine, and oil, the climate being dry, which is the contrary of the maritime parts of America, where the rains are almost continual. And from the natural plenty of grass in meadows of great extent, with the general fertility of the soil, the maintenance of all sorts of cattle would be perfectly easy, and consequently provisions would be raised with scarcely any trouble; a point of great importance when a staple commodity is cultivated, for the planter ought to be able to give all his attention to the principal article: but if he is forced to divide his strength for providing food for cattle, &c. he cannot raise such a quantity of his staple as if more favourably circumstanced.

In a word, this territory of the Ohio enjoys every advantage of climate and soil which is to be found in the back parts of Virginia, but in a much higher degree, the soil being far more fertile, and the climate more pleasant and more wholesome. The assertions in the observations on the report of the board of trade are strong to this point, and may be depended on, as several of the gentlemen in the association for establishing this colony have lived long in Virginia and Pennsylvania, and [have] appointed persons to gain intelligence of all the material circumstances concerning it. From these, and the other authorities I have mentioned, it is plain that this new colony will probably be found of the highest consequence in the production of the following commodities.

TOBACCO

This valuable staple is cultivated in Virginia upon the freshest and most fertile lands; none can be too rich for it: a newly broken up woodland is what it most affects, and is what the planters choose for it, whenever it is in their power. I before observed that such new land was no longer in plenty in the tobacco colonies, which makes this acquisition of country of the more importance: here are immense forests upon a soil the most fertile that can be imagined, and consequently such a field for enlarging our tobacco plantations as the nation has long wanted. Such a soil may well prove an inducement to many to purchase great numbers of negroes, in order to employ them on staple productions, which in such fresh and fertile lands may safely be expected to pay them better than in the old colonies, where the good land has been for some time scarce; that is private property: there is in several of our colonies great tracts that are excellent, but this is like the wastes in Britain; plenty of land is of no effect if it is not to be had by the new settlers without paying a large price for it. But the value of the lands on the Ohio is not disputed, the great point for tobacco is that of carriage; for it is so bulky, that if carriage is expensive, it cannot be brought cheap enough to market. The proprietors give the following account of the communication with the Atlantic.

During the last French war, when there was no back carriage from the Ohio to Alexandria, the expence of carriage was only about a *half-penny* a pound, as will appear from the following account, the truth of which we shall fully ascertain, viz.

	£.	s.	d.
From Alexandria to Fort Cumberland by water	0	1	7 per cwt.
From Port Cumberland to Red Stone Creek, at fourteen dollars per waggon load, each waggon carrying fifteen cwt.	0	4	2
	0	5	9

Note, the distance was *then* seventy miles, but by a *new* waggon road *lately* made, it is *now* but forty miles—a saving, of course, of above one half of the 5s. 9d. is *at present* experienced. If it is considered that [what] this rate of carriage was *in time of war*, and *when* there were no inhabitants on the Ohio, we cannot doubt but every intelligent mind will be satisfied that it is now *less* than is daily paid in London for the carriage of *coarse woollens, cutlery, iron ware*, &c. from several counties in England.

And in the enumeration of advantages quoted above, it is asserted, that *large ships* may be built on the Ohio, and sent loaded, from January to April, to Britain; also that provisions and lumber may be sent from thence cheaper to the West Indies than from New York or Philadelphia.

These accounts call for several material observations: as to the truth of them, they are advanced in such a manner, and by such persons, that we have no reason to doubt it; nor should I omit to remark that the account coincides with others, particularly with the exportation which the French are well known to have carried on from the Illinois, and do at present carry on from thence. But it was never known that the mouth of the Mississippi was navigable for *large* ships; Captain Pittman, who surveyed the river, says, a thirty-six gun frigate has gone over with her guns *out*; but after you are over the bar, he acknowledges there is a depth of water, all the way up, for *any ship whatever*. The proprietors remark, that half the 5s. 9d. is saved; but that does not appear, as the price from Alexandria to Fort Cumberland is not changed; but supposing instead of 4s. 2d. from Fort Cumberland to Redstone Creek, that it should be only 2s. then the total price per cwt. would be 3s. 7d. or per ton 3£. 11s. 8d. Now two hogsheads of tobacco make a ton, which at 8£. are 16£. from which price the deduction of 3£. 11s. 8d. more than is paid by the planters near Alexandria is too high to be submitted to, if any cheaper method can be found of conveying that product to shipping; and this cheaper method must surely be by the Mississippi, to the gulph of Florida; for if lumber and provisions can be sent by that channel cheaper than from New York or Philadelphia, as the proprietors assert, it must plainly be a cheaper way than a carriage which comes to 3£. 11s. 8d. per ton, which can never be supported by a commodity the value of which at shipping is only 16£. a ton. The reason of this carriage being so dear, must be the number of falls above Alexandria. As to wheat and other provisions, they could never be sent by such a conveyance, five quarters of wheat are a ton, which at 20s. a quarter come only to 5£. a sum that will never bear 3£. 11s. 8d. carriage before it gets to the shipping; and if it is reckoned at 30s. or 7£. 10s. still 3£. 11s. 8d. is far more than it would bear.

Relative to the mother country, it is of very little consequence whether wheat and provisions can be exported from a colony or not, because staple commodities alone are valuable to Britain; but to settlers it is an object to know if all the surplus of their products can be exported to advantage. What [whether] they may be [transported] by the Missis-

sippi is not the point at present, but certainly they cannot be
to the Atlantic. By the accounts of the proprietors it is clear
that no commodity scarcely can be raised, but what may be
sent from the Ohio to the West Indies. This concern of navigation is of great consequence to the tobacco planter, whose
product is one of the most bulky staples of America; and in
Virginia and Maryland the convenience of water-carriage is
so great that many planters load ships at their own doors;
but this is not in common to be expected, though it seems
that it might be the case along the Ohio if once the navigation of the Mississippi be well understood from practice.

In respect of the advantages for tobacco planting that
result from a great plenty of land, enabling the planter to
keep whatever stocks of cattle he wants and to raise provision for the plantation, no country in America is comparable
to the territory in question, where a country is now settling
more than 500 miles long, by from 2[00] to 300 broad, possessing, in the utmost luxuriance of plenty, every necessary
of life.

Hemp

As tobacco requires for yielding great crops a rich woodland that is rather dry, hemp on the contrary, loves a large
degree of moisture, in rich low lands. Such are found in great
plenty in all the valleys between the hills in the new colony,
where the soil is natural to this production, as we may judge
from the circumstance of such quantities of wild hemp being
found in almost all the low lands. This circumstance shews
also how well the climate may be expected to agree with it.
There is all the reason in the world to think that the nation's
expectations of having hemp from the colonies will at last,
after so many disappointments, be answered by the lands on
the Ohio. They are, it is universally agreed, of that nature

which is peculiarly adapted to the production; the vales are rich, deep, moist, and so fertile that it will be many years before they are exhausted. This is precisely what has been so long wanted; for if hemp will not pay for the employment of negroes it will never be made an article of culture in large: secondary objects are always neglected; it is only those of the first importance which enjoy that degree of attention necessary to make any thing succeed. The only thing to be feared, upon this principle, is the neglect of the planter, who, used to tobacco, may be so eager in raising that staple as to neglect every other. Neglect of this sort sometimes gives rise to ideas of incapacity in a country, when the fault is only in the cultivator: for this reason I cannot but regret that the proprietors' offer of ten thousand pounds should have been accepted; they ought to have been bound to supply the navy with a given quantity of hemp, *the growth of the colony*, annually: this would have forced them to give a degree of attention to this important article, which in the present case may not be thought of. Nothing is more common in the establishment of colonies, than proprietors to make large promises at first, and afterwards to forget that even such things were thought of. The territory of the Ohio is in no want of *encouragement* from the proprietors; but people are so apt to move only in their accustomed line and [are] so averse from all useful trials and experiments that they should in some cases be driven to do that which is equally for the interest of their country and themselves.

VINES

Of all North America, this is the tract which bids fairest for yielding wine: the native vines are in greater plenty and variety than in any other part; the country at some distance from the Ohio is hilly and very dry, and in some places even rocky; but these plants do not require the rocky soil near so much as European ones; for they thrive and bear well on rich deep soils. "We have seen," says Dr. Mitchel[l], "fifteen different sorts of native grapes there, the like of which growing wild are certainly not to be found in any part of the world. The ordinary sorts of these in Virginia yield a wine so like the common Bordeaux wine that it is difficult to distinguish the one from the other; and from another sort, some wine has been made which was compared by good judges, both here and there, to the best that is drank. Other sorts yield wine exactly like the Lisbon.[12] But instead of these, they have transplanted grapes from the hills of Normandy to the maritime parts of Virginia and Carolina, where no one could expect them to thrive nigh so well as they do. They ripen there in the beginning and middle of August, when no one can expect to make good wine; although they yield a very good wine for present drinking. But this is the most improper for their climate of any grape that grows; neither is it the true Burgundy grape for which they got it." From hence it is easy to be gathered, if the fact was not well known, that these territories on the Ohio must be well adapted to vineyards;[13] much more so than any maritime part of that continent; for near the sea the rains are almost incessant,

[12] In all probability this was wine from Estremadura shipped from Lisbon.

[13] It was along the Ohio that Nicholas Longworth (1782–1863) "the father of successful wine culture in the West" experimented with grape culture. Large tracts of his land were by 1850 devoted to the raising of Catawba and Isabella grapes. The wines he manufactured from his grapes and his wine-house were internationally famous. His gift of wine to Longfellow inspired the poem "Catawba Wine." Longworth was also interested in the cultivation of strawberries. See L. H. Bailey, *Cyclopedia of American Horticulture* (New York, 1900), Vol. II; T. V. Munson, *Foundations of American Grape Culture* (New York, 1909).

whereas upon the Ohio the climate is very dry, and on the Mississippi it rarely rains. This is a circumstance extremely favourable to the vineyard culture, which never does well in a country where much rain falls: all the fine wines come from countries which enjoy upon the whole, a climate dry on comparison with others, and some remarkably so.

Wine is another commodity which will bear no long land-carriage, since to become an object of exportation from America to Britain, it must be afforded at a low price; wines upon the par with the red port of Portugal ought not to exceed 10 or 12£. a pipe, prime cost, and perhaps not so much; this is 20 or 24£. a ton; so that hemp is, in proportion of weight, as valuable a commodity. It will certainly be found that the Mississippi must be the conveyance of both tobacco, hemp, and wine, to the sea; land-carriage will add too much to the expences; a fresh reason for the navigation of the Mississippi being immediately and accurately examined. If ships of only 100 tons could (as the proprietors assert *large* ones can) be built on the Ohio and sent, at a certain season of the year, laden to Britain with hemp, tobacco, and wine, the advantage would be the most profitable application of the timber in the world; as well as casks for the wine and tobacco.

Silk

All this territory abounds with mulberry trees, in an extraordinary manner; and it is very well known that people in the new colony will soon be in plenty, [from] the surplus of population in Pennsylvania, New York, Jersey, Virginia, and Maryland—a surplus which is great, as is well known from various circumstances before mentioned, such as numerous petitions to settle in the northern parts of New England, repeated ones for lands on the Ohio, and 30,000 people already settled there, even without the advantage of a government being established, also the well known want of *fresh* lands for tobacco. If the accounts we have had from all parts of the central colonies be well considered, there can be no doubt remain[ing] that 500,000 persons at least will, in a few years, be found in this colony, since it is that tract of country which has for so many years been the object of their ardent desires. Silk therefore certainly promises to become an article of no slight consequence, *in case the people will be persuaded to give due attention to it;* and in such cases I have often remarked that the only sensible persuasions are examples and rewards. Every person might make a pound of silk, without interruption of their agriculture, which would be to themselves, as well as to Britain, an object of consequence; but if the business was well attended to by whole families, who understood the conduct of it, then much larger quantities might be produced: and in such case it would be found, for the time it required, one of the most valuable staples in the world.

COTTON

This plant grows spontaneously from the southern parts of Pennsylvania to Florida: in Virginia they have some that is excellent, and in some respects superior to that of the West Indies, particularly for mixing with wool. Upon the Ohio, the soil, after being exhausted by tobacco, would yield large crops of this for ever; the climate is better adapted to it, and the quantity gained would be greater. Cotton is not an article of sufficient value to be the sole product of a plantation; but as a secondary object it might be cultivated with good profit. This part of husbandry is not sufficiently attended to in our colonies; the planters bestow all their time and at-

tention to their grand staple, so as to overlook all inferior
articles; but this [is] a mistaken conduct; they can have no
crop in this latitude that will employ them the whole year;
the sensible management would be to have several, so as to
employ their slaves on them in succession. Wheat may be
the most valuable product of a British farm; but this does
not prevent the farmer from sowing barley, oats, pease, and
beans; nor does corn in general prevent his cultivating turneps, carrots, and potatoes, which again leave time for clover
and grasses: and it is to this various application of his land,
that he is as much obliged for his profit as to any other circumstance. Sawing lumber does not equal (except in the lands
that must be cleared for the crops) the culture of any staple:
among these secondary objects, cotton will here be found of
no slight importance.

INDIGO

The finest indigo is that of Guatimala, the climate [there
is] exceeding hot; in St. Domingo the French raise large
quantities that is excellent; and in Carolina it is become a
staple of great consequence: the profit depends much on the
heat of the climate, as may be judged from its being cut five
times in St. Domingo in a season, three or four in Carolina,
and two or three in Virginia; for there is some indigo planted
in that province, notwithstanding its making no figure in the
exports. On the Ohio there is great reason to suppose it may
be cultivated to good advantage, the soil being admirably
rich, and the climate superior to Virginia; but a strong proof
is its having long been an article of export from the Illinois
settlements, which are full as northerly as any part of the
colony of the Ohio. In Carolina they plant it on their dry
sands, but this is for want of such a rich, deep, black mould

as is found through the new colony, where soil may make good amends for want of so hot a sun; a point which seems almost proved by St. Domingo so much exceeding Carolina, though the summers (notwithstanding the difference of latitude) are hotter in Carolina than in that island; but in the latter it is planted on fresh woodlands to prepare them for sugar, and in the former on a poor sand. This article is perfectly well adapted to the Ohio in another respect, which is that of its great value in proportion to its weight, which is so high that the price of an expensive carriage would be scarcely felt. This is a product which might (as well as silk) be sent over the mountains to be shipped in Virginia.

MADDER

An article[14] of great importance in the manufactures in England, and bought of the Dutch in great quantities at the high price of from 80£. to 90£. a ton; from which we see it ranks among those that will very well pay the expence of carriage from the Ohio to Virginia. It is amazing that this article of cultivation has never been introduced in large in our colonies, though it is beyond doubt one which would agree as well with their climate as any thing they cultivate. In Europe the finest grows in Turkey, but the most in Holland, Flanders, and the Palatinate, from whence there can be no hesitation of its suiting the excellent climate of the Ohio. Madder requires a rich, deep, flexible mould; no degree of fertility is too great for it; of all soils I should suppose a new deep woodland would be the most proper for it; in this respect it would be a rival to tobacco, but then it would

[14] An Old World dye plant from which was made various fast and beautiful pigments, such as madder purple and madder orange in a great range of color.

probably pay better for it, and in the value of the weight
infinitely exceed it. In England there has been raised fifteen
hundred per acre, and the expence *in labour* may be thus
calculated from the totals mentioned in the account.

		£.	s.	d.
1767	Four ploughings	0	4	8
	Ridging up	0	1	6
	Water-furrowing	0	1	6
1768	Planting	0	18	0
	Hand-weeding	0	12	0
	Horse-hoeing	0	2	4
	Water-furrowing	0	1	0
1769	Three hand-hoeings	1	10	0
	Horse-hoeing	0	3	0
	Water-furrowing	0	1	0
1770	Two hand-hoeings	1	0	0
	Horse-hoeing	0	1	6
	Taking up	3	0	0
	Drying, at 3s.	2	5	0
	Total	10	1	6

Produce

	£.	s.	d.
15 cwt. at 4£.	£. 60	0	0

The drying, probably, at so large an expence is peculiar to
the climate of England and Holland; but on the Ohio the
sun would be much superior to the stove drying, as it is for
the wild madder of Turkey. I shewed, under the article of
Virginia, that the expence of an acre of tobacco in labour be
6£. 1s. 8d. and the produce is only 5£. 6s. 8d. from whence
it was plain that it is an article of culture only fit for very
cheap labour, such as that of negroes; but on the contrary
we find that madder is far more valuable: 15 cwt. indeed
was the greatest crop got by one gentleman with manuring,

but then other persons in the same register got 20 cwt. and even 30 cwt. without manuring, only by planting on land of superior natural fertility: where is more fertile land to be met with than the fresh grounds on the Ohio? Now the culture of tobacco without the produce being sufficient even to pay the expence of labour of whites is extremely profitable by slaves; the proportion would hold with madder and it would be found far superior to tobacco; the expence on carriage and freight on a commodity worth 80£. a ton would not be felt.

Rich, deep, black land, moist, but not wet, is the great article wanted for madder, or else such an immense plenty of dung as will convert an indifferent loam into such a soil which can be had only in three or four situations in a great kingdom: natural fertility is what we ought therefore to seek; the price of labour evidently is of no weight—yet is this circumstance, like all others, in favour of America—for that the labour of slaves is as three to one cheaper than that of English labourers was sufficiently proved by the product of tobacco; [which] instead of yielding a profit not answering the expense, but, [yet] with negroes, being advantageous enough to give fortunes to the planters, did they know how to keep the money they make.

This object of introducing madder as a staple in the new colony, in order to save two or three hundred thousand pounds a year which we at present pay to Holland for the commodity—an absolute necessary in our manufactures—ought to be well considered. That it would thrive to admiration there cannot be doubted, since the soil in many tracts is equal to any in the world; and the climate very similar to that of Turkey, where it is a common spontaneous growth. No doubts therefore can be entertained of the produce; as to labour, the above account of 10£. in England near London would not be 4£. by means of negroes; and if the product was no more than 15 cwt. and the value 60£. in London, the account in general would stand thus:

	£.	s.	d.
Labour	4	0	0
Carriage from the Ohio to Alexandria, at 3£. 11s. 8d. per ton	2	13	9
Freight to London at 5£. 10s. per ton	4	2	6
Total	10	16	3

Thus would the Ohio planter land his madder at London at nearly the same expence that labour alone stands the Surry [Surrey] or Kentish planter in! If this is not an immense encouragement to them to enter deeply into the culture, nothing can [be]; but they will in this, as in numerous other cases, want example—visible proof; which can only be given them by the proprietors establishing a plantation for experiments in large, which would presently ascertain this and other points of great importance.

There is one circumstance in this culture which would make it suit extremely the usual economy of a plantation in North America. It is three years in the ground, and might be left four or five with proportionable profit, during which time there is nothing to do to it in winter; all the operations it requires are over between March and October, and, when taken up, the drying is over in less than a month; thus would the negroes have the whole winter to saw lumber or to be employed in other articles of culture that required winter operations: this is a point much attended to in America, and particularly by new settlers; for coming to lands, great parts of which are a forest, it is of vast consequence to them to be able to convert the wood into lumber as fast as they clear the ground, by which means they make that preparatory work pay its own charges. The great inducement to such numbers of people to settle in America is the plenty of land; but if that land, as it generally is, is covered with timber that can be converted to no use, the expence of clearing would be too great to undertake; where they now can take up an hundred acres, they would not then be able to take up ten. Here lies one of the great advantages of that noble navigation from the Ohio down the Mississippi to the gulph [gulf] of Mexico, which the proprietors assure us is a more ready and cheap conveyance than by sea from New York or Philadelphia.

Other staples might be mentioned for this colony, which would suit it in great perfection, and which ought likewise to be cultivated, but these are the material ones. It is never advantageous to have the attention of planters too much taken up with one object, as has been the case long in Virginia and Maryland; the consequence of which is, that when land fails them for their favourite staple, they have no succedaneum,[15] but must turn mere farmers for raising corn and provisions, which has actually been the case in those two colonies; whereas by giving that attention to hemp, flax, tobacco, vines, indigo, silk, cotton, madder, &c. which English farmers give to as great a variety of products, they would be certain of some valuable staple for ever; and also be able to apply every part of their estates to some profitable purpose. Tobacco, indigo, or madder, hemp, vines, silk, and cotton, might be in culture on the same plantation, and each on a different soil. This would increase the profit of planting very much, and make the produce of negroes much more than 20£. a head, which is the calculation of those employed on good land in tobacco.

[15] Substitute.

Under the articles tobacco and Indian corn, I have before remarked, that the reason the planters in America did not, on a given quantity of land, equal the profit of the farmers in Britain, was their executing much work by hand labour, which might as well and better be done by horse work. In Virginia, a negroe pays about 16£. in tobacco, and 4£. in sundry articles. It will admit of no doubt that the sums will be higher on the Ohio; but at the same time they ought by management to be carried as high as possible; which can only be done by substituting the plough and horse-hoes, instead of the spade and hand-hoe: the expence of horses on the Ohio, or in Virginia, is not what it is here, for the price of the beast is not more than a third or fourth, and his keeping not a tenth of what it is in Britain. If these ideas were adopted, their profit would rise greatly.

An English farm of an hundred acres, 60 arable, and 40 grass, or 70 [arable] and 30 [grass], or even 80 and 20, may be cultivated upon the most improved methods in common crops, by three men and four horses; and if the land is good the average product will be 4£. an acre, or 400£. a year; thus the working hands yield 133£. apiece, this is by the addition of four horses, which indeed in Britain will, if well kept, cost full as much as four more men; but taking it in that light, and call the working hands seven, the annual produce per hand will be 57£. But this is quite different in America, for the four horses would not cost more than one man if a black; and if a white, 10 horses would not equal his expence: nor have I any doubt but by a proper and ex-perienced use of horse work, every working hand might in the Ohio be made to produce 50£. or 60£. a head at least: they would then have an assignment of many acres per head, instead of which two or three per slave is the common allow-

ance; however, without supposing any such good management, it would be a very moderate supposition to calculate
the produce per working hand at 5£. more than in Virginia
or Maryland, which the great superiority of fresh lands, so
extraordinary for their fertility, may well allow; and with
the advantage of so large a range as the planters will have
here, and have not generally in the old tobacco colonies—a
point of vast consequence—would justify an higher idea. If
madder was undertaken, a much larger sum should be named;
and yet how easy to introduce this upon a plantation, and
extend the culture by degrees. Silk, madder, and indigo, of
each but a small quantity, or only madder and silk, being so
valuable, would pay the extra expence of carriage and freight
on the other commodities; but I shall suppose, by adopting
these articles in part, each working hand to pay 25£. and the
extra expence of carriage of some articles [which is here]
more than is felt in Virginia. Upon this footing I shall calculate the expences of establishing a capital plantation on the
Ohio; previous to which it may not be amiss to point out to
the first settlers some signs whereby they are to judge of the
soil, not only here, but through all these central colonies, and
also those to the southward.

The trees, which are the spontaneous product of the land,
should in general be first attended to; if they abound with
fine, tall, red hickories, white oaks, chestnut oaks, scarlet oaks,
tulip trees, black walnuts, locusts, mulberry trees, &c. they
may be pronounced good, and the value will usually be in
proportion to the size and straitness of those trees; pines,
live oaks, laurels, bays, liquid amber, and water oaks are,
among others, signs of bad land; and in general that soil will
be best which is free from under-wood: nor should the planter
take a few trees of any sort as his guide, but a predominancy

of them in whole woods. This rule of judging must be united with that of the appearance of the soil when dug into, particularly colour and depth; the black mould on a bed of loam is best; that on clay, good; but the light sandy tracts are in general bad, unless they are of a dark colour, and moist, with good trees growing from them; in that case they may be excellent; for sands differ as much as loams; the misfortune is, that in America the sands are generally white and dry, and produce little besides pines.

Besides tracts which may come under this description, he is farther to examine the meadows which are composed of similar soils but without any trees, being covered with grass; these are to be judged by the height, thickness, and luxuriance of that grass. These tracts are common on the Ohio, and prove how valuable the country should be esteemed: they, like the woodlands, should be examined with the spade, in order to know the appearance of the soil. Besides these there are marshes or swamps, but not in great quantities as in the maritime parts of America: the value of these depend on two circumstances, the richness of the soil, and the ease of being drained: the former is seen by the products; cedars are good signs, though not very common; cypresses generally are found in them, and the excellency of the land [is] perceived from the tallness, size, and beauty of their stems: as to draining, it depends on the situation, and on examining the means of carrying off the water, as in all other countries. These swamps and marshes when drained, if the soil is stiff, are the proper lands for hemp, not that it will not thrive as well on fertile uplands; but they may be applied to other crops. There are, besides these, hilly tracts and the sides of mountains, generally of a gradual ascent, but sometimes sharp and rocky; on the latter vineyards may be planted, and also olives; on the former indigo, tobacco, madder, if rich; if indifferent, cotton, &c.

These are the soils and sort of tracts which are to be met with in the new colony; and I should observe that every kind of land here is equal to any in the world for the growth of wheat, maize, barley, oats, pease, beans, &c. all sorts of roots, and every kind of garden-stuff and fruit known in Europe. Of this no doubts can be entertained when it is considered how well all these thrive in Maryland and Virginia, in the same latitude; whereas the Ohio is more fertile in soil, and far more temperate and regular in climate, being free from excessive heats and those violent colds which are found in the maritime parts of the continent.

In the disposition of new plantations it is of consequence that the planters give some attention to the situation of their house and offices, a point which, in the hurry of the first building, is seldom thought of enough, not only as a matter of convenience and agreeableness, but also of health. In this continent the north-west wind brings the severe weather and the worst seasons; a house should be well sheltered from it by wood, but instead of having any idea of shelter, planters in general attack all the timber around their houses with such undistinguishing rage, as not to leave themselves in a few years a tree within sight. For convenience, as well as health and pleasure, the best situation would be in the centre of a space of wood in form of a crescent, open to the south, and in front of the navigation which is to convey the product of the plantation, always chusing [choosing] an elevated situation, yet not the top of a hill, leaving as much ascent of wood behind the building as descent of lawn before it. At all events a spot should be chosen where the shores of the river are high and bold, because nothing is more unwholesome than to live in the neighbourhood of a marsh or flat land that is apt to be overflowed. This in many of our colonies is not attended to, but it is because situations free from it are not very common; and in the southern ones, the rice culture makes them seek for swamps, the consequence of which is the unhealthiness so much complained of.

Agriculture is followed in so imperfect a manner in our old colonies, owing to plenty of land, that one cannot expect to see it well managed here, where land is so much more plentiful; yet do I wish to see some plantations laid out in a manner that shall obviate the objections to the careless husbandry of the Americans. I here mean particularly to hint at inclosures—not to sow or plant any piece of ground that is not well and substantially enclosed with a ditch, a bank, and live hedge; the expence would bear no proportion to the numerous advantages of it; besides that uncommon superiority in point of neatness and beauty: and in the disposition of the fields, some should undoubtedly be left occupied with the timber that is upon them, as a future supply, which will be a matter of great consequence, not only to the public good of the colony, but also to the future private advantage of the planter.

And here I shall once more observe that, for gaining the requisite knowledge of so extensive a tract of so noble a country, the proprietors would act with a patriotic spirit if they were to establish a plantation in a well chosen spot, including every variety of soil for trying large experiments on the preceding list of staples, and others that might be named. The expence would not be considerable; under the direction of a sensible, intelligent overseer, who was a man of integrity, the produce would be highly sufficient, after the first expences, to pay the annual charge. In such a plantation might be introduced the culture of hemp and flax on every sort of soil, to see how far it might become the colony staple. Madder might be tried with the same design; vineyards should be planted, both of foreign and native grapes, for wines and raisins; silk should be made in large quantities; cotton tried with equal attention; and experiments made on indigo, to see how far fertility of soil in an excellent climate would make amends for the want of greater heat. The native hemp, flax, silk-grass, and other indigenous plants [should be] brought into culture, that their qualities might be known; these would be noble designs, and could not fail of proving of great advantage to the colony, and of doing great honour to the proprietors.

I shall now proceed with the design of calculating the expences and profit of fixing a capital plantation on the Ohio, supposing the person to move from Britain, and to have money enough for all necessary (but not superfluous) expences.

	£.
Freight and expences of a family of six persons from London to Alexandria, at 25£.	150
Freight of 10 tons	55
One year's living or board at 20£.	120
A second year's housekeeping	100
Fees of 10,000 acres at 30£. per 1000	300
Building a house	200
————— offices	150
Furniture	150
Carriage of necessaries from Alexandria to the Ohio	50
A canoe	50
Boats	15
Implements	200
Machine for rooting up trees	80
A saw mill	500
50 horses, mares, and stallions	250
50 cows	150
50 young cattle	50

100 swine   25
500 sheep   125
Poultry   5
Repairs of implements   50

Labour

Attendance on cattle .... £. 30
Bailiff (one year)   40
Labour in clearing 20 acres of wheat, at 1£. .   20
Ditto 40 oats, at 16s.   32
70 turneps, at 1£.   70
5 potatoes at 5£.   25
On hay, mowing and making, &c. arpent of
    natural meadows   30
On fencing   50
Orchard and garden   20
Sundries   30   *347

                       Carried over   £. 3,122

                               £.

             Brought forward 3,122
40 negroes, at 50£.   2,000
Annual expence of negroes per
    head, overseer, 1£.   40
Cloaths, 1£.   40
Sundry expences   40   160

Seed

20 acres of wheat at 8s.   8
40 oats at 8s.   16   24

70 turneps, 1s. 3   10   0   s.   d.
  5 potatoes, 8s. 2   0   0   5   10   0

Taxes   30   0   0
Two years interest on 5300£.   530   0   0

                       £. 5,871   10   0

* All these articles are usually done by negroes for a third of this expence, but they are here reckoned at the rates of the labour of white
servants, that the planter may not be supposed to have nothing but blacks
about him.

Produce of second year

40 negroes at 20£.	800	0	0

N.B. The first year of their labour reckoned 5£. a-head lower than when experienced more.

	800	0	0

Third year

Taxes	30	0	0
Buildings	10	0	0
Housekeeping	100	0	0
Repairs and addition to implements	50	0	0
Labour as before	347	0	0
Seed ditto	29	10	0
Incidents	50	0	0
Interest of 5400£.	270	0	0
Allow towards carriage or freight of bulky products	50	0	0
Expences on 40 negroes, at 3£.	120	0	0
Purchase of 20 at 50£.	1,000	0	0
£.	2,056	10	0

Produce

	£.	s.	d.
40 negroes at 25£.	1,000	0	0
20 ditto at 20£.	400	0	0
£.	1,400	0	0

Fourth year

Taxes	30	0	0
Buildings	20	0	0
Housekeeping	80	0	0
Implements	50	0	0
Labour	347	0	0
Seed	29	10	0
Incidents	40	0	0

Interest	2,000	0	0
	800	0	0
	1,200	0	0

	£.	s.	d.
At 5 per cent. 60 0 0			
Before 270 0 0	330	0	0
Freight	60	0	0
Expences, on 60 negroes at 3£.	180	0	0
Purchase of 20 at 50£.	1,000	0	0
£.	2,166	10	0

Produce

	£.	s.	d.
60 negroes, at 25£.	1,500	0	0
20 ditto at 20£.	400	0	0
£.	1,900	0	0

Fifth year

	£.	s.	d.
Taxes	30	0	0
Buildings	20	0	0
Housekeeping	80	0	0
Implements	50	0	0
Labour	347	0	0
Seed	29	10	0
Incidents	40	0	0
Interest 2,166 10 0			
1,400 0 0			
766 10 0			
At 5 per cent. 38 0 0			
Before 330 0 0	368	0	0
Freight	70	0	0
Expences on 80 negroes at 3£.	240	0	0
20 at 50£.	1,000	0	0
£.	2,283	10	0

Produce

	£.	s.	d.
80 negroes at 25£.	2,000	0	0
20 ditto at 20£.	400	0	0
£.	2,400	0	0

Sixth year

	£.	s.	d.
Taxes	30	0	0
Buildings	20	0	0

	£.	s.	d.
Housekeeping	80	0	0
Implements	60	0	0
Labour	347	0	0
Seed	29	10	0
Incidents	40	0	0

Interest	2,283	10	0
	1,900	0	0
	383	10	0

				£.	s.	d.
At 5 per cent.	19	3	0			
Before	368	0	0	387	3	0
Freight				80	0	0
100 negroes at 3£.				300	0	0
20 ditto at 50£.				1,000	0	0
			£.	2,373	13	0

Produce

	£.	s.	d.
100 negroes at 25£.	2,500	0	0
20 ditto at 20£.	400	0	0
£.	2,900	0	0

Here we find the receipt is more than equal to the annual expence, including the increase of 20 negroes bought every year, consequently the whole sum wanting for such a plantation is to be ascertained.

				£.	s.	d.
First capital				5,871	10	0
Expences of third year	2,056	10	0			
Produce of second	800	0	0	1,256	10	0
Expences of fourth year	2,166	10	0			
Produce of third	1,400	0	0	766	10	0
Expences of fifth year	2,283	10	0			
Produce of fourth	1,900	0	0	383	10	0
		Total		8,278	0	0
Annual interest				413	18	0

If no increase of negroes, the account would be:

	£.	s.	d.
Taxes	30	0	0
Buildings	20	0	0
Housekeeping	80	0	0
Implements	50	0	0
Labour	347	0	0
Seed	29	10	0
Incidents	40	0	0
Interest	413	18	0
Freight	80	0	0
Expences on 120 negroes at 3£.	360	0	0
£.	1,450	8	0

Produce

	£.	s.	d.
120 negroes at 25£.	3,000	0	0
Expences	1,450	8	0
Profit	1,549	12	0
Housekeeping	80	0	0
Interest	413	18	0
Total receipt	2,043	10	0

which from 8,278£. is per cent. 24£.

During the preceding time, no produce is supposed from cattle, that in so great a space of country they might increase to great herds and flocks; but afterwards the annual product would be very great, as the numbers would be two or three thousand head of cattle, five or six thousand sheep, and two or three thousand hogs; such herds have been known the property of single people in North Carolina, where they have not greater advantages, nor yet so great, as on the Ohio: these would yield annually near 1,000£. a year in hides, wool, and barrelled meat for the West Indies, but I shall calculate only 300£.

	£.	s.	d.
Receipt above	2,043	10	0
Cattle	300	0	0
	£. 2,343	10	0

which from 8,278£. is per cent. 28£.

This profit is considerable, not so much in itself, as in the circumstance of the planters being able annually to incorporate it into the old capital, and thereby yield a compound interest at that proportion. I am of opinion that husbandry in England will yield a greater profit than 24£. per cent. if so large a sum as 8,000£. is expended in stocking a farm. Calculations have been published of English husbandry which shew that so high as 33 per cent. may be made in any part of the kingdom by *good* and *improved* husbandry, and above 20 per cent. by the most common crops. And I am clear, that if potatoes, carrots, madder, hops, &c. were calculated (which do not come into those calculations) the profit might be carried to 40 or perhaps 50 per cent. in certain situations; in this respect I am confident that America cannot equal Britain, but in other points the superiority is entirely with her: that of the annual increase of culture is a very essential one. What a vast difference between the English farmer putting out his savings at 4 per cent. and his brother on the Ohio doing the same at 24 [per cent.] compound interest! What a difference between the one living on another man's land, with a lease of twenty-one years—which is a long one, subjected to the caprice of a landlord or a steward—or sure of quitting at the end of his term, and the other living on his own extensive freehold of 10,000 acres! What a difference between 80£. a year spent in all sorts of necessaries, even bread, meat, malt, &c. by the farmer for housekeeping; and the same sum by the planter for tea, sugar, coffee, chocolate, spices, rum, and manufactures. Bread, meat, venison, fruit, fish, fowl, game in the utmost plenty, besides the corn, &c. the expence of which is before reckoned, but no produce!

In all these circumstances there can be no comparison: at the same time that the Ohio planter makes near as great interest from his first capital as the English farmer, [and] at the same time that he is able to throw his savings annually into business at 28 per cent. compound interest, he lives like a country gentleman in Britain who has an estate of 2,000£. a year, and if the latter spends half the year at London, much better; while the farmer, it is very well known, must fare very coarsely. I draw this comparison with no design to send British farmers to the Ohio. I am clear not one in the three kingdoms will go; had I thought a book would be an inducement to them, I would not have drawn up this calculation: it is written for the use of those who will go to America, whether books are published or not; and to them it is meant merely as advice, that they make a proper choice of the colony they settle in: many go to Nova Scotia, to New England, to New York, &c. where they can raise nothing advantageous to the commerce of Britain, and where they must live in a climate that is odious to a British constitution, at least during the severity of winter. There is no object in the whole range of American affairs of more importance than the directing of new settlers, whether from Britain or foreign countries, to those parts of our colonies, which, from their staple productions, are really valuable to the mother country; yet this matter, of as great consequence as it certainly is, has not by any means been so much attended to as it ought; for [the] government has paid the freight of more men to Nova Scotia than it has to Virginia and Maryland;[16] though the former has no staple, and can only rival Britain in her fishery, and the latter one so valuable in every respect as tobacco.

[16] After the Treaty of Aix-la-Chapelle (1748), which marked the close of the War of the Austrian Succession, the British felt that they could no longer run the risk of leaving Nova Scotia in the possession of such unreliable subjects as the Acadians. Consequently a policy of allocating settlers—English, German, Swiss, and French Protestants—to the province was undertaken. In the spring of 1749, for example, alluring advertisements appeared in the public press inviting recently discharged soldiers and sailors, and all manner of artisans and husbandmen to settle in Nova Scotia. The inducements held out were free transportation, land grants, arms, and tools, with subsistence for twelve months after arrival. See J. B. Brebner, *New England's Outpost, Acadia, before the Conquest of Canada* (New York, 1927), pp. 166–69, 183–86.

CHAPTER XIX

NORTH CAROLINA

Climate of North Carolina—Productions—Soil—Common husbandry—Staples—Exports—Defects in their agriculture—Improvements proposed

THIS province lies between latitude 34½° and 36½° [north]: it is hotter than Virginia, but in other respects the climate of these two provinces is very similar; North Carolina being hotter as you advance southward, until the most southerly parts are as hot as South Carolina. This gradation of heat is such as may be supposed from the variation in latitude, but [is] not to be compared with the same parallels in other quarters of the world, no more than [are] the other American territories. In winter they have frosts here sometimes very sharp, though not in general so cold as in Virginia; and a warm day often follows a very cold night. The same distinction is also to be made between the maritime and back parts of the province that I mentioned before in Virginia; the coast, as far as it continues a flat country, is excessive[ly] hot and very unwholesome, like all the low sea coasts in these southern countries; but when the country rises, and begins to be hilly—which is about one hundred or one hundred and fifty miles from the sea—and continuing till you come to the western mountains, in this part the climate is pure, temperate, and healthy.

The products of North Carolina are rice, tobacco, indigo,

cotton, wheat, pease, beans, Indian corn, and all sorts of roots, especially potatoes. Rice is not so much cultivated here as in South Carolina: but in the latter they raise no tobacco, whereas in North Carolina it is one of their chief articles. It grows in the northerly parts of the province, on the frontiers of Virginia, from which colony it is exported. Indigo grows very well in the province, particularly in the southern parts, and proves a most profitable branch of culture. Cotton does very well, and the sort is so excellent that it is much to be wished they had made a greater progress in it. The greatest articles of their produce which is exported are tar, pitch, turpentine, and every species of lumber, in astonishing quantities.

The soil in the flat country is in general sandy, and great tracts of it but indifferent in fertility; but others are rich, and will produce cotton, indigo, and Indian corn freely. It is in this part of the country that the swamps are to be found, which when drained yield rice: this forms a distinction between North Carolina and Virginia; they have vast swamps on the coast of Virginia, but cultivate no rice, not because it would not grow, but from an idea that it requires, in order to yield large crops, a hotter sun. The swamps in North Carolina are some of them very rich, but remain undrained for want of people. In the back part of the country the soil is very fine, and in several tracts equal to the best of Virginia; and it improves as you advance towards the mountains. This is the case with all these colonies in the southern parts of America. In many of these backward tracts the land is a rich black mould, of a good depth, and highly fertile, especially the country on the river Pedee,[1] &c.

[1] The Peedee river rises in the Blue Ridge Mountains in Western North Carolina. It flows east and south to Winyah Bay, South Carolina. In North Carolina this river is often called the Yadkin.

It is extraordinary that more settlements should not have been made in this country, notwithstanding the obstacles I have mentioned, considering the pleasantness of it, and extreme fertility of the soil; these circumstances were also known many years ago, as appears by the travels through it of a Mr. *John Lawson,* surveyor-general of North Carolina in the year 1700, which were published in 1718.* There are many curious particulars in it, and especially of the appearance of the back country, as will appear from the following extracts, which I make because the book is very scarce.

We went directly for Sapona Town: that day we passed through a delicious country (none that I ever saw exceeds it). We saw fine bladed grass six feet high, along the banks of pleasant rivulets. Coming that day about thirty miles, we reached the fertile and pleasant banks of Sapona river, whereon stands the Indian town and fort.² Nor could all Europe afford a pleasanter stream, *were it inhabited by christians,* and cultivated by ingenious hands. These Indians live in a clear field, about a mile square, which they would have sold me. This most pleasant river may be something broader than the Thames at Kingston, keeping a continual pleasant warbling noise with its reverberating on the bright marble rocks. It is beautified with a numerous train of swans and other water-fowl. One side of the river is hemmed in with mountainy ground, the other side proving as rich a soil to the eye of a knowing person with us as any this western world can afford: it is as noble a river to plant a colony on as any I have met withal. Next morning we set forward; all the pines were vanished, for we had seen none for two days. We passed through a deli-

---

* *The History of Carolina,* small quarto.

² The John Mitchell map of North America, prepared at request of the Board of Trade, first drawn in 1750 and reproduced again in 1755, shows the Sapona river as the principal western branch of the Peedee, and Sapona Town, not far from the confluence of the Sapona and the Peedee, in what is now West Central North Carolina. See C. O. Paullin and J. K. Wright, *Atlas of the Historical Geography of the United States* (Washington, 1932), pp. 13–14, and plate 89.

cate rich soil this day, no great hills, but pretty risings and levels, which made a beautiful country; we passed likewise over three rivers on this day. We were much taken with the fertility and pleasantness of the neck of land between these two branches. It is called *Haw* river,[3] from the *Sissipahaw* Indians who dwell upon this stream; there being rich land enough to contain some thousands of families, for which reason I hope, in a short time, it will be planted. This river is much such another as Sapona, both seeming to run a vast way up the country. There is plenty of good timber, and especially oak; and as there is stone enough in both rivers, and the land is extraordinary rich, no man that will be content within the bounds of reason can have any grounds to dislike it. Some Virginia-men we met, asking our opinion of the country we were then in, we told them it was a very pleasant one; they were all of the same opinion, and affirmed that they had never seen twenty miles of such extraordinary rich land, lying all together like that betwixt *Haw* river and *Achonedry* town.[4]

Long after this account was written (viz. near seventy years) Dr. Mitchel[l] gives it in general the same character.

There are five large rivers (says he) which rise in the inland parts of North Carolina, the banks of which are rich and fertile, although the hills between them still partake of the barrenness of Carolina, as we are well informed by several whom we have recommended to settle in the country. This seems to be the most improveable part of all the British dominions on this side of the Mississippi. But they have no navigation nor ports to the more fruitful parts of the country, if it be not by the river *Pedee,* which runs through all this inland part of North Carolina, and falls into the sea at Wineau (or Winyaw) which now belongs to South Carolina, and for that reason it is neglected and never used by the other, which possesses the fruitful lands belonging to this port.

[3] The Haw river in North Central North Carolina with the Deep river forms the Cape Fear river.
[4] This was situated in the upper valley of the Peedee river.

From all which accounts it is extremely plain that these back parts of North Carolina are to be ranked among the finest in our colonies.

Notwithstanding these great advantages, there are very few people in North Carolina; this has been owing to several causes: there were obstructions in settling it, which occasioned some to leave the country, and a general idea was spread to its disadvantage; but the principal evil was the want of ports, of which there was not one good one in all North Carolina: the river Pedee falls into the sea at Winyaw, which is in South Carolina, and that has prevented an exportation of products from thence of the growth of North Carolina. And this want of good ports, and a trading town, has checked the culture of rice a good deal; but it has had another effect, which may probably prove a great advantage; it has driven the new settlers back into the country, and thrown them very much into common husbandry, on a soil and in a climate that will do for productions much more valuable than rice; these, such as silk, indigo, and cotton, are coming in by degrees, and will in a few years change the face of this colony entirely and enrich it prodigiously; it is this spreading about the country that makes the produce of the woods almost the staple at present of the colony.

It is this circumstance that has thrown them into common husbandry, as I observed before; and it is this common husbandry which deserves our attention particularly, since in many respects it is different from that of any other part of America.

The two great circumstances which give the farmers of North Carolina such a superiority over those of most other colonies, are, first, the plenty of land; and, secondly, the vast herds of cattle kept by the planters. The want of ports, as I said, kept numbers from settling here, and this made the land of less value, consequently every settler got large grants; and, falling to the business of breeding cattle, their herds became so great that the profit from them alone is exceeding great. It is not an uncommon thing to see one man the master of from 300 to 1,200, and even to 2,000 cows, bulls, oxen, and young cattle; hogs also in prodigious numbers. Their management is to let them run loose in the woods all day, and to bring them up at night by the sound of a horn; sometimes, particularly in winter, they keep them during the night in inclosures, giving them a little food, and letting the cows and sows to the calves and pigs; this makes them come home the more regularly. Such herds of cattle and swine are to be found in no other colonies; and when this is better settled, they will not be so common here; for at present the woods are all in common, and people's property has no other boundary or distinction than marks cut in trees, so that the cattle have an unbounded range; but when the country becomes more cultivated, estates will be surrounded by inclosures, and consequently the numbers of cattle kept by the planters will be proportioned to their own lands only.

It may easily be supposed that these vast stocks of cattle might be of surprising consequence in the raising [of] manure, were the planters as attentive as they ought to be to this essential object: they might by this means cultivate indigo and tobacco to greater advantage than their neighbours; some few make a good use of the advantage, but more of them are drawn from it by the plenty of rich land, which they run over, as in the northern colonies, till it is exhausted, and then take fresh, relying on such a change, instead of making the most of their manure, which would add infinitely to their profit.

Their system is to depend (where they have no navigation,

and are at a considerable distance from it, which however is not the case in many parts) on the hides of their cattle, and on barrelled meat, with some corn, roots, and pitch and tar, &c. for the profit of their plantation; but the most bulky of these commodities yield but little, unless near some river; accordingly there are not many plantations at any distance from water, since it is not an inland navigation that is wanted in North Carolina, but ports at the mouths of the rivers that will admit of large ships.

The mode of common husbandry here is to break up a piece of woodland, a work very easily done, from the trees standing at good distances from each other; this they sow with Indian corn for several years successively, till it will yield large crops no longer: they get at first fourscore or an hundred bushel an acre, but sixty or seventy are common: when the land is pretty well exhausted they sow it with pease or beans one year, of which they will get thirty or forty bushels per acre; and afterwards sow it with wheat for two or three years: it will yield good crops of this grain when it would bear Indian corn no longer, which shews how excellent the land must be. But let me remark that this culture of wheat to such advantage is only in the back part of the province, where the climate is far more temperate than on the coast; upon the latter it does not succeed well, a circumstance much deserving attention; for we may lay it down as a universal rule, that where wheat thrives well, *there* the climate is healthy, and agreeable to the generality of constitutions: it does well neither in extreme cold, nor in great heat.

In this system of crops they change the land as fast as it wears out, clearing fresh pieces of woodland, exhausting them in succession; after which they leave them to the spontaneous growth. It is not here as in the northern colonies that weeds come first and then grass; the climate is so hot, that, except on the rich moist lands, any sort of grass is scarce; but the fallow in a few years becomes a forest, for no climate seems more congenial to the production of quick growing trees. If the planter does not return to cultivate the land again—as may probably be the case, from the plenty of fresh [land]— it presently becomes such a wood as the rest of the country is; and woods are here the pasture of the cattle, which is excellent for hogs, because they get quantities of mast[5] and fruit, but for cattle is much inferior to pastures and meadows.

Besides these crops they cultivate all sorts of roots, particularly potatoes, of which they get large crops; some they sell into Virginia, and the rest are given to their hogs. Fruit in none of the colonies is in greater plenty, or finer flavour; they have every sort that has been hitherto mentioned in this work; peaches, as in the central colonies, are so plentiful, that the major part of the crop goes to the hogs. In a word, all the necessaries, and many of the luxuries of life abound in the back parts of this province, which, with the temperate climate, renders it one of the finest countries in America; so fine, that every body must be astonished at finding any settlements made on the unhealthy sea coast, which is nearly the reverse.

Respecting their staples: tobacco I have been so particular in treating of under the article Virginia and Maryland that little remains to be said here, as the management of it is the same; the climate for this plant is not better than that of Virginia; but as there are more lands that are fresh, the crops will for some time be larger: four hogsheads have been made for a share here on a small plantation (near the northern forks of the river Pedee) for several years; and five have

---

[5] The fruit of the beech, oak, chestnut and other forest trees was used extensively in Europe as food for swine.

been known for a season or two in the same plantation. Such crops, and even less, would well pay the expence of sloops taking the crop to the ships at sea which cannot come into port.

Rice is cultivated only in the maritime part of the province, in the swamps. As this article of husbandry is the grand staple of South Carolina, where infinitely greater quantities are made, I shall not enter into the process here: but observe that the planters do not make so great a profit by this article as many do in South Carolina, which may be owing to the latter country being hotter, and perhaps the swamps are somewhat richer.

Pitch, tar, and turpentine are made throughout this province in vast quantities, which is a proof, among others, that the country is very far from being well settled even yet. These commodities are the produce of that species of pine called the *pitch pine;* they are all made by different preparations from the resin of this tree. Turpentine is this resin or gum as it flows from the tree through holes cut for that purpose; the heat of the sun assists this extraction, and the operation is performed while the tree is growing. It is well known that oil of turpentine is a distillation of it. From the holes cut to gain the turpentine, little channels are made in the trees to conduct the resin down to the foot of them, where boxes or bowls are placed to receive it. After the oil is distilled from the turpentine, the residuum is the resin in a very thick consistence, which is dried, and then is in the lumps we have it in England.

Tar is the same gum, but gained in a different manner; the method is as follows, which I shall give in the words of an intelligent writer: "First, they prepare a circular floor of clay, declining a little towards the centre, from which there is laid a pipe of wood, extending, near horizontally, two feet without the circumference, and so let into the ground that its upper side is near level with the floor: at the outer end of this pipe they dig a hole large enough to hold the barrels for the *tar,* which when forced out of the wood naturally runs to the centre of the floor, as the lowest part, and from thence along the pipe into the barrels: these matters being first prepared, they raise upon that clay floor a large pipe of dry pine wood split in pieces, and inclose the whole pile with a wall of earth, leaving only a little hole at the top, where the fire is to be kindled; and when that is done, so that the inclosed wood begins to burst, the whole is stopped up with earth, to the end that there may not be any flame, but only heat sufficient to force the tar out of the wood, and make it run down to the floor: they temper the heat as they think proper, by thrusting a stick through the earth, and letting the air in at as many places as they find necessary. In order to gain pitch they boil the tar, and the solid part being separated in that operation, is the pitch." It is found much more profitable to apply the timber they cut down to this use than to saw it or export it in any kind of lumber; and the tar &c. being far more valuable in proportion to bulk, is a circumstance of great importance in a country that does not abound with good ports.

To shew what the back part of this colony is capable of, I shall insert the account of the labour of ten negroes in one year upon the plantation on the Pedee above-mentioned, premising that it is not to be taken as an *annual* product, this being an extraordinary year; the account does not contain all the circumstances I could wish, but as it is put into my hands, so I insert it.

Products raised and made by ten negroes in one year
in the plantation

	£.	s.	d.
31 hogsheads of tobacco at 8£. 5s.	255	15	0
400 bushels of Indian corn and pease at 1s. 6d.	30	0	0
114 barrels of tar at 6s. 9d.	38	9	3
Skins	8	10	0
Shingles 4,000 at 12s. a 1,000	2	8	0
£.	335	2	3

which is 33£. 10s. per head, besides making corn and other
provisions for the family, cattle, poultry, &c. and keeping
the buildings in repair.

Upon good fresh land this may often be equalled, but
doubtless there are many tracts of country in which the
negroes do not equal half this profit. But if the conduct of
their husbandry was well looked into, and their modes of
culture minutely examined, the low products would be found
oftener the result of bad husbandry than the fault of either
soil or climate; it is so in Britain, and doubtless in a much
greater degree in America. It is however of consequence to
know what in good years and on good land may be done in
planting tobacco; we see here a product of 25£. per head in
that staple alone, besides the other articles of the plantation.
This is a point at which emulation should strive to arrive;
and spirited endeavours have a wonderful efficacy in gaining
points; but planters, like farmers, are too often content to
move on in the old line, without daring to think that a devia-
tion can be beneficial.

The following are the exports from this province.

	£.
Rice, 2,000 barrels at 40s.	4,000
Tobacco, 2,000 hogsheads at 8£.	16,000
Pitch, tar, and turpentine, 51,000 barrels at 7s.	17,850

Boards, staves, joists, shingles, masts, and lumber .. 15,000
Indian corn, pease, and other grain 7,000
Live stock of different kinds 5,000
Skins of different kinds 5,500

Total*   70,350

But I must remark that this account does not at all agree with another which has been given on good authority; yet this account is drawn up for the years since the peace; and that which I am now going to insert, for the year 1753. The former ought to be much the greatest, instead of which it is the least.

	£.	s.	d.
Pitch, tar, and turpentine, 84,012 barrels at 7s.	29,404	4	0
Staves 762,330 at 4£. 5s. a 1,000	3,230	0	0
Shingles 2,500,000 at 11s. 5d. per 1,000	1,427	1	0
Lumber, 2,000,647 feet at 5£. per 1,000	10,000	0	0
Corn, 61,580 bushels, suppose 2s.	6,158	0	0
Pease, 10,000 bushels, 1s. 6d.	750	0	0
Pork and beef, 3,300 barrels, 23s.	3,795	0	0
30,000 deer skins†	5,500	0	0
Rice omitted, therefore taken from the other account	4,000	0	0
Tobacco (ditto)	16,000	0	0

Besides wheat, bread, potatoes, bees-wax, tallow, candles, bacon, hogs-lard, some cotton, and a vast deal of squared walnut timber and cedar, and hoops and headings, also some indigo

Total‡   80,264 5 0

* *American Traveller*, p. 89. [By Alexander Cluny (London, 1769). See the editor's note on page 91, above.]

† The price by tale not known, the sum is therefore taken from the first account.

‡ *An Account of European Settlements*, II, 260. [For a description of this work, usually attributed to Edmund Burke, see the editor's note on page 29, above.]

There can be little doubt, from the number of articles omitted, but the total must amount to 100,000£. and it is well known that this province is now making a great progress in its cultivation and exports: after being long neglected it was but little known, but since the back country has been settled, the planters have succeeded so well as to draw great numbers after them, so that there is scarcely a part of America that is at present filling faster: the new colony on the Ohio will give a check to this; had not that been established, North Carolina must have soon become as flourishing as her want of ports would allow, which must ever keep her comparatively low. The country would thrive more if their husbandry was better, but, like all the American farmers, they are spoiled for good husbandmen by plenty of land.

Among the defects of their agriculture, I shall mention in the first place, their almost total neglect of inclosures; this they carry to a degree that is not even found in the provinces I have already described. Even their corn-fields are open to the depredations of their own and others cattle; nor are the fences of their rice and tobacco grounds made with that care and attention which in England is bestowed on the least valuable fields. This circumstance, wherever it is found, is a sign of extreme bad husbandry: it is owing to the planter being sparing of expence in every article that is not of immediate consequence; the expence of fences in Carolina, where wood grows with such amazing luxuriance, would be trifling and the advantages of good ones too great to need expatiating on.

The system pursued here is as faulty as in most other parts of America; it consists in cropping the land with tobacco as long as it will bear it; then they will take two crops of maize, and after that throw in wheat, pease, &c. for several years longer; after which they leave the land to become forest again; as fast as they want more, they take it from the old woodland, serving it in the same manner. It is owing to this wretched system that many of their corn-fields are so full of weeds that in some it is difficult to know what is the crop.

Even in the northern parts of the province, upon the frontiers of Virginia, where they give their principal attention to the little tobacco they cultivate, they do not manage it with any spirit; not being in several instances so good planters of that commodity as their neighbours. They do not seem so attentive to keeping the hillocks clean from weeds; this may be owing to the general circumstance of the planters not being so rich, or [not] having such large stocks of negroes; for in North Carolina it is but of late years that men of property have settled in it; and they observe in America as well as in all other parts of the world that the richer the cultivator, the better will the land be cultivated, whether the crop be tobacco, rice, corn, sugar, indigo, or whatever it may. In one respect, however, they have made an improvement in North Carolina in the tobacco culture, which is the introduction of a machine between the rows of tobacco instead of a plough, being between a plough and a harrow, and something in the nature of horse-hoes used in England. It is not however a common tool there, but from its use, it is expected to become more general.

Another very great defect in their management is the careless manner in which they conduct their cattle: immense herds are kept that yield a profit to the planters more inconsiderable than can at first be imagined; this is not for want of a market, since no commodity more readily yields its price in North America than beef and pork in barrels; and hides are every where a commodity easily to be turned into money; but it is owing to a want of attention—to keeping a proper proportion

of them to the winter food—to not fatting them well, and
many not at all, which is owing to a want of pasturage, and
also to leaving them too much to themselves in the woods
without a sufficiency of attendants to watch and take care of
them. The mere multiplication of cattle is not the only object,
though it sounds greatly; bringing them up in health and
vigour, of a due size and fatness, are [is], as essential; but
the stunted diminutive size of all the cattle in North America,
to the northward, as well as in the southern colonies, shews
plainly the great want of pastures: cattle will live and multiply in their woods, but they will never be cattle of any value
and yielding [will yield] a profit as inconsiderable as their
worth.

In raising manure, they are, notwithstanding their numerous herds, no less negligent. This is owing also to plenty of
land; while they can get good crops of any thing on fresh
land without dung they care little about raising any; but with
the advantage of fresh and good land, aided by their numbers
of cattle, they might very well make three and a[n] half
or four hogsheads of tobacco a share, which would be 28£. or
32£. a head, and, with lumber, tar, corn, &c. would make their
slaves on an average worth at least 30£. apiece to them, which
would be a profit their neighbours very seldom reap.

As to the improvements which might be made in this colony, they are as great as in any other, if not more so, for it
has been more neglected than most. What I should propose
is that the new settlers that came there should fix themselves
in the very back part of all the country, upon the rivers that
run among the Ap[p]alachian mountains, of which there are
the Pedee with five considerable branches, Cape Fear river,
and others: some of these are navigable for middling sized
boats above two hundred and fifty miles from the sea coast;

and it is in this country, at the foot of the mountains, where the soil ranks among the richest in America, and where the climate is perfectly temperate, healthy, and agreeable. I would not propose them to settle here to raise bulky com- modities, because the navigation is not good enough to convey them away and because there are other territories better sit- uated for them; but for indigo, silk, cotton, and some other valuable commodities, no situation in all America exceeds this: here the soil is so fertile, so deep, and of such an excel- lent nature, that the products of indigo, &c. would be far greater than what is known in South Carolina; and these commodities are all so valuable that very small boats would carry the amount of a great value. Indigo and cotton would here pay at least 25£. a head for all labouring hands, besides raising necessaries for the support of the plantation: this would prove of greater advantage to the settlers than any thing they could do with other products. The navigation of Virginia and Maryland, and the Ohio will give them a superiority in tobacco; and the same circumstance, with better swamps, and a hotter sun, will render South Carolina superior in rice; but in the commodities I have mentioned, the lands in question would have a yet greater superiority. Nobody disputes the excellence of the soil in the back parts of North Carolina; it excels that of South Carolina; and the climate is known to be equal to any in the world, being as different from the maritime parts of the continent, as much as Hudson's Bay varies from Jamaica.

This is an improvement which would much advance the interests of Britain, for indigo, cotton, and silk are commod- ities which she buys of foreigners at a great price;[6] and if she

---

[6] This point was repeatedly stressed by English writers. See G. L. Beer, *British Colonial Policy, 1754-1765* (New York, 1922), chap. viii.

had more than supplied the consumption of her own manufactures, they are articles of ready sale all over Europe, so that nothing more demands the attention of the mother country than such parts of her colonies as are fitted by nature to produce them. Silk can only be produced in proportion to the number of people in the country; but then it is of consequence that the inhabitants of our wide spread plantations should all make as much as they can. It is a common observation on this point of producing silk in the colonies, that the country is not populous enough to make any progress in a business that requires so many hands, but nothing can be more mistaken than such reasoning. The culture of silk is of that nature, that if there were only one solitary plantation in a whole province, the same quantity of silk might be made on it, as proportionably in a whole country, though ever so populous; it is a business that requires only a few weeks in a year, were it therefore otherwise, it could not answer to any one to meddle with it. Every person might make one or two pounds of silk annually with very little or no interruption of their usual occupations. Hence we may assert that nothing can be more absurd than the argument of the inutility of silk because the country is not populous; when the country becomes populous the quantity will be an object of consequence; but if the work is not begun till then, it will probably never be begun at all: a few people in one colony, a few in another; some thousands here, some thousands there—separately taken, the quantity of silk they could make might not be a national object; but when all these numbers were added together, and united with the people in all the colonies, who enjoy a climate that would do for the business, the affair is then no longer a trifle: this we may be convinced of by reflecting on the numbers we have from Florida to Jersey inclusive; in all which tract silk might be produced in any quantities the population of the country would admit of: would but all the people in this line of country make each a pound per head, it would supply Britain with all she uses and more, and be worth both to her and the colonies much above a million sterling per annum.[7]

It is upon this principle therefore that it ought to be recommended particularly to enter into the business of making silk, however thin the population; and especially in such excellent climates as the back parts of this province at the foot of the mountains: for more than an hundred miles in breadth, quite among the mountains, the whole territory is covered with mulberry trees; nature points out what *might* be done in this country, but if the industry of man will not co-operate it is in vain to see these rich gifts on every side.

No part of America would be more proper for the growth of wine than this; but at present we know not of a navigation that would be sufficient for the cheap conveyance of it. Yet I should remark that the rivers in this country are not sufficiently known. Nothing is of more importance in the management of our American concerns than to know accurately how far the waters in that continent are navigable, and for what boats; surveys should be made of them with the greatest care possible: tracts of country may be neglected under a notion of the rivers not being navigable, while the fact may be quite otherwise. In the back and hilly parts of this province are numerous situations which would do admirably well for vineyards, the soil and climate equally promising success

[7] The author of *American Husbandry* was only one of many who urged England's colonies to engage in the silk industry. The high cost of labor seems to have been the main deterrent to its success in America. See S. Matsui, *History of the Silk Industry in the United States* (New York, 1930).

and the wild vines every where found in immense quantities. Nothing is supposed to be wanting but a navigation, which ought to be well enquired into.

Every reason of effect conspires to shew the propriety of settling the back parts of this province in preference to the maritime ones; in the latter rice must be the staple, which is not wanted, since it is the grand staple of South Carolina, where there are swamps sufficient to raise more than they will ever be able to sell. Indigo they may cultivate, but the crop will be far inferior to those on the rich, deep, black land in the back country; and as to tobacco, the soil on the coast is not comparable to that on the Ohio, where the planters will rival them entirely, not to speak of the want of ports. At the same time that these points give such a great superiority, there is an equal one in the articles of health and pleasure. A temperate and healthy climate is, for profit as well as pleasure, of the greatest importance; the life of a negroe employed on indigo in the back parts of the province, would be worth ten years purchase more than one employed on rice in the maritime part: and the same difference must necessarily be found in the population of whites. The destructive swamps in which rice is cultivated must never be expected to breed people; whereas the high, dry, and healthy regions of the western parts are so liberally blessed with every circumstance of climate, soil, and productions, that the people would increase prodigiously, as in fact they are found to do in all the back settlements of the southern colonies.

In the next place let me recommend to the planters of North Carolina, whether living in the eastern or western part of the province, to pursue a better conduct relative to their cattle. Instead of keeping such vast herds of half starved,

stunted beasts, let them provide good pastures, and keep
fewer beasts; the consequence of which will be that five head
will pay them better than twenty. In the very backward parts
of the colony they have good meadows and pastures, but these
are where the settlements are most scattered; and in all the
rest of the country all the pastures the cattle have are the
woods: this ought on every account to be remedied, so as to
draw a greater profit from the stocks and at the same time
make them contribute largely to manuring the plantations,
which at present they are far enough from doing. This good
effect is only to be brought about by providing them pastures,
as I said; in order to [do] which the system of crops which
I have so often condemned must be changed, and the land,
when corn, &c. is no longer sown on it, must be left in sufficient order and sown with grass seed that good pastures may
come in succession, instead of the land becoming forest again.
There are sorts of grasses indigenous in the country, which
might be brought into culture, that would answer this purpose; but the readiest way to effect it would be to sow lucerne,
which I before recommended to other colonies: the hotter
the climate, the greater the necessity of employing this grass,
or some one similar to it in the great length of the root, which
penetrates so deeply in the ground as to secure the plant from
all damage by the heat of the sun beams; most grasses, from
having fibrous roots which spread near the surface, are in these
climates burnt up, but lucerne will bear the hottest sun, and
thrive in it. By means of the culture of this plant they would
be able to provide well for their cattle, both horned cattle,
sheep, and swine, to all whom it is equally grateful; a few
acres cropped with it would go as far as a great number of
woodland: the cattle would thrive, their size and breed be

improved; and, instead of yielding little or no profit, they would become one of the best branches of the planter's business.

In England it has been found necessary to plant lucerne in rows, in order to keep it free from the natural grass, which otherwise soon choaks and destroys it; but in such climates as Carolina, the heat of the sun is such an enemy to the vegetation of grass that none is to be found in the flat country but in rice swamps: this precaution therefore would be unnecessary, and it might be sown broad-cast with the last crop of corn, in the same manner as clover in England. This would (if properly introduced in the system) prove of wonderful utility to the cattle, and be of more consequence to the planter than almost any other improvement. But I am aware that a North Carolina man would be apt to sow lucerne with the last crop of such a system as this:

1. Tobacco.	6. Indian corn.
2. Tobacco.	7. Wheat.
3. Tobacco.	8. Pease.
4. Tobacco.	9. Wheat.
5. Indian corn.	10. Wheat.

In which case he must not expect it to prove the valuable plant I have mentioned: for such a system leaves the land a caput mortuum[8] for some time, until the growth spontaneous to the country appears, which is wood of several kinds; and it is not to be expected that a crop of any value should grow after such treatment. But lucerne being to planters, circumstanced as the North Carolina ones, of great value, it would well deserve better treatment. Suppose the system begins with fresh woodland; it should be sown with the last crop of some such system as this, in which I have partly allowed the plant-

[8] Dead or without ability to produce; robbed of fertility.

ers to be bad husbandmen, as they all will be, till the luxuriance of the fresh land is a little tamed.

1. Tobacco.	6. Cotton.
2. Tobacco.	7. Indian corn.
3. Indigo.	8. Potatoes.
4. Cotton.	9. Cotton.
5. Wheat.	10. Potatoes.

11. Oats, or pease, and with it, lucerne.

In case cotton is not planted, some crop should be taken, instead of it that is not a great exhauster of the land. There are other roots which thrive well in the climate, as turneps, carrots, and several sorts of cabbages. These should certainly be introduced in the field culture to yield food for the cattle in winter, which is as necessary as lucerne for the summer, since hay is to be had only in rice swamps cleared or in the natural meadows near the mountains.

It is only in the introduction of such plants in their systems of crops that they can be able to keep their lands in tolerable heart or vary their present bad husbandry: no land, however good, will bear such exhausting crops for ever, as tobacco, indigo, and corn; it must be exhausted, vary them how you will; but by introducing potatoes (which is a native plant to the Carolinas), turneps, carrots, cabbages, or other plants, for the winter food of cattle, the land would be kept fertile twice as long and be in good heart when laid down to lucerne.

The present general management of the cattle I should adhere to, that is, to let them wander about the woods all day, and keep them at home in the night, with only this variation, they should in the pens and folds be *well* fed both winter and summer, which at present is far enough from being the case. In summer lucerne should be mown and given green in racks; and in winter they should have roots or cabbages, or the hay of lucerne: and the hogs also [should be] well fed with roots or cabbages, and such offal as the plantation yields: the advantages of this conduct would be great, not only in the superior growth of the cattle and the larger quantity of produce yielded by them, but also in that article essential to all husbandry, *dung;* thus managed they would make much more dung, and of a quality far superior to that which the planters gain at present; for every farmer knows the difference between the dung of cattle well fed and that of cattle half starved: this would be a new assistant to them in keeping their fields in good heart, and would vastly increase the profit of their plantations.

This conduct would soon make a great change in the appearance of the country and in its value; now almost as much returns to forest as is broken up, by the strange management they have of roaming from piece to piece and touching none without ruining and exhausting it. What a great difference would it make, if, when they took in a fresh piece of land, the old one was kept in value under lucerne, or some grass that would suit the climate. We should then see extensive and wide-spreading pastures of excellent herbage, instead of those numerous spots, which, having been under culture and exhausted, lie absolutely barren for some years and then are covered gradually with weeds, bushes, and rubbish, among which forest trees at last shoot up. This great change would make cattle as profitable to them as their staples, instead of keeping monstrous herds which yield little or no produce. The planters should remember that in proportion as the country settles, the woodlands diminish, and the number of their cattle must necessarily fall off; then they would find the advantage strongly of keeping the land under good grass which they had had in culture: without this precaution, they will by and by, instead of boasting of a thousand or fifteen hundred head of cattle, with difficulty be able to keep a fourth of the number; and they will then be forced to the very culture of grass and other food for cattle as a necessary; it will then be a difficult and expensive business to get good grass on land so ruined and exhausted as their old plantations will be found.

In carrying such ideas into execution, supposing it ever done, fences should be much more attended to than they are at present in North Carolina: it ought to be an universal rule, never departed from, to bring into culture no piece of ground without previously fencing it in a secure and lasting manner by a live hedge, bank, and ditch. There is no part of the world in which this can be done better than in Carolina, from the quick growth of wood in land not exhausted by planting. And these fences should not only be kept up while the land yields a crop, but afterwards when it is under grass or lucerne, that the fences may be secure enough to keep all cattle out in order for mowing the crop to feed with at night. When the lucerne began to fail from age, or the planter wanted the land again for corn, &c. then he would find the fences prove of great utility. It is observable that under grass or lucerne the land, if well laid down, and in heart, would continually improve in fertility until in some years it would prove highly profitable for a fresh system of crops.

There is no greater defect in the husbandry of this province than the foulness of the crops with weeds, &c. the improvement in this case would follow of course from adopting a different system of crops, as recommended above.

CHAPTER XX

SOUTH CAROLINA

Climate of South Carolina—Productions—Soil

THE province of South Carolina lies between latitude 31° and 35° N. but no idea is to be formed of the climate from that parallel, which in all other countries is found to be the finest on the globe; whereas this province experiences degrees of heat and cold rarely felt in other countries. This will appear from the following authentic account, said to be written by governor Glen.[1]

Our climate is various and uncertain, to such an extraordinary degree, that I fear not to affirm there are no people upon earth who I think can suffer greater extremes of heat and cold; it is happy for us they are not of long duration. No idea of either one or the other can be formed from our latitude, which on other

---

[1] Born in Scotland in 1701, James Glen belonged to a set of young Scotchmen who sought political offices in London and in America. A man of considerable knowledge and good manners, but wanting in experience, he was named governor of South Carolina in 1738 and continued in that capacity until 1755. His conduct in respect to the Indians and to the settlement of the back country has been severely criticised. Among other things, he has been charged with deliberate sacrifice of the public interest to promote his own private aggrandizement. Nevertheless his administration is indissolubly associated with the beginning of an era of prosperity for the province. During his governorship the area of the colony was greatly enlarged and population increased. Glen's volume, *A Description of South Carolina* (London, 1761), though exaggerated in some respects, is a useful source of information. See Edward McCrady, *The History of South Carolina under the Royal Government, 1719–1776* (New York, 1899), pp. 230 ff.

continents is found to be very desirable; nor dare I to trace by any physical reasoning the causes of these extremes, lest I should amuse with vain conjectures those to whom I would not write any thing but truth; I shall therefore content myself with setting down what we are sure of by experiments. In summer the thermometer hath been known to rise to 98 degrees, and in winter to fall to 10 degrees. The weather perhaps is no where more variable, with respect to heat and cold, than in Carolina; the changes are frequent, sudden, and great; but the decreases of heat are always greater and more sudden than its increases. On the 10th of January, 1745, at two o'clock in the afternoon, the thermometer was at 70 degrees, but the next morning it was at only 15 degrees, which was the greatest and most sudden change that I have seen.

In summer the heat of the shaded air at two or three o'clock in the afternoon is frequently between 90 and 95 degrees; but such extremes of heat, being soon productive of thunder showers, are not of long duration. On the 14th, 15th, and 16th of June, 1738, at three o'clock in the afternoon, the thermometer was at 98 degrees, a heat equal to the greatest heat of the human body in health! I then applied a thermometer to my arm-pits, and it sunk one degree; but in my mouth and hands it continued at 98 degrees. Sixty-five degrees and a half may be called the temperate heat in Carolina, which exceeds 48 degrees, the temperate heat in England, more than that exceeds, 32 degrees, the freezing point. The mean heat of the shaded air, taken from the mean nocturnal heat, and from the mean heat at two or three o'clock in the afternoon, during the four seasons of the year, is as followeth: in spring 61 degrees, in summer 78, in autumn 71, and in winter 52. The mean heat of the shaded air, at two or three o'clock in the afternoon, is 65 degrees in the spring, 82 in the summer, 75 in autumn, and 55 in winter. The mean nocturnal heat in those seasons is 57 degrees in the spring, 74 in the summer, 68 in autumn, and 49 in winter. Therefore our winter's mean nocturnal heat exceeds the temperate heat in England.

As the weather here is generally very serene, the sun's rays exert more constantly their full force; and therefore when we are abroad, and exposed to the sun, we are acted upon by a much greater degree of heat than that of the shaded air; for the thermometer, when suspended five feet from the ground, and exposed to the sun and to reflected rays from our sandy streets, hath frequently risen in a few minutes from 15 to 26 degrees above what were at those times the degrees of heat in the shaded air. But I have never yet made that experiment when the heat of the shaded air was above 88 degrees; when therefore we are in the streets in a serene day in the summer, the air we walk in and inspire is many degrees hotter than human blood; for supposing the heat of the shaded air be 88 degrees when the thermometer would rise 26 degrees higher if suspended and exposed to the sun, &c. as before mentioned; or suppose that the heat of the shaded air be 98 degrees when the thermometer would rise 26 degrees higher by such suspension and exposure: in the first of those two cases, the heat of the air in the streets would exceed 98, the natural heat of the human blood, by 16 degrees; and in the last case it would exceed such heat by 26 degrees.

The first instance of intense cold that I shall mention, relates to a healthy young person of my family, who at the time was two or three and twenty years of age, and usually slept in a room without a fire: that person carried two quart bottles of hot water to bed, which was of down, and covered with English blankets; the bottles were between the sheets, but in the morning they were both split to pieces, and the water solid lumps of ice. In the kitchen, where there was a fire, the water in a jar, in which was a large live eel, was frozen to the bottom; and I found several small birds frozen to death near my house; they could not have died for want of food, the frost having been but of one day's continuance. But an effect much to be regretted is, that it destroyed almost all the orange trees in the country; I lost above three hundred bearing trees; and an olive tree of such a prodigious size, that I thought it proof against all weathers; it was near a foot and a half diameter in the trunk and bore many bushels of excellent olives every year. This frost heppened on the 7th of February, 1747.

Another account, written also by a person who resided long in Carolina, gives some other particulars deserving notice.

The air is more clear and pure here than in Britain, being seldom darkened with fogs; the dews howe[ve]r are great, especially in the end of summer, and beginning of the fall. The rains are heavy, but commonly short, and observe no particular season or time of the year.

The winds are generally changeable and erratic, blowing from different points of the compass without any regularity; about the vernal and autumnal equinoxes they are commonly very boisterous; at other seasons are moderate. The northerly winds are cold, dry, and healthy—they disperse fogs and mists, giving a clear sky—the north-west is the coldest we have; it comes to us over an immense tract of land, and from the snow-capped Ap[p]alachian mountains; whenever it blows the air is cool, and in the winter it generally brings us frost, and often snow: it is vulgarly and deservedly called the great physician of the country, as by its force it clears the air of the putrid autumnal effluvia; and by its coldness shuts up the pores of the earth, and of the trees, keeping in their vapours, the principal sources of the epidemics of the warm season. This refreshing, invigorating, and bracing wind is anxiously expected about the month of October by all, but by those particularly who have the misfortune to be afflicted with the more obstinate intermittents, to whom it generally affords relief: the easterly winds are always cool: from them we have our most refreshing summer showers; when they blow for any continuance they occasion coughs and catarrhal fevers. The south and south-west winds are warmest and most unhealthy; in whatever season they blow the air is foggy and affects the breathing: in summer they are sultry and suffocating; an excessive dejection of spirits and debility of body are then an universal complaint; if this constitution lasts any considerable time, hysterics, hypo, intermitting and remitting, putrid, slow, or nervous fevers are produced. This province is subject to frequent and dreadful tempests of thunder and lightning in May, June, July, and August.

From this account of the weather in South Carolina is to be drawn several important conclusions; that the maritime part of the country is in one of the most unhealthy climates in the world cannot be doubted. The heat rises to an extreme which is felt in very few, if any places on the globe, of which accounts have been given: at the same time the changes to intense cold are so violent and sudden, that instances are to be met with no where but in America, and not in that quarter to such a degree as in South Carolina. Now of all other circumstances of weather, there are none that are found so insalubrious to the human constitution as such sudden changes, nor any which demands so much caution, in dress and living. Another point to be observed is [that] this immoderate and excessive heat of climate is in a country the major part of which is spread with stagnated waters of no depth, for such are the marshes, swamps, and all the rice grounds; from the mud of these stinking sinks and sewers the heat exhales such putrid effluvia as must necessarily poison the air and render it more similar to the Campania of Rome[2] than anything else an European can compare it to.

But at the same time that this character is perfectly just to the marshy sea coast, and generally to all the flat country, we must observe that it holds no further: this flat country reaches from eighty to a hundred miles from the sea coast, but then the soil begins to rise into little hills and beautiful inequalities, which continue increasing in height and variation till you reach the Ap[p]alachian mountains, at three hundred and three hundred and fifty miles from the sea. In all this range of country the climate is nearly the reverse; they have neither those extremes of heat, nor the excess cold that is felt on the

[2] Campania, the Roman name for inhabitants first of the town of Capua and its district, and subsequently for the very fertile plain about Rome.

coast. On the contrary, they have a charming, pleasant, and temperate climate, which in health and agreeableness yields to none in the world. This is to be attributed to the difference in the surface of the two countries; in one it is high, dry, and hilly—and wherever a country is of that sort or rocky, let it be in whatever latitude it may, it is sure to be healthy; but the other is a flat, marshy tract, full every where of stagnant water, and this is throughout the world a never failing sign of an unhealthy air.

Hence therefore a distinction is to be made in every article that depends on climate between the eastern and western parts of this province: an inhabitant of Carolina may assert that country to be one of the most healthy and pleasant in the world, and nothing can be more true: an inhabitant of Carolina may assert that country to be in unhealthiness the sink of the earth; nothing more true: but let them explain; one will be found to live in the east of it, the other in the west; countries as different almost as Iceland and Bengal. If it is asked how it comes that any people will live in the flat country when the back parts are so superior, it must be attributed to two causes; the one is the contiguity to the ports and trade, the other, the necessity of swamps for cultivating their grand staple, rice; were it not for these it is to be supposed that all the inhabitants would flock backwards.

Relative to the products of South Carolina, it will be necessary to know them with tolerable precision, as they will mark the nature of the country better than any other circumstance. I shall begin with timber: the uncultivated parts of the province are one continued forest, with not much under-wood. Among the trees are found oaks of several sorts, viz. the *chestnut oak*, which is the largest in the province; some are three or four feet in diameter, and sixty feet high to the first bough: they grow chiefly in low land that is stiff and rich. *Scarlet oak,* used, as well as the former, in ship-building; it grows on dry land. *Red oak* grows sometimes very large and lofty, but it is porous, and not durable; used for rails, staves, &c. *Spanish oak,* more durable, is used sometimes in ship-building and rives well into clapboards. *Bastard Spanish oak,* used for rails and clapboards. *Black oak* is durable under water, used also for building. *White iron oak,* very durable, is reckoned the best of all for ship-building; grows on dry lean land. *Live oak,* the most durable of all, but unfortunately affords not long plank clear of boughs. The weight and firmness of this wood is extraordinary; the particles have such an adhesion, that when a nail is once driven in, it is almost impossible to draw it out again; it grows in fresh water ponds and swamps. *Willow oak,* so called from the near resemblance of the leaf to that of a willow: these are not all the sorts of oak found in this province, there are several other varieties, but these are the principal distinctions: I must remark that all of them yield acorns, generally in plenty, and some of them in immense quantities, that scarcely ever fail; and several of them that are as good for swine as chestnuts, having a strong resemblance to that fruit; and they are in general much better food for hogs than our English acorns; and such as will not only keep hogs, but fat them admirably, without any expence to the planter. This is a great object to the Carolina people; for there is not a farmer or planter in the country who has not great stocks of hogs kept in the woods, and even fattened there.

Ash is a common tree here, but differing somewhat from that of England. Elm they have of two sorts; one grows on the high lands, which resembles that of Britain; the other sort grows in low lands. Tulip trees grow to an immense size;

some of them have been found one and twenty feet in circumference, and some even ten feet in diameter; they have also a story current in Carolina, that a new settler, not having a better habitation, took his abode for some time in a decayed tulip tree, in which he had his bed and other furniture; yet this man, poor as he may seem from hence, lived to become a considerable and wealthy planter. The use the wood of this tree is put to is generally that of shingles, wainscot, planks for buildings, and lasts longer under ground.

Beech is often met with, and grows to a large size; it is very like that of Europe; the only use it is applied to in Carolina is for firing; it yields plenty of mast for swine.[3] Hornbeam is common here. Sassafras is one of the articles of their exportation; it comes sometimes to a large size, even to two feet [in] diameter; they use it for turners ware, housebuilding, posts, and [it] does well for all ground work. Dogwood is very plentiful, and generally found on light lands that are rich; they use it in building, where it is not exposed to the air. Laurel comes here to a great size; so that planks are sawn out of it, but it is not durable when exposed to the air: both bay and laurel grow principally in low swampy ground. The red cedar grows chiefly on swamps or sand banks; it is much valued for durability, and used for building sloops, boats, &c. as well as by the joiners; nor will the worm touch it for many years, and the sloops built of it are esteemed for good sailers. White cedar is no less esteemed for other uses, particularly top masts, yards, booms, bowsprits, &c. and the best shingles are made of it.

The cypress grows to an immense size, perhaps larger than any other tree in Carolina, both in respect of height and thickness; some have been found of thirty-six feet in circumference.

[3] Nuts, especially beechnuts.

The Indians make their canoes of single cypress trees scooped out, and some of them have been thus made large enough to carry thirty barrels; and others that are split down the bottom, and a piece added thereto, will carry eighty or an hundred.

The locust tree is very durable, and will bear being exposed to the weather; it is never found in swamps or low places, being a general sign of dry, healthy, good land. They have four sorts of pines here; the pitch pine grows to a great size: I before mentioned this tree yielding tar, pitch, &c. The white pine they saw in various species of lumber; it makes also masts, yards, &c.; the almond pine does also for masts. The dwarf pine is of no great account. The hickory is a kind of walnut, the timber not all durable. The common walnut is called the *black* walnut, to distinguish it from the hickory: it affects good land, and grows therein to a vast size: it is hard and durable. The maple is common here. The chinkapin [chinquapin][4] is a sort of chesnut, and durable in the weather; it is used in building boats, shallops, &c. Birch grows on the banks of the rivers, high up the country, but [is] seldom found on the coast. Willows, sycamores, and hollies are found here. Three sorts of mulberry trees abound in Carolina, wherever the land is light; and rich shumac and hazel wood are also common.

In the next place we are to attend to the fruit trees of this country, which are very numerous.

Among these we find the wild fig, which grows only on the mountains or their neighbourhood. The wild plums are of several sorts; they are of quick growth, bearing in five years from the stone. They have a kind of currants, the bushes of which grow seven or eight feet high. Apples of various sorts, and in great plenty. Three or four sorts of pears. Three sorts

[4] Sometimes referred to as the dwarf chestnut.

of quinces, the fruit of which is very large, and much beyond those of England. The least slip of this tree planted will bear in three years; a surprising vegetation. Peaches are the most common fruit in the country, and no wonder, for every stone that falls becomes a bearing tree in three years; all are standards; the quantity of this fruit is so great that the hogs have much the larger share of it: they are generally such great bearers that the branches of the trees are broken down with the weight of the fruit; they grow to the size of common apple trees.

The apricot grows to a very great size, exceeding most apple trees: they are raised from the stone. Red and black cherries are found very plentifully. Gooseberries do not agree well with the climate, but common currants do well. Raspberries are plentiful. Strawberries thrive greatly, and bear amply. Native vines are met with all over the province; but the finest are in the back parts upon the dry hills, where they are five times as large as on the coast. From the native black grape, which does not ripen till October, wine has been made of an excellent quality and very strong; but the vineyards which have been tried of European grapes have all failed from their ripening in August.

Besides these fruits, South Carolina produces others more valuable and sought after, as oranges, sweet and sour, lemons, citrons, limes, olives, pomegranates, all sorts of melons, watermelons, &c. Oranges and lemons are an article of exportation, great numbers being sent abroad annually. Olives are not cultivated in common, which is a neglect; though none of these fruits can be depended on, as in a country where no frosts are felt; whereas in Carolina, as before remarked, they are sometimes so severe as to kill all tender trees to the root.

In the kitchen garden are found every sort of useful plant

that is commonly cultivated in the gardens in England. Potatoes no where thrive better, and they have them of several sorts; many sorts of pease and beans, with cabbages, broccoli, cauliflowers, &c. Some of these are in a perfection which is unknown to us in Britain, owing to the superior heat of the climate; yet in general we should remark, that garden-stuff which will grow at all in the climate (fruits excepted) is preferable more to the north, in Maryland, Virginia, and the southern part of Pennsylvania; but in the back parts of Carolina, near the mountains, all these articles are yielded in a perfection that cannot be exceeded.

The products which respect husbandry in particular are Indian corn, which thrives very well here; wheat, which does well in the backward parts, but very badly in the maritime side of the province; barley the same; both these grain, as well as oats, are very little cultivated, nor can they be till the settlements reach further back; beans and pease of several sorts, particularly the Indian kinds, thrive well all over the province. As to the staples of rice, indigo, &c. I shall speak more particularly of them in another place.

The soil of Carolina must like the climate be divided, before one can speak of it with any precision, into the eastern and western parts of the province; that is, the maritime part, and the back country; the former reaches above an hundred miles from the coast: this tract contains several kinds of land, which the planters distinguish by calling them pine land, oak land, swamps, and marshes.

Pine land is much the most general, containing perhaps four-fifths of the country; the soil is a dry white sand, covered with pines: if there is any under-wood it is very poor, only the whortleberry and chinkapin, which Dr. Mitchel[1] calls the *heath* of America. This land is very poor, and will bear scarcely any thing but its spontaneous growth; in spots it contains a little grass, but of so bad and sour a nature, that cattle will not touch it unless half starved. The writer I just now mentioned has an observation on this pine land, which deserves attention.

These pines with which all our southern colonies are covered for one hundred or one hundred and fifty miles from the sea coast, and in some all over them, are the most pernicious of all weeds; they not only destroy every thing upon the face of the earth, but the very land they grow upon; insomuch that nothing will grow among them, and hardly any thing after them. It is a general observation, that the lands are not only barren on which they grow naturally, but if they happen to come up on other lands, they spoil them, and render them more or less barren. Having often examined what this could be owing to, I could not attribute it altogether to their large spreading roots, which spread all over the surface of the earth like a mat and exhaust its substance, but chiefly to the strong acid juice of their leaves, which distills from them in the spring of the year like oil of turpentine, and poisons both the earth and every thing upon it; as it is well known that all acids are a poison to vegetables, and all alcalies [alkalis] a rich manure. But whatever may be the cause, the matter of fact is certain, that nothing will grow among pines in America; and M. du Hamel makes the same observation in France. The whole surface of the earth is covered with their acid leaves; they overtop and destroy every thing; and if a little grass should happen to come up among them where they grow thin, it is so scarce, yellow, and sour, that to see any beast feed upon it is a certain sign of the miserable poverty of a country, where they are reduced to the last extremity. Yet these are the only pastures they have in many of our colonies: what is worse, these pernicious weeds are not to be extirpated; they have a wing to their seed, which disperses it every where with the winds, like thistles, and in two or three years forms a *pine thicket*, which nothing can pass through or live in. Thus the land becomes a perfect desart instead of a profitable pasture, in a few years after it is cleared. Corn upon such land looks as yellow as the turpentine with which it is fed, and grass will not grow.

There is a great deal of truth and good sense in this passage; but at the same time it is not strictly true, that nothing will grow *after* these pines, for it is well known that the planters get Indian corn and pease from these lands after they are cleared; and when they lie low enough to be flooded, rice. But the principal use they are put to is for indigo, in which they answer tolerably; but this is only because they have no better that is dry; for indigo delights in dry, rich, deep, black mould. When you abuse their pine barrens, a Carolina planter will answer you by saying, that they do for their richest crop, indigo; which is very true, as I just observed; but they do for it only as poor sands in England do for the culture of wheat: the farmers sow it because they have no better, and get half crops, which is just the case with indigo on pine barrens.

Oak land is another sort; it is a black, rich sand, and produces oaks, walnut, hickory, and black mulberry trees, and is to all intents excellent land; but the misfortune is that the quantity of it is very small; it is found only in narrow strips between the swamps and pine barrens, and between the latter and creeks or rivers. This is the only land they have that will produce good crops of corn and indigo.

Swamps are of several sorts, and they judge of them by their produce; the best are the white oak swamps, which have generally a clayey foundation; but these are rare in South Carolina, or else being on the large rivers are too deep to clear and drain. Others bear canes, and are therefore called cane swamps: these are generally rich and good; but the most general are cypress ones, which is the spontaneous growth of all, where the soil surrounding them is a poor land. However, it is to be noted that all these swamps, when drained, produce the grand staple of the country, rice, yielding crops of it, as in other cases, of a goodness proportioned to their fertility. The face of the country in general is that either of a swamp or a pine barren. Marshes they divide into the salt and fresh water marshes; when the water is low enough they pasture them with horses and cattle; and if they bestow the labour of draining on them they make tolerable good meadows.

There can be no doubt but that all this maritime part of America has been covered with the sea, it has every sign of it; upon digging you find no clay, stones, rocks, nor minerals, it is all sand, or beds of shells; and the flatness of the country, with the gradual shallowness of the sea, shew it sufficiently.

The varieties of land just given include all the maritime part of the province; but the back country, which reaches to the Ap[p]alachian mountains, is very different; swamps and marshes are there unknown, or at least but rarely met with, from whence proceeds the healthiness of it. The face of the country is hilly, and either covered with tall stately trees or spread into extensive meadows of dry, rich, deep land; which is the general nature of the soil, except where rocks abound, which is on the broken parts of some of the mountains and on the banks of some of the rivers. Pines are in this part of the province seldom met with; on the contrary, the timber is oak, elm, hickory, walnut, and mulberry: no lands in the southern part of North America have an appearance of being more fertile; and the most retired of our plantations, which are seated only where this fine country begins, find that one acre will yield as much produce of any kind as three in the maritime part of the province. The fresh woodlands here are deep, and *black* for two feet deep; such is the right land for indigo, tobacco, corn of all sorts, and, in a word, for every thing that is sown upon it. This extraordinary fertility of the soil is united with a climate as mild, temperate, healthy, and agreeable, as that of the eastern part of Carolina is the reverse. It is the rice swamps that alone keep the inhabitants near the coast; the planters are accustomed to that culture, and will not change it for a different one: no rice is to be cultivated here, which is the circumstance that is the glory of the country: from this country it is that silk and wine must come, if ever they are had from Carolina.

It is the peculiar blessing of these back tracts of country, that they have every product that is valuable, which is known in the maritime part of the province, except rice; and at the same time they are exempted from those of little or no use, or that are pernicious, such as the pine; a character we may fairly give it (notwithstanding its yielding tar, pitch, &c.) whenever it grows on land that could be applied to any other use.

This is the part of Carolina to which all new settlers should be recommended; here they will increase their numbers greatly from the healthiness of the country, which is not the case with the swamps and marshes on the coast. They may raise much better and more valuable staples than rice.

CHAPTER XXI

SOUTH CAROLINA

Staple productions—Rice—Culture of it—Management
of the plantations—Profit—Indigo—Culture—Profit
—Observations—Other staples—Remarks

RICE is yet the grand staple production of South Carolina, and that for which the planters neglect the healthy, pleasant back country in order to live in the *Dismals* on the coast, for so the Americans justly call the swamps:[1] rice can only be cultivated in land which lies so low as to admit of floating at pleasure, and all such lands in Carolina are necessarily swamps. The first business is to drain the swamp, in which work they have no particular methods deserving notice, or which are unknown in England. The moment they have got the water off they attack the trees, which in some swamps are very numerous; these they cut down at the root, leaving the stumps in the earth, and, oftentimes even the trunks and branches of the trees are left about the ground: some planters pile them up in heaps, and leave them to rot; others, more provident, cut them into lengths, and convert them into some sort of lumber. However they do not wait for the ground being cleared of them, but proceed to plant their rice among the stumps. In March, April, and May they plant; the

---

[1] The largest of these swamps is Dismal Swamp; it extends from southeastern Virginia into northeastern North Carolina. It is about twenty miles long and ten miles wide, but originally was much larger.

negroes draw furrows eighteen inches asunder, and about three inches deep, in which the seeds are sown; a peck is sufficient for an acre of land: as soon as planted they let in the water to a certain depth, which is, during the season of its growth, repeated, and drawn off several times; but most of the growth is while the water is eight, nine, or ten inches deep on the land. The great object of the culture is to keep the land clean from weeds, which is absolutely necessary, and the worst weed is grass: if they would say a man is a bad manager, they do not observe such a person's plantation is not clean, or is weedy, but *such a man is in the grass;* intimating that he has not negroes enough to keep his rice free from grass. This is the only object till it is reaped, which is usually about the latter end of August or [the] beginning of September. Like wheat in England, they prefer cutting it while the straw is a little green, leaving it on the stubble to dry and wither two or three days in case the weather is favourable: after which they lay it up in barns or stacks, in the same manner as corn in Europe.

The next operation, as in other sorts of corn, is the threshing of it, after which it is winnowed, which was formerly a very tedious operation, but now much accelerated by the use of a windfan.[2] When winnowed it is ground, to free the rice from the husk; this is done in wooden mills of about two feet diameter: it is then winnowed again, and put into a mortar large enough to hold half a bushel, in which it is beat with a pestle by negroes, to free it from its thick skin; this is a very laborious work. In order to free it from the flour and dust made by this pounding, it is sifted; and again through another sieve, called a market sieve, which separates the broken

---

[2] A device for forcing air through threshed grain for the purpose of removing the chaff.

and small rice, after which it is put up in barrels, and is ready for market.

The reader must observe upon this account that the cultivation of it is dreadful: for if a work could be imagined peculiarly unwholesome and even fatal to health, it must be that of standing like the negroes, anc[k]le and even mid-leg deep in water which floats an ouzy [oozy] mud, and exposed all the while to a burning sun which makes the very air they breathe hotter than the human blood; these poor wretches are then in a furnace of stinking putrid effluvia: a more horrible employment can hardly be imagined, not far short of digging in Potosi.[3] We are told indeed that South Carolina breeds more negroes than she destroys, which is certainly a fact, as appears by the annual exportation of a few; but then let it not be imagined that it is in these properly denominated *dismals*: we are to remember that the proportion between the domestic and other negroes and planting ones, is as 30,000 to 40,000 when the total is 70,000; and we are further to remember, that many are employed on indigo where there are no rice swamps, and also in other branches of culture; all these with the 30,000, may certainly increase greatly; but it does not from hence follow that those employed on rice do not decrease considerably, which is a certain fact, and it would be miraculous were it otherwise. It will therefore be no impropriety to determine that there must be a considerable expence in recruiting those negroes that are employed on rice and more considerable far than what attends others employed on tobacco, indigo, or indeed any plant not cultivated in a swamp.

As to the product of rice, it varies much, which is in pro-

[3] Long after its discovery in 1545 the slope of the Cerro de Potosi, in what is now southern Bolivia, was the richest source of silver in the world.

portion to the goodness of the swamp, and to the culture that
is bestowed on it; the land it likes is the stiff, deep, miry
mud on clay; the worst is the swamp with only a sandy
bottom. Governor Glen observes that thirty slaves are a
proper number for a plantation, and to be attended by one
overseer. The common computation throughout the province
is, communibus annis,[4] that each working hand employed in a
rice plantation, makes four barrels and a half of rice, each
barrel weighing four or five hundred pounds weight neat
[net]; besides a sufficient quantity of provisions of all kinds
for the slaves, horses, cattle, and poultry of the plantation
for the year ensuing; the price 6s. 5d. per 100 lb. or from
1£. 5s. to 1£. 12s. per barrel; but since this gentleman wrote,
the price has risen to 2£. and 4£. per barrel. We are told in
an account written in 1710, that the product was from 30 to 60
bushels; suppose 40, and that a bushel weighed 65 lb.; at 450
lb. a barrel this would be 5¾ [barrels] to the acre; and at
2£. the amount would be 10£. 5s.

The first account of 4½ barrels at 2£. is 9£. per working
hand, at the price rice is at present. A late account of Carolina,
published in 1770, makes the labour of the slaves 10£. each;
these agree therefore very well. But Dr. Stork[5] makes the

[4] That is, in average years.
[5] Dr. William Stork, doctor, naturalist, and traveler, was much interested in what is now southeastern United States. In company with John
Bartram, who through the influence of Peter Collinson had been appointed
botanist to King George III, Dr. Stork made a careful study of parts of
the southeast which was published in 1766 under the title *An Account of
East Florida with a Journal Kept by John Bartram of Philadelphia, Botanist to His Majesty for the Floridas; upon a Journey from St. Augustine
up the River St. Johns.* In the same year Stork published a similar document entitled *An Account of East-Florida with Remarks on Its Future
Importance to Trade and Commerce.* An examination of this work indicates that he was not only a mercantilist but was interested in land speculation. (See below, p. 361, footnotes 3 and 4.)

profit per head 20£. by this culture, and says that where the soil and climate are proper for rice, there is no grain in the world yields so much profit to the planter; this is evidently a mistake, and a great one. If we allow 10£. a head upon the former, and better authority, we cannot be far from the truth. I before calculated the annual expence of the negroes as follows:

	£.	s.	d.
Overseer	1	0	0
Cloaths	0	10	0
Sundries	1	10	0
	3	0	0

But the decline of value must be in all reason reckoned in rice work; if 2£., the expences will be 7£. and the produce but 10£. so the planter's profit per head will be only 3£. from which must be farther deducted the interest of his cost, or 50£. which at 5 per cent. (not reckoning the rate per cent. of the colonies) come to 2£. 10s. and leaves neat [net] from the slave 9£. 10s. But as this would by no means pay the planter for his other expences and his time, he makes a shift to save something in the articles of overseer and cloathing; but still the product from rice alone would be insufficient: the method in which they make it up is partly by lumber, as the slave will have time in the winter to thresh and dress more rice than he can plant in the summer; and consequently can spare it for sawing lumber. But yet rice would not answer were it not for other assistance; this is chiefly indigo. I before remarked that between the pine barrens and swamps are dry slips of oak land, which is rich and good; on this they plant indigo, and to good profit, with this further advantage, that indigo requiring no winter work, the slaves may assist in manufacturing rice, and sawing lumber, &c. Upon this plan indigo is

extremely profitable, but for want of enough of it, they plant
it likewise on the pine barren, where it is but little better than
rice. It is this secondary object of the rice planters which
makes their business advantageous enough to support them;
but upon this circumstance I must make a few observations.

What can induce them to have any thing to do with an
article of culture, which, taken singly, would not even pay
charges? That this is the fact is not to be disputed, for we
have the produce per working hand from the best authority,
the governor of the province who resided in it many years;
and let any person judge if a negroe can stand in less than 7£.
or 8£. a year in so pernicious an employment as that of making rice. And it is also clear enough that the wear of tools,
buildings, charges, incidents, interest of other money, &c. &c.
must likewise come to something considerable.

What, therefore I say, can induce the planters to engage
in such a business?

Possibly it is owing to habit, and being accustomed to consider rice as their grand dependance, which it was to their
fathers before indigo, silk, cotton, &c. were known here; and
having been used to this idea, they find it difficult, like all
cultivators of the soil, to change old customs. If it is not owing
to this, it is difficult to say to what it can be owing. In the
back country of the province the land is of infinitely greater
fertility, and would produce much more valuable staples, at
the same time that the healthiness of the climate would both
to the planter and his family, as well as his slaves, be invaluable: their being so much addicted therefore to rice is
founded on no good and substantial reasons.

There is another circumstance which should make the government attentive to encouraging every staple—but particularly indigo, tobacco, silk, wine, &c.—more than rice, which

[circumstance] is its being a rival to one of the most valuable articles of our trade, that of corn; for all the rice sold to Spain and Portugal is but enabling them to do without so much of our wheat; and that is partly the case with Germany: not that I would insinuate that restrictions on rice should be laid for obvious reasons, and particularly, the not knowing whether we can supply those markets with corn,[6] supposing they would take it of us—and also the value of the rice being all laid out in British commodities. But indigo, tobacco, &c. have all the same advantages without *any* disadvantages, nor even the appearance of any.

INDIGO

There are three sorts of indigo cultivated in South Carolina —the *Hispaniola*, the *Bahama*, which is a false Guatimala, and the *native*; the two first are the most valuable, but the last is much better adapted to the climate. The former is an annual plant, but the wild sort, which is common in the country, is perennial; its stalk dies every year, but it shoots up again next spring; the indigo made from it is of as good a quality as the other, the superiority of that being owing to the superior fertility of the West Indies, and a better climate for it. Dr. Mitchel[1] reckons Carolina to have a great inferiority to the West Indies in this article: his words are,

Indigo thrives very indifferently either in the soil or the climate. Indigo is one of those rank weeds like tobacco, which not only exhaust the substance of the earth, but require the very best and richest lands, and such as have a natural moisture in them; whereas the lands in Carolina are extremely poor and sandy, and have a barren dryness in them, which renders them very unfit to produce such a crop as this to any manner of advantage. This is planted by the French on the fresh woodlands of St. Domingo,

[6] Grain.

which are too rich and moist even for sugar, and is intended to exhaust their luxuriant fertility, as we do with tobacco, in order to render them fit for that and other crops. They likewise cut it every six weeks, or eight times a year, and for two years together; whereas in Carolina it is cut but thrice; and as the land has not substance and moisture to make it shoot after cutting, and the summers are too short, the third cutting is but of little value, as even the second is in Virginia. Neither does the soil or climate seem to be fit to yield that rich juice which makes this dye in any plenty or perfection. The French and Spaniards make great quantities worth eight and ten shillings a pound, when the little we make in Carolina is not upon an average worth above two shillings, and a great deal has been sold for a shilling and less.[7]

The proper soil for indigo is a rich, light, black mould, such as is commonly found in the back country; but in the maritime part they chuse oak land for it, not having the other; and as this is but in small quantity, they are forced to cultivate their poor white sands for indigo, which will not yield near the produce which all cultivators of this commodity ought to be desirous of, and indeed which will always be gained when proper land is employed for it. The deficiency of common products appears from Governor Glen's account,[8] who asserts that 30 lb. an acre is all that is to be expected in common, though good land will produce 80 [pounds].

Respecting this point of produce our accounts differ greatly, and none yet in print are fully to be depended on; Mr. Glen's account is that one acre of *good land* will produce 80 lb. and one slave may manage two acres and upwards, and raise provisions besides, and have all the winter months to saw lumber

[7] Mitchell, *The Present State of Great Britain and North America with regard to Agriculture, Population, Trade, and Manufactures* (London, 1767), pp. 148–49.

[8] See Edward McCrady, *The History of South Carolina under the Royal Government, 1719–1776* (New York, 1899), pp. 262–74.

and be otherwise employed: 80 lb. at 3s., the present price, is 12£. per acre; and 2½ acres at that rate amount to 30£. per slave, besides lumber, which is very considerable: but I should observe, that there is much indigo brought now from Carolina which sells in London for from 5s. to 8s. a pound, and some even higher, though the chief part of the crop may not yield more than 3s. or 4s.; this will alter the average price, but how much, is almost impossible to ascertain, as it depends on many unknown circumstances.

Before I quit this subject, I shall, in order to give the reader all the satisfaction possible, transcribe part of an account of the indigo culture, written in 1755, before the province had got so largely into the management of it as it has done since.[9]

Whoever plants indigo must be careful to have a good command of water in his reservoirs, which if in the center of his field, the better, to save time in bringing the plant when cut to the vats. We plant two kinds of land in Carolina, viz. high land and low land. The first is of the richest kind, overgrown with oak or hiccory, in which the plant will strike its roots very strait and deep. The second is either our river or inland swamps, where we plant rice, which lands are generally covered with huge oaks and cypresses; so that to gain a field of twenty acres in this country, as many noble trees must be felled and burnt as in England would bring many thousands sterling.

This low land is banked, ditched, trenched, and drained; but the soil must lie on a clay bottom, otherwise indigo will not thrive in it. In those lands the indigo roots spread horizontally, as in the high lands perpendicularly.

—This idea of our author seems contradictory to the best accounts I have received, which confine the culture of indigo to hickory land and pine barren, as it requires a dry soil,

[9] James Glen, *A Description of South Carolina* (London, 1761).

though as fertile as possible, and consequently a swamp must be well *drained* indeed to be rendered proper for it: but what he says himself shews that the high land is the best for it, since all plants that strike a perpendicular root ought to be planted in a soil that will admit such roots shooting: a perpendicular root spreading horizontally proves clearly that the soil is improper; it meets with the wet retained by the clay, which prevents its running deeper. His situation within forty miles of Charles Town, prevented him, I suppose, from mentioning the deep black loams of the back country which are the only ones that will yield *great* crops of indigo. But to return,

If the planter prefer the quality before the quantity of his indigo, he will be very careful to let his plants but just blossom before he cuts; for the more young and tender the plant, the more beautiful will be the colour of the indigo, though it will not yield perhaps so much as if cut a week or two later; but what he loses one way he will gain another. On the contrary, if he lets his plants be overgrown, and stand too long, he can never expect bright indigo. Indigo has a very disagreeable smell, while making and curing; and the *fœces*,[10] when taken out of the steeper, if not immediately buried in the ground (for which it is excellent manure) breeds incredible swarms of flies.

The quality of indigo, when made, may be known by its brightness, closeness, and fine violet blue, inclining to copper. It is better by being kept some time, and ought to be light enough to swim on the water; the quicker and more it sinks, the worse its property. The very best and finest is of a fine lively blue, inclining to the violet; brilliant, of a fine shining colour when broke, and more beautiful within than without. A bushel of good indigo weighs about 50 or 55 pounds. The methods for trial of its goodness is first to throw a cake into a glass of water, where it will soon dissolve entirely if pure and well made, but if mixed with

[10] Sediment.

any foreign matter, the heterogeneous parts will sink. Secondly, another method is to burn it: good indigo entirely consumes away; but if adulterated, it will be discovered by the false mixtures remaining after the true indigo is consumed.

Our indigo making ceases with the summer. As soon as cold weather sets in, little or no fermentation can be excited. Double beating and labour is required; and in drying the indigo the cakes will break into powder. The first frosty night concludes our season.

Expence of purchasing a plantation in Carolina within 40 miles of Charles Town

	£.	s.	d.
To 1,000 acres of land (one third of which ought to be good swamp, the rest oak and hickory, with some pine barren) at 11s. 5d.	575	0	0
To a dwelling house, barn, stable, overseer's house, negro huts, &c.	142	15	0
To two valuable negroes (a cooper and a carpenter) at 71£. 7s. 6d.	142	15	0
To 26 other negroes (two thirds men and one-third women) at 35£. 10s.	927	10	0
To two ordinary old negroes to look after the poultry, kine, hogs, &c.	57	0	0
To a waiting boy	28	10	0
To a house-wench	40	15	0
To 20 head of oxen, cows, &c. at 1£. 8s.	28	0	0
To 2 stallions and 4 breeding mares, at 5£. 14s.	11	8	0
To hogs, sheep, and poultry	21	8	0
To plantation tools, a cart, plough, &c.	21	8	0
To 2 riding horses, for yourself, family, overseer, bridles, saddles, &c.	28	0	0
To clothes, provisions, &c. for negroes, seed, vats, &c. for the first year	35	15	0
To contingencies, nails, oil, &c.	15	15	0
£.	2,075	19	0

The plantation per ann. after the first year.
N.B. *This calculation is for good years, and
exclusive of accidents*

	£.	s.	d.
To the overseer's wages, and allowance for rum, &c.	35	15	0
To 32 pair of shoes for negroes, at 2s. 6d.	3	0	0
To 160 yards of white plains (5 yards each negro) at 1s. 5d.	11	6	8
To thread, buttons, &c.	50	1	8
To one third of 32 blankets given every third year	3	17	0
To physic for each negro, as per agreement with the doctor	4	14	6
To Osnaburg,[11] lime, oil, nails, and iron ware	8	13	6
To freight and cooperage of 50 barrels of rice, at 2s. 10d.	7	1	8
To ditto of 6 of indigo, at 3s. 2d.	0	19	0
To tax and quitrent of 1,000 acres of land	2	2	6
To tax of 32 slaves, about	4	4	0
To purchase of two slaves annually, to keep up the original stock, which it is judged this and their increase may do	71	5	0
To wear and tear	14	10	0
£.	168	3	1

By the produce of 60 acres of indigo at 50 lb. per acre, at 2s. 10d. per lb. or 7£. 1s. 8d. per acre	425	0	0
By 50 barrels of rice, on 25 acres, each barrel 500 lb. net, at 6s. per cwt.	66	18	0
By 50 barrels	3	13	6
Total,	495	11	6
Expences	168	3	1
Balance, planter's profit	327	8	5

[11] A kind of coarse linen originally made in Osnabrück, North Germany.

N.B. It is here supposed, that the family resides on the spot, and that the surplus of hogs, poultry, &c. raised above their own consumption, will be sufficient to find the family in butcher's meat, and other necessaries, save cloathing.

This computation is made of two acres of indigo and one of rice to each hand; they raise their own provisions besides.

If rice is not planted, some of the hands may be employed in the winter season in making naval stores, cutting of lumber, shingles, &c.*

There are some valuable particulars in this account; but in others it is either erroneous, or does not hold good at present, when they reckon that the slaves, well appointed and taken proper care of, keep up their own numbers with any new purchase, which indeed appears from Carolina generally exporting a few. As to the rice, if 66£. in 500£. with a loss of lumber, is all the recompence for fixing in the low swampy country, it shews at once how just my former observations were, that the back country is not only in point of health and agreeableness infinitely superior to any thing within forty miles of Charles Town, but also by far the most profitable to the planter. The soil is there greatly superior for every production except rice; this superiority would alone more than equal the amount of 66£. besides the produce of lumber. All the accounts we have had of this country only confirm the truth of the general observation, that the back country is that to settle.

Besides rice and indigo, there are some other staples cultivated in Carolina, which though not of any great importance, yet demand a little attention. Cotton thrives well in the soil and climate, and though it is applied at present only to the home consumption of the province, yet it might certainly be extended so as to become a considerable article of exportation.

* *Gentlemen's Magazine,* XXV, 258.

Indigo and rice at present engross all their attention, not because they cannot raise other staples, but because these, while the demand is great, are more profitable. Cotton will hereafter be a valuable staple. Wine, silk, oil, hemp, and flax, are other products which in the back country may be cultivated in the greatest plenty; but this is not to be expected till the value of that healthy and fertile part of our southern colonies is better known and peopled.

It is an observation that demands much national attention that this very important colony should cultivate more staples than rice and indigo; it is of consequence that our colonies should not depend on one or two staples which are not of a permanent nature: indigo is the only article that ranks among the staples of South Carolina which is secure of a future sale, proportioned to the future increase of culture: I do not think that this is the case with rice, the sale of which depends very minutely on the plenty of corn in Germany, the North, Spain, and Portugal; for in those countries is its principal sale; and the immense growth of the rice plantations in Carolina has of late years been much owing to a great failure in the corn crops[12] of Europe, a failure which has been and is at present likely to prove of no slight advantage to this colony.

But silk, wine, oil, hemp, flax, &c. not forgetting tobacco, would, if well attended to in the back country, secure to this province those advantages which can only flow from the possession of various staples in common demand throughout the world; by which means, their profit would be greater than at present, and under the security of a much longer duration than ever will be found attendant on the exportation of rice.

Besides these articles, which are at present cultivated in large or small quantities (it is to be observed that every one

[12] Grain crops.

of the products here mentioned are planted for private use, and in some in small quantities for sale), there are others which deserve mention; among these we find an exportation of the same fruits which are sent from Spain and Portugal, oranges, lemons, citrons, &c. pitch, tar, turpentine, rosin, naval timber, potash, sassafras, lumber, tallow, wax, leather, skins, &c. These are articles which demand attention, and for which all endeavours should be tried to increase, since it is a number of staples upon which a flourishing colony depends for any permanency of prosperity: and this is the more necessary, as in proportion as the settlements extend, in such proportion does the benefit of lumber fall off; since the clearing the woods pays the expence in lumber only in the maritime part of the province: now in plantations which are deprived of the advantage of lumber, there must accrue a certain loss, if a variety of staples be not introduced. Indigo and tobacco employ only the negroes the summer half of the year, and leave time sufficient for silk in the spring, an harvest in summer, and a vintage in autumn, besides the winter for other purposes, and completing the labour of other staples.

This object deserves the more attention, from the circumstance of the eagerness of the Carolina planters in the culture of their grand staples, rice and indigo, which is carried on to such a degree as to render them little solicitous about other objects. Herein they consult what we are to look for from all mankind—great attention to what they think their present interests and very little idea of futurity. This disposition which is so general among all people does very well for the present time and for present interests, but it will rarely, if ever, bring in those improvements, which, in the introduction of new staples, become, in future, objects of the greatest importance. It is in such points as these that the attention of government is wanted, which can alone effect such material improvements by bringing people to an attention to other objects besides their immediate interests, by rewards and other encouragement.

The administration of our government has in these instances shewn too great an inattention to such important objects; our colonies have increased greatly in population and product, which has satisfied us, although the benefits received might have been greatly increased and been of such a nature as to promise a much longer and more secure duration than what they enjoy at present.

CHAPTER XXII

SOUTH CAROLINA

*Account of the means, expence, and profit of forming a
plantation in South Carolina—Explanation—Remarks*

SOUTH CAROLINA has of late years increased in a most
prodigious degree, both in people and the exportation of
valuable staples, which has been owing to several causes I
shall mention hereafter; and this great increase, with the fortunes made by planting in this part of the continent, have induced very great numbers to settle in this province, and it is
much to the advantage of Great Britain that this is so; for in
all these provinces to the south, valuable staples are produced,
which enable the inhabitants to purchase the manufactures of
Britain, a case not to be met with in the northern settlements:[1]

[1] Exports from England from Christmas to the same date the following
year as given in the British Board of Trade Commercial Series and cited
by G. L. Beer, *British Colonial Policy, 1754-1765* (New York, 1922),
p. 138.

	1746–1747	1751–1752	1756–1757	1761–1762	1766–1767
Newfoundland	£ 49,021	£ 46,995	£ 23,537	£ 34,387	£ 53,550
Carolina	95,529	150,777	213,949	194,170	244,093
Hudson's Bay	2,994	3,380	4,033	4,122	4,981
New England	210,640	273,340	363,404	247,385	406,081
New York	137,984	194,030	353,311	288,046	417,957
Pennsylvania	82,404	211,666	268,426	206,199	371,830
Virginia and Maryland	200,088	325,151	426,687	417,599	437,628
Georgia	24	3,163	2,571	23,761	23,334
Nova Scotia	4,408	19,310	70,600	25,071	25,094
Florida					30,963
	£783,092	£1,217,812	£1,726,518	£1,440,740	£2,015,511

for this reason it is highly expedient that the profit accruing from agriculture in this province be well understood, that all those persons who are in doubt which part of America they should go to, may be induced to make choice of those colonies which produce staples for Britain; among which South Carolina figures greatly.

A calculation drawn from actual experience of the expences, produce, and profit of a considerable plantation in this province

	£.	s.	d.
Freight and expences of six persons in one family from London to Charles Town, at 25£.	150	0	0
Freight of 10 tons, at 40s.	20	0	0
A couple of riding horses	40	0	0
Expences in searching for plantation	40	0	0
Patent fees of 10,000 acres	62	10	0
Building a house	200	0	0
———— offices, rice barns, &c.	700	0	0
———— tobacco house	20	0	0
———— saw-mill	500	0	0
Furniture	150	0	0
A canoe	50	0	0
Boats	30	0	0

That the southern continental British colonies—Maryland, Virginia and the Carolinas—were exporting large quantities of commodities not grown in England, such as rice, tobacco, and indigo, is evident from the following:

Imports into England from

	1757	1761	1762
New England	£ 27,556	£ 25,985	£ 41,733
New York	19,168	21,684	58,882
Pennsylvania	14,190	22,404	38,091
Virginia and Maryland	418,881	357,228	415,709
Carolina	130,889	206,534	181,695

See G. L. Beer, *British Colonial Policy, 1754–1765* (New York, 1922), p. 150.

	£.	s.	d.
Year's housekeeping	120	0	0
Implements of culture	200	0	0
20 horses at 5£.	100	0	0
100 cows, at 30s.	150	0	0
Swine	20	0	0
Poultry	5	0	0
Wear and tear of implements	20	0	0

Sundry labour exclusive of negroes

				£.	s.	d.
On cattle	15	0	0			
100 acres of wheat at 20s. ..	100	0	0			
40 acres of oats at 16s.	32	0	0			
10 potatoes at 40s.	20	0	0			
Making hay	20	0	0			
Orchard and garden	15	0	0			
Sundries	30	0	0	232	0	0
40 negroes at 50£.				2,000	0	0

Expences on ditto

				£.	s.	d.
Overseer	1	0	0			
Clothes	1	0	0			
Sundry expences	0	10	0			
Province tax	0	3	0			
	2	13	0	86	0	0
				[*sic.*]		

Seed

				£.	s.	d.
100 acres of wheat, at 8s. ..	40	0	0			
40 oats 8s.	16	0	0			
10 potatoes 8s.	4	0	0	60	0	0
Taxes; a quit-rent of 2s. per 100 shares ..				10	0	0
				4,965	10	0
Two year's interest at 5 per cent				496	10	0
				5,462	10	0
Interest				273	10	0

Produce of second year

	£.	s.	d.
1,000 acres of wheat, 20 bushels an acre, at 3s.	300	0	0
40 negroes at 15£.	600	0	0
	900	0	0

Third year
Expences

	£.	s.	d.
Taxes as before	10	0	0
Repairs of buildings	50	0	0
Housekeeping	100	0	0
Implements	40	0	0
Labour	200	0	0
Incidents	50	0	0
Interest	273	1	0
Freight of products to shipping	80	0	0
Expences on 40 negroes at 2£. 13s.	86	0	0
	889	1	0

Produce of Third Year

	£.	s.	d.
Wheat	300	0	0
40 negroes at 25£.	1,000	0	0
A saw mill of 7 saws will cut 5,000 feet of boards per week, at 6s. per 100 feet, 15£. per week, which is per annum 780 0 0			
Deduct labour, repairs, freight and sundries 280 0 0			
Remains 500 0 0			
But say	0	0	0
£.	1,300	0	0

Fourth year
Expences

	£.	s.	d.
Taxes	10	0	0
Repairs of buildings	50	0	0

	£.	s.	d.
Housekeeping	100	0	0
Implements	40	0	0
Labour	200	0	0
Incidents	50	0	0
Interest	273	1	0
Freight	80	0	0
15 negroes at 50£.	750	0	0
Expences on 55 ditto at 2£. 13s.	145	15	0
£.	1,698	16	0

Produce

Wheat	300	0	0
40 negroes at 25£.	1,000	0	0
15 ditto at 20£.	300	0	0
	1,600	0	0

Fifth year
Expences

Taxes	10	0	0
Buildings	50	0	0
Housekeeping	100	0	0
Implements	40	0	0
Labour	200	0	0
Incidents	53	0	0
Interest	273	1	0
Freight	110	0	0
10 negroes	500	0	0
65 ditto at 2£. 13s.	172	5	0
£.	1,508	6	0

Produce

Wheat	300	0	0
55 negroes at 25£.	1,375	0	0
10 at 20£.	200	0	0
Saved last year	300	0	0
£.	2,175	0	0

Sixth year
Expences

	£.	s.	d.
Taxes	10	0	0
Buildings	50	0	0
Housekeeping	100	0	0
Implements	40	0	0
Labour	200	0	0
Incidents	53	0	0
Interest	273	1	0
Freight	140	0	0
25 negroes at 50£.	1,250	0	0
90 ditto at 2£. 13s.	238	10	0
£.	2,354	11	0

Produce

	£.	s.	d.
Wheat	300	0	0
Cattle (supposed by this time to bring in a regular profit)	100	0	0
65 negroes at 25£.	1,625	0	0
25 ditto at 20£.	500	0	0
£.	2,525	0	0

Seventh year
Expences

	£.	s.	d.
Taxes	10	0	0
Buildings	50	0	0
Housekeeping	100	0	0
Implements	40	0	0
Labour	200	0	0
Incidents	53	0	0
Interest	273	1	0
Freight	140	0	0
30 negroes at 50£.	1,500	0	0
120 ditto at 2£. 13s.	318	0	0
£.	2,684	1	0

Produce

	£.	s.	d.
Wheat	300	0	0
Cattle	100	0	0
90 negroes at 25£.	2,250	0	0
30 ditto at 20£.	600	0	0
£.	3,250	0	0

Eighth year
Expences

Taxes	10	0	0
Buildings	50	0	0
Housekeeping	100	0	0
Implements	40	0	0
Labour	200	0	0
Incidents	53	0	0
Interest	273	1	0
Freight	180	0	0
36 negroes at 50£.	1,800	0	0
156 ditto at 2£. 13s.	413	8	0
£.	3,119	9	0

Produce

Wheat	300	0	0
Cattle	100	0	0
120 negroes at 25£.	3,000	0	0
36 ditto at 20£.	720	0	0
£.	4,120	0	0

Ninth year
Expences

Taxes	10	0	0
Buildings	50	0	0
Housekeeping	100	0	0
Implements	40	0	0
Labour	200	0	0
Incidents	53	0	0
Interest	273	1	0

	£.	s.	d.
Freight	180	0	0
60 negroes at 50£.	3,000	0	0
216 ditto at 2£. 13s.	572	8	0
£.	4,478	9	0

Produce

	£.	s.	d.
Wheat	300	0	0
Cattle	100	0	0
156 negroes at 25£.	3,900	0	0
60 ditto at 20£.	1,200	0	0
£.	5,500	0	0

Tenth year
Expences

	£.	s.	d.
Taxes	10	0	0
Buildings	60	0	0
Housekeeping	150	0	0
Implements	80	0	0
Labour	200	0	0
Incidents	53	0	0
Interest	273	1	0
Freight	200	0	0
80 negroes at 50£.	4,000	0	0
296 ditto at 2£. 13s.	784	8	0
£.	5,810	9	0

Produce

	£.	s.	d.
Wheat	300	0	0
Cattle	100	0	0
216 negroes at 25£.	5,400	0	0
80 ditto at 20£.	1,600	0	0
£.	7,400	0	0

Eleventh year
Expences

	£.	s.	d.
Taxes	10	0	0
Buildings	60	0	0

	£.	s.	d.
Housekeeping	150	0	0
Implements	80	0	0
Labour	200	0	0
Incidents	53	0	0
Interest	273	1	0
Freight	200	0	0
110 negroes at 50£.	5,500	0	0
406 ditto at 20£.	1,075	18	0
£.	7,601	19	0

Produce

	£.	s.	d.
Wheat	300	0	0
Cattle	100	0	0
296 negroes at 25£.	7,400	0	0
110 ditto at 20£.	2,200	0	0
£.	10,000	0	0

Twelfth year
Expences

	£.	s.	d.
Taxes	10	0	0
Buildings	60	0	0
Housekeeping	150	0	0
Implements	80	0	0
Labour	200	0	0
Incidents	53	0	0
Interest	273	1	0
Freight	200	0	0
150 negroes at 50£.	7,500	0	0
556 ditto at 2£. 13s.	1,473	8	0
£.	9,999	9	0

Produce

	£.	s.	d.
Wheat	300	0	0
Cattle	100	0	0
406 negroes at 25£.	10,150	0	0
150 ditto at 20£.	3,000	0	0
£.	13,550	0	0

And now having arrived at the greatest number of negroes met with on any plantation in Carolina (above 500, which are found on two or three), it will be proper to close the account with the next year, by supposing no new ones bought.

Thirteenth year
Expences

	£.	s.	d.
Taxes	10	0	0
Buildings	70	0	0
Housekeeping	150	0	0
Implements	80	0	0
Labour	200	0	0
Incidents	53	0	0
Interests	273	1	0
Freight	200	0	0
556 negroes at 2£. 13s.	1,473	8	0
£.	2,509	9	0

Produce

	£.	s.	d.
Wheat	300	0	0
Cattle	100	0	0
556 negroes at 25£.	13,900	0	0
	13,900	0	0
Expences	2,509	9	0
Profit	11,390	11	0
Housekeeping	150	0	0
Interest	273	1	0
Total receipt £.	11,813	12	0

This profit is immense, and yet upon revision there do not seem any articles that are calculated too low. I am sensible that there are not any planters in South Carolina that lay up, or make an income of 12,000£. a year; but calculations of what may be done can take no cognizance of private conduct. There are some planters in this province who have more than 500 slaves; but very many causes may conspire to reduce their profit to a trifle, compared with what we see here: of 556 negroes only 40 were here supposed to be originally bought; all the rest were purchased annually by savings out of the preceding years products; but if instead of this the planter spends his income and borrows money to increase his stock of slaves, the profit at the end of the term will turn out very differently. The great profit here stated is entirely owing to an accumulation of profits for twelve years, the planter living upon 100£. or 150£. a year; but the event would prove very different if he takes at first a larger sum for his housekeeping; and if, instead of waiting the first twelve years patiently, in order afterwards to live more at his ease, and in almost any degree of affluence he pleases, if, instead of this, he frequents the taverns and concerts of Charles Town more than his plantation, any man may, without much sagacity, account for calculation turning out differently from real life. The only means of coming at useful truth in such cases as this, is to calculate what may be done—what such a business, under given circumstances, can produce: as to the caprices of individuals, they are beyond the power of calculation; but the profit here supposed will admit of great deductions in several articles which seem the lowest set in expence, and yet the remainder will turn out so considerable as to prove that planting in this country may be made the way to immense fortunes.

Now it must be apparent, at first sight, that no husbandry in Europe can equal this of Carolina; we have no agriculture in England—where larger fortunes are made by it than in any other country—that will pay any thing like this, owing to several circumstances which deserve attention. First, land is so plentiful in America, that the purchase of a very large estate costs but a trifle, and all the annual taxes paid afterwards for ten thousand acres, do not amount to what the window duty in England comes to on a moderate house;[2] no land-tax, no poor's rate, no tythe. This plenty of land, which is at the same time so excellent, enables the planter to proportion his culture every year to the saving of the preceding [year] which is the grand circumstance in the increase of his fortune; since it is this which converts simple interest at 5 per cent. with an English farmer, to compound interest at 100 per cent. with an American planter. Were the waste lands of Britain in the same situation as those of America, to be granted to whoever would settle and engage to cultivate them, this would be the case with them; but the profit from the inferiority of the land and the dearness of labour would not equal that above stated. As these wastes are private property and cannot be gained by other people, there is no comparison remains between them; and as to common agriculture, the profit of 20 or 30 per cent. without any ability of increasing the business annually, it cannot be named with this of America. Secondly, the price of labour is incomparably cheaper in Carolina than in Britain: a negro costs 2£. 13s. per annum, to which if we add 2£. 10s. the interest of his prime cost, the total is only 5£. 3s. and as the common calculation is, that one English labourer does as much work as two negroes, a labourer to the planter costs 10£. 6s. a year, whereas to an English farmer he costs from 20£. to 25£. The difference is 125 per cent.; this article therefore is very decisive in favour of

[2] The window duty here referred to was one of the numerous English taxes levied at the time to furnish revenue. It was first imposed in 1695 and abolished in 1851.

the planter. Thirdly, we are to remember the peculiar circumstance of the prices of the planter's products and consumptions: his crops, whether of indigo, tobacco, &c. are of a constant high value, the price rising, as it has done indeed for these fifty years; but his consumption of corn, meat, fruit, fowls, game, fish, &c. being chiefly the produce of his own plantation, stand him in little or nothing for his family. The common idea of the article game and fish is, that one Indian, or dextrous negroe, will, with his gun and netts, get as much game and fish as five families can eat; and the slaves support themselves in provisions, besides raising the staples mentioned above; but in Britain the servants kept in the house cost the farmers 12£. or 15£. a head in board, besides his own housekeeping being in the same articles as those he sells from his farm, so that he cannot in his sale have the advantage of high prices without being proportionably taxed in his consumption. This point in a large family is of great importance, and would, if calculated for a course of years, be found to amount to a very considerable sum. Besides this great superiority in respect of profit, the pleasing circumstance of being a considerable freeholder and living in a most plentiful, and even luxurious manner, is a point that has nothing among British farmers for opposition to it.

These three grand articles—plenty of good land free from taxes, cheapness of labour, and dearness of product sold, [together] with cheapness of that consumed—are, united, sufficient to explain the causes of a Carolina planter having such vastly superior opportunities of making a fortune than a British farmer can possibly enjoy.

Considered in a national light, no bad consequences can result from making known the great profit which may be made by planting in Carolina; for all the inhabitants of this province are well employed for Britain, and husbandry is too profitable an employment for them to suffer any one to think of manufactures; all their cloathing, furniture, tools, and a variety of other articles, come from Britain, besides the exportation and importation employing many ships and seamen for the mother country. Nor are we ever to forget the great importance of taking every measure to induce new settlers in our colonies, emigrants from Europe, to fix in those settlements, which from climate, soil, and staples, are of such importance to Britain, as the West Indies, Carolina, and the tobacco colonies are found to be.

If the state of Europe at present be considered—which is that of a military state, from one end to the other, insomuch that in some parts of this quarter of the world the military out-number the rest of the men—if this be considered, surely all mankind must think with peculiar pleasure of a country which holds forth an asylum to protect them from the cruelties of the military government and the horrible oppressions of the despotic sway in all other matters; these are such curses on human nature that it is astonishing any men of small fortunes, or to the amount of from one to five or six thousand pounds, should remain in such countries that deny them most of the comforts, enjoyments and security of life. On the contrary, these southern colonies of the British dominions in America hold forth the very contrast to the unhappiness they experience in Europe. They may have whatever land they please at a price next to nothing; that land is [as] rich, if chosen with judgment, as in any country in the world; in a climate that produces the richest commodities, and at the same time abounds with all the necessaries of life, in a plenty not to be equalled throughout any other countries on the globe; and at the same time that both soil and climate, and plenty of land, join to yield such advantageous offers; the government is the most mild in being;[3] liberty reigns in perfection; taxes are too inconsiderable to be mentioned; no military service; no oppressions to enslave the planter and rob him of the fruits of his industry. When all these great and manifest advantages are considered, I think it must appear surprising that more emigrants from different parts of Europe are not constantly moving from thence to America: nothing but that love for the native country, universal thro' mankind, could prevent whole crowds of people from flying from misery and oppression to wealth and freedom.

The calculation here inserted is that only of a considerable plantation; but it is a circumstance, peculiarly fortunate in the husbandry of those parts of America where negroes are used, that a small, and even the smallest, plantation is proportionably as profitable as the largest. There is no necessity of employing an overseer for the negroes; if the number is small, the planter himself takes that office on him. Men establish even such small plantations as employ only two or three negroes, and make by them a sum proportioned to what their more considerable neighbour enjoys from as many hundreds: indigo is of that nature in the culture that even a single negro may be employed on it, since the apparatus for it does not even, for three or four slaves, cost above ten or a dozen pounds. Husbandry in England on so small a scale is carried on with scarce any advantage; for no profit, public or private, accrues from the smallest scale of farms, since our best writers on the subject of husbandry agree that the occupiers of such farms live much harder and fare worse than our day-labour-

[3] South Carolina was at this time a royal province. See Edward McCrady, *The History of South Carolina under the Royal Government, 1719–1776* (New York, 1899).

ers.[4] But nothing can be more different than this from Carolina, where the little planter whose freehold amounts only to one or two hundred acres, with his two or three negroes makes not only a most comfortable living for himself, but also such an annual profit that if he is at all saving and diligent he may speedily increase his negroes and his plantation and in no long term of years become a man of handsome fortune.

And here let me once more observe that the calculations which have been given are particularly deduced from the circumstances of the back country and not from the culture of rice in the destructive and unwholesome swamps on the coast; so that this large degree of profit is to be gained in a country whose climate is equal to the soil, being healthy and pleasant to as great a degree as any country in a hot climate that is to be found in the world; and to the generality of constitutions, taking the world through, perhaps more wholesome than many parts of Europe. Was such a profit only to be made by cultivating rice swamps, I should be far enough from dwelling upon the advantages of it; but as they flow not from rice, but [from] indigo, tobacco, corn, hemp, flax, &c. which admit of culture better in the back country than on the coast, all the benefits I have dwelt on are reaped without any such attendant inconveniencies as are met with in the rice plantations; a circumstance of infinite importance to the mother country as well as to the colony.

[4] Encouraged by high profits, approved by the economists, and justified by necessity, English agriculture advanced rapidly along the lines of large capitalized farms during the second half of the eighteenth century. Arthur Young, for example, was an ardent advocate of large farms, large capital, long leases, and the most improved methods of cultivation and stock-breeding. The little farmer, he asserted, was not in a position financially to pursue modern practices. See Young, *A Six Months' Tour* (London, 1770), pp. 70–71; and The Right Honorable Lord Ernle, *English Farming, Past and Present* (5th ed., London, 1912), pp. 200–206, 214–15.

CHAPTER XXIII

SOUTH CAROLINA

Exports of South Carolina at different periods—Rapid progress of the trade of this province—Present state—Remarks

THE great increase of the population of the northern colonies is not near of such advantage to Great Britain as that of the southern ones, which in proportion to the increase of population has a corresponding increase in the production of true staple commodities, the circumstance on which the interest of Britain depends; those colonies which have not staples, we have found from long experience, can afford to purchase but a small part of their manufactures and other necessaries from the mother country; common agriculture will not effect it; accordingly we see, that in the northern settlements, that is, the settlements to the north of Maryland, they are forced to make up their deficiency of staples by fisheries and commerce, in both of which articles they interfere considerably with Britain; so that their import of manufactures is by no means of the value of that of the southern settlements, as they get the money to make their purchases by rivalling the fisheries and commerce of Britain. Hence therefore appears the constant expediency of watching anxiously the increase of population in the southern parts of America and [of] taking every measure to increase it. Nor can any conduct in the administration of our government be of such great importance as inducing the people settled in the northern colonies to quit them in favour of the southern ones. The truth and propriety of these sentiments will appear from the following tables of the exports of South Carolina.

Exports from Charles Town from Nov. 1747, to Nov. 1748

COMMODITIES

Corn and Grain	Quantity	Rates				Amount Sterling
Rice	55,000 bushels	0	6	5	per 100 lb. .	£. 88,600
Indian corn .	39,308 bushels	0	1	5	per bushel .	2,789
Barley	15 casks	0	14	3	per cask ...	10

Roots and fruit

Oranges ..	296,000 in number	0	17	1	per 1,000 .	251
Pease	6,107 bushels	0	1	5	bushel .	432
Potatoes ...	700 bushels	0	0	8	bushel .	23
Onions .... {	10 casks	0	14	3	cask ..	7
	200 ropes	0	0	4	rope ..	3

Cattle, Beef, &c.

Live stock						
Bullocks .	28	1	11	5	bullock .	44
Hogs	158	0	8	6	hog ...	63
Sundries ..						357
Beef	1,764 barrels	0	18	6	barrel .	1,631
Pork	3,114 barrels	1	8	6	barrel .	4,436
Bacon, about	2,200 lb.	0	0	4	lb.	36
Butter	130 casks	1	2	10	cask ...	148

Naval stores

Pitch	5,521 barrels	0	6	5	barrel .	1,771
Tar						
Common .	2,784 barrels	0	5	0	ditto	696
Green ...	291 ditto	0	7	1	ditto	103
Turpentine .	2,397 ditto	0	7	1	ditto	847
Resin	97 ditto	0	7	1	ditto	34

Naval stores	Quantity	Rates	Amount Sterling
Masts	9 in number	2 2 10 each	19
Bowsprits ...	8 "	0 17 1 each	7
Booms	6 "	1 8 6 each	8
Oars	50 pair	0 2 10 pair	5

Vegetable produce of other sorts

Indigo .....124,118 lb.	0 2 6 per lb.	16,764
Pot ashes .. 3 barrels	2 17 1 barrel .	8
Oil of turpen- } 9 jars	1 8 6 jar	13
tine } 7 barrels	2 2 10 barrel .	15
Cotton wool 7 bags	3 11 5 bag ...	25
Sassafras ... 22 tons	2 2 10 ton ...	67

Lumber

Boards ..... 61,148 feet	5 14 3 per 1,000 feet	349
Cedar boards 8,189 ditto	0 17 1 per 100 ...	70
Cedar plank 1,331 feet	0 1 5 a foot	92
———— posts . 52 ditto	0 1 5 ditto	3
Cypress boards 21,000 ditto	5 14 3 per 1,000 .	111
Ditto ...... 979 boards	0 1 9 each	84
Heading ... 13,975 ditto	5 14 3 per 1,000 .	79
Ditto ......127,652 feet	4 5 8 ditto	546
Ditto pine ..148,143 ditto	5 14 3 per 1,000 .	840
Ditto ...... 1,293 boards	0 0 10 each	53
Ditto plank . 22 in number	0 2 1 ditto	2
Baywood plank .... 98 ditto	0 8 6 ditto	41
Scantling ... 2,000 feet	0 10 0 per 1,000 .	10
Shingles ....635,170 in number	0 11 5 ditto	364

Naval stores	Quantity	Rates	Amount Sterling
Staves	132,567 ditto	4 5 8 ditto	567
Timber	4,000 feet	0 14 3 per 100 ...	28
Ditto	9 pieces	0 5 8 each	2
Walnut	739 feet	1 14 3 per 100 ...	13
Ditto	66 pieces	0 2 10 each	10
Hogsheads ..	80 in number	0 8 6 each	34
Tierces	43 ditto	0 7 1 ditto	16
Hoops	3,000 ditto	1 14 3 per 1,000 .	5
Canes	800 in number	0 5 8 per 100 ...	2
Pumps	1 set		3

Animal produce of other sorts

Skins			
Beaver ...	200 lb.	0 4 3 per lb.	42
Calf	141 in number	0 5 8 each	40
Deer	720 hhds.	50 0 0 ditto	36,000
Tallow	81 barrels	1 8 6 per barrel .	115
Hogs lard ..{	25 jars	0 17 1 jar	20
	26 casks	2 0 0 cask	52
Raw silk ...	8 boxes	28 11 5 box	229
Wax			
Bees	1,000 lb.	0 0 8 lb.	33
Myrtle ..	700 lb.	0 0 8 lb.	22

Manufactures

Leather			
tanned ...	10,356 lb.	0 5 0 lb.	2,589
Soap	7 boxes	1 8 6 box	10
Candles	34 ditto	2 2 10 each	73
Bricks	7,000 in number	0 14 3 per 1,000 .	5

£. 161,361

Sundry articles exported from Charles Town in 1754

	Quantities		Rates				Amount Sterling
Rice	104,682 barrels	1	15	0	per barrel	.	183,193
Indigo	216,924 lb.	0	2	6	lb.	....	27,115
Deer-skins	460 hhds.	50	0	0	each	.....	23,000
Pitch	5,869 barrels	0	6	5	per barrel	.	1,881
Tar	2,945 ditto	0	5	0	ditto	.....	736
Turpentine	759 ditto	0	7	1	ditto	.....	266
Beef	416 ditto	0	18	6	ditto	.....	384
Pork	1,560 ditto	1	8	6	ditto	.....	2,223
Indian corn	16,428 bushels	0	2	0	per bushel	.	1,642
Pease	9,162 ditto	0	1	5	ditto	.....	648
Shingles	1,114,000 in number	0	11	5	per 1,000	.	631
Staves	260,000 ditto	4	5	8	ditto	.....	880
Total of these articles	....					£.	242,529

These articles not containing the whole export, the total does not shew the full increase; but rice and indigo being the two grand staples of the province, their increase shews how quick the cultivation of South Carolina had advanced in those years.

Exported in ten months, 1761, from Charles Town

Rice	100,000 barrels	1	15	0	per barrel	.£.	175,000
Pitch	6,376 ditto	0	6	5	ditto	....	2,043
Tar	931 ditto	0	5	0	ditto	....	232
Turpentine	4,808 ditto	0	7	1	ditto	....	1,702
Oranges	161,000 in number	0	17	1	per 1,000	.	137
Ditto	141 barrels						
Pork and beef	1,149 ditto	1	13	0	per barrel	.	1,894
Bacon	13 barrels						
Indigo	399,366 lb.	0	2	6	per lb.	...	49,920

	Quantities	Rates				Amount Sterling
Deer-skins ..	422 hhds.	50	0	0 each		21,100
331 bundles						
300 loose						
Tanned leather ..	5,869 sides					
Pease and corn	11,126 bushels	0	1	5 per bushel .		784
Bees wax ...	6,721 lb.	0	0	8 lb. ...		224
Staves .....236,850 in number		4	5	8	1,000 .	1,014
Boards, &c. .466,186 feet		5	14	0	1,000 .	2,657
Hoops ..... 29,600 in number		1	14	3	1,000 .	50

Besides many other articles . . . . £. 256,767

This incomplete table shews another considerable increase of export, and the following will continue the progression.

Exported from South Carolina upon an average of three years succeeding the peace of 1762

	£.	s.	d.
Rice, 110,002 barrels at 40s.	220,000	0	0
Pitch, tar, and turpentine, 8,000 barrels, at 6s. 8d.	2,666	13	4
Pickled pork and beef	25,000	0	0
Deer and other skins	45,000	0	0
Indigo 500,000 lb. at 2s.	50,000	0	0
Boards, masts, staves, joists, &c.	20,000	0	0
Indian corn, pease, beans, and calavanches[1]	12,000	0	0
Live stock and sundries	15,000	0	0
Ships built for sale, 10 at 600£.	6,000	0	0
Total £.	395,666	13	4

[1] Calavanches is a name, now little used, for certain varieties of legumes.

And since this account I have been favoured with another for the year 1771, which is as follows:

	£.	s.	d.
140,000 barrels of rice, at 3£. 10s.	490,000	0	0
Pitch, tar, and turpentine, 10,000 barrels at 10s.	5,000	0	0
Pork and beef	30,000	0	0
Corn and other provisions	13,500	0	0
Deer-skins, &c.	50,000	0	0
Lumber	32,000	0	0
Live stock	17,000	0	0
Ten ships	6,000	0	0
Indigo, 750,000 lb. at 3s.	112,500	0	0
Total £.	756,000	0	0

This account shews in how extraordinary a manner the improvement of South Carolina has been carried on; and it has been a peculiar felicity to this province that the prices of its staples have risen considerably at the same time that the quantity raised has increased immensely. This circumstance, which is of such uncommon value, has advanced the interests of the country prodigiously, and now renders it one of the most flourishing colonies we possess in America; at the same time that the quantity of land which yet remains to be cultivated, is beyond comparison greater than what is yet improved. It is also to be remembered that the parts unsettled —being more rich, fertile, and healthy than the coast which yields the commodities hitherto exported—is in particular far more luxuriant in the production of indigo: now it is to be observed, that the grand staple of this province, rice, has not so good a probability of future increase as indigo; the latter is so valuable a drug, and produced in so few countries, that Carolina may look forwards to almost any quantity, even till the whole consumption of Europe, America, and parts of Africa and Asia are satisfied, before a stop will be put to her market for this commodity; for there is little doubt of her being able to undersell both French and Spaniards. But with rice, the case may be different; for being an article of food, it is rivalled by other articles: good harvests of wheat in Europe and Africa would sink the price; for it has risen from 15s. and 20s. a barrel to 3£. 10s. and 4£. from the high price of wheat in Europe; if grain should fall much, the price of rice must fall with it: indeed it is at present so dear that the rate may fall greatly and yet leave the planter sufficient inducement to increase the culture of it.

The exports of this province will not be many years in rising to a million sterling; it will gain this point of equality with Virginia and Maryland put together, before it has a fifth of the inhabitants found in those provinces, which shews how valuable the climate is to produce so largely in exportable staples. I do not compare the staples, for certainly tobacco is far more valuable to Britain than rice, and perhaps than indigo; but tobacco is produced in the back part of South Carolina, and of a quality superior to that of Virginia; the quantity however is but small yet: a navigation for large canoes that will carry from five to ten ton is wanting, when you get far back, which navigation in the culture of tobacco is very necessary.

CHAPTER XXIV

SOUTH CAROLINA

Improvements proposed in the culture of this province

HOWEVER wealthy the production of staples may make a country, it is common husbandry alone on which first depends the interest of any people; and it ever beho[o]ves them much to carry this to as high a degree as possible. All our American colonists are very bad farmers; this is a remark I have had occasion to make when treating of every one of them: it is almost uniformly owing to the great plenty of land, which enables everybody to gain the necessaries of live [life] with so much ease that an accurate and industrious cultivation appears useless.[1]

The productions of common husbandry in Carolina, by which I mean corn and provisions of all sorts, have risen of late years to so high a price, that I have been assured by

---

[1] The dictum uttered by John Locke that "an infallible sign of your decay of wealth is the falling of rents, and the raising of them would be worth the nation's care," was a widely accepted economic doctrine at this time. Moreover, it was thought to be an absolutely necessary spur to agricultural progress. So long as land remained cheap, farmers, it was maintained, would be content with antiquated practices. In other words, the dearer or more costly the land, the more energetic and enterprising the farmer necessarily became. Arthur Young went so far as to say that the spendthrift who frequented London club-houses and raised rents to pay his debt of honour, was a greater benefactor to agriculture than the stay-at-home squire who lived frugally in order to keep within his ancestral income. See The Right Honorable Lord Ernle, *English Farming Past and Present*, (5th ed., London, 1912) pp. 213–14.

several considerable planters and merchants in this province
that the farmers who have employed their negroes on these
objects alone have in several years made a larger profit than
has been gained from rice and indigo; and that, on an average,
there has been an equality. This is a circumstance of prodigious consequence, since the common husbandry is exercised
in the healthy and agreeable back country, while rice only is
to be had in the swamps in the flat, maritime, and unhealthy
part.

The articles cultivated are wheat (which grain will not
thrive in the flat country) Indian corn, Indian pease, barley,
buckwheat, [po]tatoes, and other roots, fruit, &c. The hilly
part of the province is wonderfully fertile in these products,
yielding, in very bad modes of culture, crops equal to what
good husbandry will produce on many tracts of land in
Britain. But this excellence of soil and climate is very badly
seconded by the skill of the farmer. Indian corn is the principal grain they raise, which is managed in the manner I have
described before; they are very defective in the article of
keeping the plantations of it clean from weeds: the culture
the intervals receive is only that of an insufficient hand-hoeing
or two; but, instead of this, the horse-hoeing husbandry
should be applied: the spaces between the rows should both
ways be horse-hoed, for the double purpose of keeping them
free from weeds, and in a loose pulverized state; and likewise for earthing up the plants, which might be performed
with a plough much more effectually than with hand-hoes,
and for a tenth of the expence: the latter never cut deep
enough, only skimming the surface, whereas horse-hoeings
and hoe-ploughs loosen it to any depth, giving the roots of
the plants the power of penetrating into fresh earth, instead
of confining them to their hillocks. This single improvement

in the management of Indian corn would vastly increase the profit of that culture.

It is the custom in all the southern colonies to sow Indian pease with Indian corn, for the sake of their twining up the stalks of the latter; this renders the culture the more beneficial, as the product of pease is as valuable, and sometimes more so, than that of the corn itself. I would by no means condemn a custom which has an appearance of reason for it; but as such practices in most other branches of husbandry are found very disadvantageous, it is at least worth some accurate experiments to decide whether as much is not lost in the Indian corn as is gained in the pease by this method, which may possibly be the case; the produce of such large and vigorous plants as maize usually is proportioned to the nourishment the roots meet with, and certainly the pease cannot grow out of the same hillock, without robbing them of much nourishment. A good hop planter would think it very bad management to set a cabbage or a pea in a hop-hillock; bad ones plant the intervals, but good hop farmers decline even this practice; not because crops so gained would not be valuable, but because more would be lost in hops than gained in the other plants.

As to the preparation of the land for maize, wheat, barley, &c. it is nearly similar; they take a piece of fresh land, and plant it perhaps with indigo, which it yields as long as any heart remains sufficient in the soil for that exhausting crop; then they plant it with wheat or Indian corn, and afterwards with barley; and when it will yield nothing any longer, they leave it to itself, and treat other pieces in succession in the same manner. This is the system of all the provinces from New England to Florida; and it is a system from which they will all by and by feel the most monstrous inconvenience.

When indigo is not planted, the first crop is Indian corn, which they follow by a second and perhaps a third of the same grain; then wheat or barley as long as the land will allow.

To this miserable husbandry it is owing that the province wants pasture, which is only to be found in the woods or in drained rice swamps; though the planters all know the importance of cattle to them, they never think of sowing any grasses, but exhaust and ruin the land by corn, &c. and leave it, not a pasture, but a desart: the heat of the climate is so great that there is a want of good meadow in summer, and this makes the woods the natural pasture of the country in its unimproved state. But this evil might be remedied by sowing grasses, provided the land was laid to them while it was in some heart. The grass, when properly conducted, would be as profitable as the corn, and it might be gained without any decrease in the quantity of corn, in a country where land is so plentiful: this observation is particularly applicable to Carolina, where the land is cleared with so much ease; a given quantity of acres in this province is cleared of all the timber with infinitely more ease than one tenth of the land would be in Europe, with the advantage also of the timber paying the expence; and if oak or pine, more than the expence.

Suppose a planter has negroes sufficient to have every year 500 acres of corn, 250 acres Indian corn, 150 wheat, 100 barley, buckwheat, &c. If his system of crops is

1. Indian corn.
2. Ditto.
3. Ditto.
4. Wheat.
5. Wheat.
6. Barley.
7. Barley.

he then is able to support the system, by taking in a seventh of the 500 acres for fresh land every year, that is, 71 acres; and he has always 500 acres in culture, with no other profit from the rest of his estate than what the woods yield him; he leaves 71 acres barren and useless every year, which will soon run through a large grant; for some years the land is absolutely nought, then shrubs come, and by degrees forest wood rises, and it is an age before it can yield any profit. Now on the contrary, let us suppose his system

1. Indian corn.
2. Ditto.
3. Potatoes, pease, beans, legumes, &c.
4. Wheat.
5. Barley, and with it clovers, sainfoine,[2] or lucerne.

In this system he must take in 100 acres every year, and he every year lays down 100 acres to grass. The second year of pursuing such a plan he has 200 acres grass; the third year 300; the fourth year 400; and so on. By which means his whole estate will be in a profitable condition, and he will every year have a greater plenty of food for his cattle; the consequence of which will be his stocks of cattle will be larger, and better fed; he will raise much greater quantities of manure, and two acres of his corn must inevitably produce more grain than three in the other system.

Relative to the grass, which should upon these principles be cultivated, the heat of the climate will make it necessary to have recourse to such plants as have a long tap root, because by rooting deep they will be more out of the power of the sun: sainfoine and lucerne I should suppose would be found of singular utility, especially the latter; both these plants have been brought into the colder parts of Europe from very

[2] A perennial legume belonging to the lucerne or alfalfa family.

hot countries. Lucerne is indigenous in Media and Asia
Minor, and sainfoine in Calabria and Barbary; there can be
no doubt therefore of their succeeding admirably on the dry
tracts of land in the back parts of Carolina, and also in all
the sandy hilly parts of the province. The culture would be
attended with none of those inconveniencies which have been
found in England, from the moisture of the climate choaking
the plantations with natural grass and weeds: the heat of climate would entirely prevent these evils upon land well prepared; nor can any doubt be made but the crops would be
very considerable upon the fertile black loams of the interior
country, and yield such plenty of food, both green and in
hay, as to enable the planters to increase their stock of cattle
prodigiously.

It is much to be doubted whether the clovers would succeed
in the maritime parts of the province; but no hesitation can
be made about it in the interior country; and in this I ground
my opinion upon the case of wheat, which thrives admirably
two hundred or two hundred and fifty miles from the coast,
but will come to nothing in the flat country: there can be no
doubt but it would be the same with clover, which has been
found profitable in all countries where wheat is cultivated.
It should be made the general preparation for wheat in every
system, as it is equally (in this respect) adapted to all climates
in which it will grow, and to almost every sort of land. In
such climates as South Carolina there is likewise a circumstance in it, as a preparation for wheat, that much exceeds any
other; a fallow or a tillage crop leaves the soil in so loose
and hollow a state, that the roots of wheat, or any other
fibrous-rooted plant, are too much exposed to the sun's rays;
whereas, if it is sown in a clover lay, the particles of the soil

are kept in a state of adhesion by the roots and fibres of the clover, which is an effect that in such a climate must be attended with excellent consequences. With a view to this, the clover husbandry, common in Britain, of leaving it only one year upon the land, might not be so adviseable in Carolina; it might be better to let the clover be two, or perhaps three years old before it is ploughed for wheat, in order the more completely to bind the soil together, especially in sandy land. The crops of this grass would, like sainfoine or lucerne, prove of great use to the planter, either in green food, or mown for hay, and maintain him twenty times the stock that the same land would do if under wood.

In the system above proposed as an improvement of that of the Carolina farmers, there are several corn crops in succession, under the supposition that they [the farmers] would not at once come into an entire change, but the true principles of good husbandry are the same in Carolina as every where else; successive *exhausting* crops ought never to be found: between every two of that nature, one should intervene which is of a meliorating nature, or at least which does not exhaust. It has been found in all the countries where the clovers have been cultivated, that the land improves under them. The same observation has been made upon potatoes, carrots, and other roots. Turneps and cabbages, yielding crops before they perfect their seed, have the same quality. The grand principle of modern husbandry is to use these plants as follows, or [as] preparations for exhausting crops: and the principle is equally good, whether the exhausting crop be sugar, wheat, indigo, or barley. The only distinction to be made is for the planter to chuse such of them as will pay best in his country: fortunately, all of them are food for cattle—and there is no part of the world in which cattle are not valuable, or in the cultivated parts of it, where good husbandry does not greatly depend on cattle. In South Carolina nothing pays better, and the near neighbourhood of the West Indies affords an excellent market for as much meat and live stock as can possible be raised: but the importance of having plenty of cultivated food for cattle increases every day in this province; in proportion as the country is cultivated, the forest which was spread over the whole of it decreases and consequently will maintain the less; this is so much felt in some districts, that many planters, who formerly kept immense herds of cattle, can now have but very moderate ones: it therefore much beho[o]ves them to cultivate grass and winter food for cattle, as well as corn. Potatoes in this province yield as good a price, both for home consumption and the West Indies, as in many parts of Britain; for of late years they have sold at 1s. and 1s. 3d. a bushel, consequently no crop can be more profitable.

Upon these principles, might not such a system as the following be rationally recommended to the farmers of South Carolina?

1. Indian corn.
2. Potatoes.
3. Indian corn.
4. Pease or beans.
5. Barley.
6. Clover.
7. Wheat.

In this system no two exhausting crops come together; pease or beans, and in general the plants which bear a leguminous flower, being of a different nature from corn in this respect. Or to suit particular purposes, variations might be made.

1. Indian corn.
2. Potatoes.
3. Barley.
4. Clover.
5. Wheat.
6. Turneps or cabbages.
7. Indian corn.
8. Pease or beans.
9. Wheat.
10. Potatoes.
11. Barley.
12. Clover.
13. Wheat.
14. Cabbages, &c.
15. Wheat.
16. Lucerne, or other grasses, to remain.

In such a system of crops, the land would always be rich and clean; the planter would be able to keep vast stocks of cattle; in fifteen years he would sell nine crops of corn and two of potatoes, and at the end of it he would have a much more fertile pasture than he found at the beginning.

Partial trials of new recommended practices may turn out very unsuccessful without proving anything against them. Suppose a Carolina farmer, struck with the idea of clover, sainfoine, or lucerne, was to throw it in among the second or third crop of wheat or barley, which followed two or three of maize; in such a mode of conduct, chance, perhaps, might give him a poor crop instead of none at all, which he would have reason to expect; he might neglect those grasses in future from such an experiment, but surely with very little reason; for such a conduct would be like expecting a great crop of rice on a mountain-top, or fields of pine apples in the snows of Lapland. For this reason, such recommended practices had better not be tried at all, than to be partially or incompletely tried; since conclusions, however absurd, are sure to be drawn from all experiments, and people will not be so ready to discriminate and enquire into the causes of a failure as to look at the single point, *such a thing was tried*, AND IT FAILED. A comprehensive way of judging and talking, which saves the trouble of understanding reflection.

Besides rectifying the very erroneous systems pursued in this province, it will be necessary to remark that the farmers are not attentive even to making the most of the spontaneous growths, of which the natural meadows, are a proof; in many plantations they have savannah land,[3] which in the back parts of the province is very good meadow; but the planters let their cattle run over the whole in summer, without ever thinking of mowing hay, notwithstanding the crops would often be considerable and notwithstanding their cattle are sometimes half starved for want of it: it is not sufficient to say that a climate admits the cattle to be unhoused all winter; their being in the woods or pastures is of little consequence if they can get nothing to eat: the best planters find the necessity of baiting [feeding] their herds well every night when they come home from the woods in winter; for though the climate is at times amazingly hot, yet, as I have elsewhere shewn, the frosts in winter are severer than those of England.

This part of their ill conduct is owing in a good measure to another branch of it, which is their neglect of fences: it would not be true to say that they had none, but the fact is, that they are not confined too much to the care of their rice, indigo, or other valuable crop, and are apt to attend to a field no longer than while it is so occupied: none of them would think (unless it were a few sensible, and at the same time wealthy men) that a meadow or pasture was worth fencing: this is through that neglect which arises from their great plenty of land.

It would be in vain to adopt an advantageous system of crops, if at the same time the planter was not attentive to have all his fences equally good; since in good husbandry, that field which is at present under a crop of small value will in a

---

[3] An open, level region; usually a meadow.

few years be occupied by one of the greatest; the necessity therefore of this attention must be striking. In the management too common, one part of an estate is under corn and all the rest is forest; but in the proposed improvement, every part once cultivated is always to be of value; cattle will be grazing in clover or lucerne in the midst of fields of Indian corn or wheat, and consequently all the fences under an equal necessity of being good.

In the culture of roots, &c. for the winter food of cattle, they are very deficient. Where there is a very great ability of keeping any stocks in summer, but a confined opportunity in winter, it is much to be questioned whether those crops which may be used as winter food will not pay better in such an application than when sold; and this particularly with potatoes: there are many advantages in using such crops upon the plantation; freight and carriage are saved, which are articles of importance; but the great point is the ability which the planter reaps from it of keeping so many more cattle and raising so much the more dung, which they all agree is of the first consequence in making the most profit of their plantations: the effect we see in every part of Britain is similar to this; for the good farmers make it a rule never to sell those articles of their produce which are food for cattle, unless they bear a very great price, being sensible that it answers better to consume them at home.

In the culture of indigo, the Carolina planters are not so attentive as they might be: they err in their ideas of the soil which they chuse for it; because it will grow in a poor white pine barren, it has been very absurdly thought that this is the proper soil for it: indigo requires, if great crops would be gained, a rich, black, deep mould, such as is no where to be found near the sea, or at least only in small narrow slips adjoining the swamps, and even in them not comparable in fertility to large tracts in the interior country. Those planters who would wish to cultivate this drug to great profit should fix in the back parts of the province, where the land is not only plentiful, but excellent; here they would raise treble the products they are able to do upon the coast, and the dye of a finer colour. In the culture of the plant, they are also too inattentive; the hand-hoeings given by the negroes are very insufficient and not comparable to the use of several horse-hoes, which for other purposes are used in England. Hand-hoes in all operations between the rows of any crop should give place to horse-work, which is deeper, more regular, and in every respect more effective; at the same time that the expence of it does not near approach to that of hand-work.

There is another improvement which deserves mention here; it is the culture of that species of rice which succeeds on dry ground, and even on hills and mountains. This sort is known in several parts of the East Indies, and would, in the back country of South Carolina, be of use as a new dependance for the planters there fixed; and it would be much more advantageous to have this grain from a healthy country, than from the unwholesome swamps in the maritime part. It would be no difficult task to get some seed of it from India, and would at least be worth the trial.

The culture of vines has been attempted in the back part of South Carolina, and with success; but the husbandry has not been prosecuted with that vigor and attention which so important an object well deserves. The moment any individuals shewed a desire of undertaking this branch—as soon as there was the least reason for thinking the plan feasible—their wishes ought to have been prevented [promoted]—their wants supplied—and every difficulty that arose, smoothed with the minutest attention. But instead of such a conduct being pursued, specimens of excellent wine have been sent home, and tasted by Lords of Trade, with application for encouragement in the undertakings made, and all without success. Were our governors bribed by the owners of the vineyards of Champagne and Burgundy, a more impolitic conduct could not have been pursued: had a due attention been paid to those ingenious and industrious foreigners who have settled in these southern colonies and entered upon the vineyard culture, by this time American wine would have been common in the London vaults; and the importance of this nation's buying her wines by the sale of her manufactures is too obvious to need expatiating on. Such an undertaking as that, of planting vineyards in these provinces, should be taken in hand by government, at least in giving every assistance that could reasonably be required by those undertakers, who seemed to be well acquainted with what they were about; but unfortunately, a very different conduct has been pursued. Knowledge in this branch of agriculture was some years ago much wanting, but that is no longer the case; there are many settlers that have arrived within a few years in South Carolina, perfectly acquainted with the business, but whose mean circumstances have proved the only obstacles they have met with: it is such men to whom public assistance should be given, for the public is more interested in their success than even themselves.

This is an object which ought not to be left to itself; the import of wine into this kingdom carries out of it an immense ballance in cash, which throws a dead weight into very considerable branches of our commerce. North America consumes large quantities of Madeira, which consumption will in part be varied to that of their own wines before they can be expected to be brought in any quantities into this kingdom: hence the necessity of acting with some vigour, if we expect to see any beneficial consequences of many years.

Silk is another object which should be attended to with great seriousness; the back parts of this province are full of mulberry trees, and the climate is of that due temperature which is requisite for success in this culture: as fine silk has been brought from Carolina as ever came from China, insomuch that at some of our mills it is preferred to any we receive either from the East Indies or Italy. The common objection of a want of people, I have before shewn, is weakly founded in any case, since a few people, nay a single family, may make as large a proportion of it as if the whole country was employed about nothing else: it is so much a head that may be made in a season, perhaps a pound and a half, or two pounds; so that if a family consists of twenty persons, they may make thirty or forty pounds annually; if it consists of two hundred persons, the proportion will be the same; but if it is only two or three, it is equally so: the population of the country therefore has perhaps less to do with it than in any other article of culture. The object wanting is to induce the people to undertake it—to give them instructions how to feed the worms, and to manage the cocoons; but this is easily learned, and might become general through the province if proper measures were taken for it; which might be executed at an inconsiderable expence. It would be a very fine thing for this nation if all the inhabitants of our colonies, possessing a proper climate, were to make, each, only a pound of raw silk; it would be as valuable an acquisition as this nation could make: to acquire a Martinico [Martinique] or a Guadalupe [Guadeloupe] would probably cost thirty or forty millions sterling; but such a matter of mere internal management would be far more valuable, and might be had for one quarter of as many thousands. In every instance that can be named, domestic improvement is of more consequence, and easier of attainment, than military acquisition; yet is mankind ever panting after one, and neglecting the other.

No trials have yet been made of madder in Carolina, though there are tracts of a rich, deep, black, and reddish loams in the back parts of the province which would undoubtedly produce great crops of it, and the climate would probably suit it better than that of England; for it is not the madder of Zealand that is the most extraordinary; that of Turkey, Asia Minor, and Cyprus is of a vastly greater size and better quality without any culture at all; no doubt can therefore be entertained of the climate suiting it. There is no crop upon which they can go that would pay them better; madder is worth from 80£. to 90£. a ton; in England the deduction of 6£. or 6£. 10s. for freight would be but a small proportion. An acre of good land, well chosen and properly cultivated, would, in the climate of the back part of South Carolina, yield from a ton to a ton and a half; and one negroe would manage above an acre very well, and have the winter months to be employed on fences and lumber besides: there are no crops in America that would answer much better than this, since it would be above 40£. per slave per annum. The value of the commodity would also make it peculiarly adapted to those tracts of country that had not a good water-carriage for bulky commodities; a small canoe, which would run up any little branches of the rivers, would carry a ton of it, which would be more valuable than a ton of many other commodities: for the same reason indigo and silk should be particularly encouraged in those districts where water-carriage is indifferent or at some distance.

Hemp in this respect is not of the same importance, but for their lower grounds on a strong clay foundation in these back parts, where the low grounds are far more fertile than in the maritime part of the province, hemp would be a very valuable article of culture, if near a good navigation. Such tracts are numerous, and would, if well cultivated under hemp, save us no slight proportion of those immense sums which we annually pay to the Baltic for this commodity.[4] Improvements in our colonies in this article ought every where to be most assiduously promoted; not in one settlement, by making it an only staple in the nature of the rice, indigo, or tobacco (it will not admit of this, because it is nice in [requires special] soil), but all the spots suitable to it in all our colonies, from Nova Scotia to Florida, should be thus appropriated; no planter, unless he was particularly situated, need have hemp for his principal dependance; but all should have some of it that had but a small field of right soil: America would then much more than supply all our demand and her own too; and as the colonies increased in cultivation, Europe would be a constant market for all they could pro-

---

[4] England's chief source of hemp in the mid-eighteenth century was Russia. In an effort to free England from this dependence, Parliament early in the eighteenth century offered large bounties to encourage the production of hemp in the colonies. This policy failed completely. In 1763, however, a number of London merchants who had trade relations with North America petitioned for a revival of these bounties. In reporting on this suggestion on February 9, 1864, the Board of Trade attributed the former failure of this policy to lack of population in the most desirable hemp-growing areas, and to the greater profits to be derived from the production of other commodities. The whole report stressed the cost of labor and transportation. Nevertheless, the Board recommended a renewal of the policy by suggesting that colonial hemp receive a bounty of £.8 a ton for the first seven years, £.6 for the second seven years, and £.4 for a third period of the same length. In 1764 Parliament adopted this recommendation, but these bounties did not accomplish the desired result. See G. L. Beer, *British Colonial Policy, 1754-1765* (New York, 1922), pp. 215-18.

duce. It is a fortunate circumstance that hemp grows best in
a soil that is not suitable to any of the other staples of America, so that it could not rival them: it delights in a moist, low,
rich loam, on a clay bottom, and never thrives to good advantage in a dry or light soil, however rich, but will not do
in a swamp, unless very rich and perfectly drained. Indigo
and tobacco require the black dry loam, regardless of the
stratum under it, provided it be not wet; and rice can only
be had in a swamp under water: it is upon this account that
hemp would not rival their present staples, in the soil it
requires, which is a matter of consequence; for in many
plantations the land suitable to these productions is not so
plentiful as to make it a matter of indifference how the planter
disposes of it, especially in the maritime part of the province.

Those who think the success met with in South Carolina in
the culture of indigo and rice a reason sufficient for excluding
or neglecting other articles of produce are much mistaken in
that idea. It is in all countries of vast importance that the
profit of agriculture should not depend on one or two productions; since in that case a failure in one is of fatal consequence,
or a falling off in the sale of it may prove the ruin of a
country. But when the husbandry of a people is employed
about many objects, they have the beneficial chance that if
one fails others will succeed and thereby prevent any great
evils following; it is also of consequence that the labour attending the products of a plantation be so divided that as
many hands be employed at one season as at another; for if
the slaves are only employed in summer, or only in spring
and autumn, the planter cannot make such profit by his business as if they were employed regularly the year through.
The planters of Carolina and our other colonies have not yet
felt the necessity of this doctrine, from the circumstance of

sawing lumber for the West Indies finding them employment at all leisure times; but this branch of their business is confined to the amount of the West India market; besides there are numerous tracts of country in which the timber has been long ago destroyed, but which are full of plantations, and it is very plain that in them lumber can be no dependance.

Winter sowing of several crops, threshing, clearing, carrying, and selling others, building fences, manuring, and other works, should keep all the slaves of a plantation in regular employment through the winter season, without a dependance for it on lumber. Spring sowings, and the vernal attendance on crops, with making silk, would fill up that season. The summer culture and cleaning which most plants require, with the harvest, are always sufficient to fill up several months; then should succeed the vintage, and making crops of madder, hemp, &c. In such a disposition of the lands and business of a plantation, the planter would find much greater profit than what he now makes by the assistance of two or three months of the slaves at lumber. And this is reason sufficient were others wanting—which however is far enough from being the case—for inducing the Carolina planters to divide their attention more in imitation of the best husbandmen in Europe.

AMERICAN HUSBANDRY

CONTAINING AN ACCOUNT OF THE
SOIL, CLIMATE,
PRODUCTION AND AGRICULTURE
OF THE
BRITISH COLONIES
IN
NORTH AMERICA AND THE WEST INDIES

WITH

Observations on the Advantages and Disadvantages
of settling in them, compared with

GREAT BRITAIN AND IRELAND

BY AN AMERICAN

IN TWO VOLUMES
VOL. II

LONDON
Printed for J. BEW, in Pater-noster-Row
MDCCLXXV

CHAPTER XXV

GEORGIA

Climate—Situation—Soil—Productions—Agriculture—
Exports—Observations

GEORGIA is in many respects the same country as Carolina, differing very little in climate, but generally in
favour of [favored by] it. Upon the coast it is not above sixty
or seventy miles from north to south; but in the internal
country the distance is upwards of one hundred and fifty
miles. The climate upon the coast is hot, damp, and unwholesome, like Carolina, though there are hilly spots which form
strong exceptions. The flat country extends in general about
two hundred miles from the sea, and the interior tract, which
reaches from thence to the Ap[p]alachian mountains and is
about one hundred miles broad, ranks in every respect among
the very finest in all America. The climate at the same time
that it is hot enough to produce the most valuable staples is
healthy and agreeable to an extraordinary degree; free from
those sudden changes and violent extremes that are felt in
the maritime part of the province and which are so pernicious
to health wherever found. In this country the soil is of a
fertility that even exceeds the back parts of South Carolina,
especially on the river Savannah and its branches to the west
and north-west of Augusta, and indeed all round that town:
no flat lands are found, no swamps, no marshes, but high, dry
tracts, waving in gentle hills, and the vales watered with

numerous streams. The soil [is] a deep black loam, so rich that there is scarcely any exhausting its fertility: it was for a long time unknown that such a country existed here; but upon first settling Georgia, and for many years afterwards, the flat sandy coast was the only part of the province attended to or known; and as long as this has been the case with any of our colonies to the south of New York, they have languished, and emerged from their languor as soon as they penetrated into the rich and healthy part of the country. Georgia was a very inconsiderable province as long as the people confined themselves to the coast; but the efforts since made here have been by means of removing backwards, where silk, indigo, and other commodities of great value are cultivated with a success far greater than was ever found in any of the maritime parts of our colonies. But however clear the excellencies of these interior parts of Georgia may appear, to such as have viewed them with an understanding eye, yet are they not one tenth peopled: it is but a few years since any attention at all has been given to this province by American or European settlers; but after the arrangement of the American governments in 1763[1] had confined all the colonies to as narrow bounds as the encroachments of the French before the war and their operations in it, they then found good land, unpatented, scarce; which pushed them upon a more industrious search: this was the cause of Georgia receiving since the peace such an accession of people that settled in numbers in the back parts of it; and it was the same cause that contributed to the peopling several districts in North Carolina, which had been long neglected.

The soil and face of the country in the maritime part of the province resembles South Carolina; it consists of a flat

[1] The Proclamation of 1763.

territory, very sandy, and in general either pine barrens or swamps; the slips of oakland are not large or numerous: the swamps are inferior to those of Carolina in the production of rice, and in general the country is not so good for the whole breadth of the flat part; but this inferiority is not great; all the sea coast of America, from Jersey to Florida, has a strong similarity.

The vegetable productions both of trees, shrubs, roots, flowers, &c. are the same as those of South Carolina; nor is there much difference in the growth, for though Georgia lies to the south of that province, yet is the climate not hotter than that of Carolina; and there are some parts of the latter, particularly Charles Town, much hotter than most in Georgia. Relative to a further account of the soil, climate, and products of this province, I shall here insert an extract from a letter written by a planter who went from England and settled not far from Augusta, and has resided there eight years.

I must freely own, that in some instances I was much disappointed in my expectations of this country—I thought the soil had been more generally good, and the climate I was taught to imagine was more agreeable to an English constitution; but in summer I find the heat very oppressive, and gives one, for two or three hours in the afternoon, a languor which I never experienced in England even in the hottest days; going out is then disagreeable, and the only way to be tolerably at ease is to keep one's self perfectly quiet, to sit still in rooms that admit much air but no sun, and to be cautious in diet: this season lasts through July, August, and most of September. The way to enjoy the agreeable parts of any avocation during these months, is to rise early in the morning and to transact whatever business requires your being abroad, by eleven o'clock, or at most by twelve (unless the days are cloudy), and then to keep the house till five in the afternoon; in the evening the air is cool enough to render the fields pleasant. What I have now told you is not general with all constitutions;

I have a servant who came from England with me that feels no more inconvenience from being exposed through the heat of the day to the sun than the very negroes themselves, who generally delight in the most meridian beams; and among my neighbours, I know two or three who are of the same temperament. But my own constitution is very different, for a fever would be the least consequence I believe—and indeed I partly know it from experience—which would ensue from my using any fatiguing exercise from one to three o'clock in the afternoon in summer, when the sky is clear; for with a south wind the sun's beams are so intensely hot that the only pleasure I feel is to be perfectly at rest.

But at the same time, Sir, that I describe these inconveniencies, let me remark that I should use very different terms if I lived near the coast: I have been often at Savannah, when I have longed ardently to be at home; the climate is there beyond comparison worse than at Augusta, and the farther west we go, the better it becomes. This will doubtless appear very strange to you, as there is so little difference in the latitudes of these places; but that is a circumstance which has little to do with climate in this part of the world. I attribute the great contrast there is between the sea coast and the western part of the province, to the flatness of one, and the varied surface of the other—also to one being full of swamps and marshes, and the other being entirely free from them. Flat countries have always less wind and agitations in the air, which render it far more pure and wholesome to breathe in, as they carry off speedily every noxious quality; there is scarce an instance on the globe, of a hilly or a mountainous country being unhealthy; even under the line or the tropics such are always inhabited by a hardy and robust race of people. The other circumstance is of yet more consequence; the effluvia of stagnant waters in a hot climate, and especially of such as rice-swamps—which are shallow, sometimes fields of mud, at others thinly covered with water—cannot but prove prodigiously injurious to the health of the human body, at the same time that it renders the heat not only burning, but close and suffocating: such a thick heavy atmosphere, in a country so flat as not to be windy, must necessarily make the maritime part of this province far more hot than the internal part, creating a difference greater than what many degrees of latitude could occasion.

In the observations [I] have made on the climate's being uncommonly hot, I confine myself entirely to the hottest part of the summer, July, August, and part of September, and perhaps, but not always, a week [of] the latter end of June. As to the rest of the year, you have no idea in England of the charms of this climate at a distance from the sea. March, April, May, and June, are a warm spring, in which scarce a day offends you: the sky is a clear expanse, clouds rarely to be seen, and the heat nothing offensive; the beauty of our country is then enjoyed every hour of the day—in short, no season in any part of the world can hardly be more agreeable than these months in the back country of Georgia. The latter part of September and October are also perfectly agreeable, in being sufficiently warm without a melting heat. But this is not all I have to say in our favour, for to me the winter is a most pleasing season here; the degree of heat is that of a warm spring, with some days as hot as a common summer; but in some months in the latter country I have felt days as hot as are generally experienced in Jamaica: ideas of heat should not therefore be taken from the height to which the thermometer rises in certain days, but to the mean height when every day is registered. In the winter season, and also in spring, we have extreme cold winds, particularly the north-west; and also sharp frosts; but the sudden changes from heat to cold, which are so much complained of on the coast, are rarely felt with us in any such degree as is common there. I have heard many of my neighbours complain of these frosts and cold winds, but to an European constitution they are natural, and are certainly wholesome whenever the changes are not sudden from heat to cold; and even in that case they are better than constant heat, if any caution is used in dress. I must say for my own part, that neither frost nor wind have ever proved disagreeable to me; and that upon the whole, I much prefer the climate to any in which I have lived before; and yet I have resided at Cadiz, Naples, and the West Indies, not to speak of Boston and England. But whatever I have mentioned on this head is relative only to the country to the west of

Augusta, that is, the western half of Georgia; for the other part does not by many degrees enjoy so good a climate.

In another letter was written as follows.

The soil in this neighborhood is good; in general, we have very little that is bad; and none that will not produce some useful crop or other. Like you in England we have wastes uncultivated, which spread almost over the whole province; but our wastes are such only for want of people to accept their property, whereas yours are such from being of a poor and almost worthless soil. I have travelled over parts of Scotland, and even the northern counties of England, which carry such an aspect of barrenness, and are so dreary and waste, as nothing in all this country can be opposed to them. All land here that is uncultivated is either a very rich and valuable forest or a meadow, which in its natural state would be worth ten or twelve shillings an acre in England. On the coast they have swamps which produce nothing, tho' not many, but here swamps are rare; the low grounds on some of the rivers are more properly marshes; they are small, and such as are found in the best and most beautiful counties of England; low meadows on rivers, wherever they are found, were (in a state of nature) marshes: we have none but what might easily be drained, and would then be the richest meadows in the world, especially if kept as watered ones. Even these marshes are with us found full of tall and beautiful cedars and cypresses.

Our flat tracts, or more properly the surface of gentle waves of country, rather than levels or hills, are of a rich loamy soil; the surface from twelve to eighteen inches deep of a fine light, black, sandy loam, which has the appearance of being the earth which has been formed by the rotting of vegetables; and yet, which is extraordinary, we have this soil where no trees are found. Under this loam we find another of a reddish brown colour, three, four, or five feet deep, and then meet with clay and in some places rock; this under-stratum of loam has the appearance of being admirable land. Other tracts of this sort, and especially the sides of hills, are covered with a reddish loam with many stones in it, from one to two feet deep, and under it rock: the appear-

ance of this soil is not so good, but on experience we find it to be
very fertile. In some vales, between gentle hills, we find the black
loam three or four feet deep, a soil which I am persuaded might
be applicable to any purpose in the world. A true clay on the
surface is scarcely ever found in these tracts; but in the low lands
on the river sides the soil is a very strong loam, near the clay.
Some of the rivers, however, run among the hills, with high rocky
shores. For 150 miles from the sea the country abounds with
what they call a *pine barren*, which is a light white sand, very
poor, covered with pines; it is reckoned the worst part of that
country; we are not entirely without it; here and there is a pine
barren, but they are rare. There are other varieties of soil, but
not in considerable quantity; we have sandy tracts, which though
light are very rich, and of a nature entirely different from the
pine barren sand. Some spots on the rivers and the highest hills
are rocky, and so rough as not to admit of culture; but these are
covered with forest trees, and add very much to the beauty of
the country.

Uncultivated tracts of country in this part of America are very
different from such in other parts of the world; the plenty of the
finest timber is astonishing to an European upon his first arrival.
We have several sorts of oak which come to a prodigious size,
twice or thrice as large as oaks in England; and some of these
are much more excellent for ship-building than is commonly
imagined: an injudicious choice of the sort of oak was for some
years the cause of this idea; but later trials have diffused a more
correct knowledge of the value of our timber, for some has been
found superior in duration even to British oak. This wood is also
cut into various articles of lumber, which are exported to the
West Indies; pine, cypress, and cedar are likewise appropriated
to the same use: this a vast advantage annexed to those parts of
the country which have a good water-carriage, since these sorts
of woods converted into lumber will pay the expences of clearing
the thickest forests in this country, even if a proportion of the
timber be of other sorts and not used in building: when this is the
case therefore, a man enters not only into the possession of an

estate without expence, but even an estate that is ready to cultivate.

Our forests are generally open, consisting of large trees, growing so thin that you may generally ride through every part of them, rarely having any under-wood, and in some tracts they are wide enough for waggons to pass every where: the labour, therefore, of clearing, when the wood is not of a proper sort for lumber, is not great. We have immense numbers of wild mulberry trees, upon the leaves of which we feed our silk-worms, without forming any plantations for that purpose. Walnuts and hickories are also very plentiful upon the best lands, and grow to a very great size.

A third letter contained the following particulars.

My plantation is situated on a small but navigable creek, which falls into the river Savannah, about thirty miles west of Augusta; when I first came, I had a very large tract of country to chuse in, for the settlements to the west of that town at any distance from it were not numerous; had I then been as well acquainted with agriculture as I am now, I could have made choice of a plantation, consisting more entirely of rich land; but as it is, I have no great reason to complain, and what I lose in soil, I gain in the extreme beauty of the situation.

My house is on the side of a hill; behind it is a fine spreading wood of oak, walnut, hickory, &c. before it a large tract of grass which I have cleared, and which is bounded by the river, whose course I command from almost every window, for three miles on each side: on the other side of it, and all round the lands adjacent to my house, are the fields which I have in culture. The whole plantation, which is my property, consists of 6,340 acres, at least, in the rough manner in which the surveyor-general's people reported the survey, that is, the quantity registered; the only fence which surrounded it for some years was trees marked with a hatchet, or crosses dug in the meadows, with here and there a post set up; but other settlers having since fixed near me, who have taken up small grants of land, their fences have been made in some places in my boundary line, which have saved me the trouble. In some places I am yet open to the country not granted away; for this tract of land containing a large proportion of excellent soil, I paid not quite one hundred pounds, including every charge and fee incurred in order to procure it.

The method here taken is for the person who wants land to fix upon a spot and take what he likes, under condition of peopling it in a given number of years: I had twenty allowed me, but they are now giving only ten or fifteen years. It is not common to see people fixing by each other; they generally plant themselves at a distance, for the sake of having an uncultivated country around them for their cattle to range in: all the country not granted away belongs to the king, and is [held in] common for every man to turn his cattle upon, but not in the manner such right is enjoyed in England, where the same thing is done not by permission but by right; for here every new comer has a liberty of fixing in this common part of the country, and inclosing his property immediately if he pleases; so that the lands on which we turn our cattle farther than our own bounds, are continually decreasing: the consequence is, the planters who on this account have not range enough for their large stocks, take up new grants of small quantities of land farther to the westward for the sake of sending their cattle thither, by which means they are enabled to keep very great stocks, even so far as a thousand head. I have four hundred and forty head of cows, oxen, bulls, heifers, &c. but their value is far from what it would be in England.

The plenty of timber in this country is a great advantage to new settlers, in rendering their buildings and many of their utensils of no other expence than that of labour, tools, and a little iron. My house, a barn, a stable, and some other conveniencies cost me no more at first than one hundred and seventy-four pounds in cash and the labour of ten negroes during three months; this was done by hiring carpenters and paying them by the month; and two of the slaves learnt so much of the art in that time, that by working since with them occasionally, they are become good carpenters enough to raise a shed, or build any plain outhouse, such as you see common in England in little farmyards: our woods is of so little value, that their making waste is of no consequence. I have made many additions to my house since, at a small expence, so that it is now a very convenient and agreeable habitation.

When I consider that for one hundred pounds a man may in this rich and plentiful country buy an extensive tract of land; that for two more he may raise a good house and offices; that he may buy slaves for thirty or forty pounds apiece, or hire white labour a very little dearer than in England; and that he may settle himself with as few as he pleases, and increase them as he can; when this is considered, it surprises me to think that more people of small fortunes do not come among us, but that they should prefer the narrow way in which they must live in Europe. The plenty of this country is much greater than you can think of; a little planter, that is a good gun-man himself, or has a slave that is so, may in half a day kill much more game than two families will eat in a week; and in parts of the country where it is comparatively scarce, an easy walk will yield him a day or two's subsistence of this sort for a moderate table. By game we here understand deer, rabbits, wild kine, and wild hogs, turkies, geese, ducks, pigeons, partridges, teal, &c. Our rivers are equally abounding with excellent fish, which is an advantage not inferior to the other; and the two together in hunting, shooting, and fishing, affording a diversion equal to what is met with in any part of the world, and superior to most. Sporting here is carried on with unlimited freedom, and in a style far superior to what I have any where else met with; and whoever keeps house in this country must presently find the immense advantages attending the great plenty of these articles, which reduce all expences of this sort very low. And now [that] I am giving you the information you want on this head, I shall add that our great plenty of fruit is another point in which this country is very fortunate; we have melons, cucumbers, water-melons, peaches, pears, apples, plums, &c. &c. in any quantity we please, almost without trouble or culture. The climate is so favorable that to plant them is all the attention requisite. Upon a new settler fixing, one of his first works is to inclose and plant a large orchard. Peaches are the most plentiful of any kind of fruit: a stone set, becomes a bearing tree in three years, and the fruit that drops from it rises in young trees; so that a single tree would become a wood of peaches in a few years, if they were not grubbed up.

You see, Sir, from this account, upon the truth of which you may absolutely relie, that you want for nothing in this country that nature can give us. Rich land is plentiful; building no where so cheap; game, fish, flesh, fowl, and fruit, and in the utmost profusion; labour by slaves very cheap, by servants not dear. And to this may be added a government mild and equal, in which more liberty is no where to be found; taxes too trifling to be mentioned, and where neither tythes nor poor's rates are to be found: may I not therefore conclude, that if mere living well, plentifully, and at ease, be considered, no country can exceed, perhaps not equal, this. In respect of society, we are deficient; but this is made up to a studious person, or one who does not dislike retirement, by the amusements of the field, by the employments of agriculture, and by reading; not however that we are without company; I have eight or nine neighbours within twenty miles of me, with whom I visit; and some of them are families in which a rational conversation is by no means wanting!

In a successive letter the same person gave the following particulars.

Respecting the agriculture we pursue, about which you enquire, I shall give you the best account I am able: the objects most attended to are Indian corn, wheat, and provisions, which long occupied this country chiefly; but for a few years past silk and indigo have made great strides among us. The country near the sea is not near so fertile in corn and provisions as that about us; we therefore not only send great quantities for the West India export, but also to feed the towns and rice plantations in part. I am much in doubt whether the common husbandry of raising corn and provisions be not as profitable as that of indigo or rice; the best planters we have, and it is the same in Carolina, do not reckon they make in total product above 20£. or 25£. each for their working hands: I have exceeded this some years by

Indian corn, wheat, &c. and some of my neighbours have carried it much farther than me, by more skill and closer application.

The first business in our husbandry is clearing the ground, which is for corn generally done by grubbing the trees up by the roots in order for the plough to go: this method I have followed in all the land I have cleared: the expence is small, from the ease of stirring the light soil; and after raising my house, offices, and negroe camp, with lengths and posts for fences, &c. the residue I have sent down the river in several sorts of lumber, as boards, planks, staves, pieces, casks, &c. to Augusta and Savannah, but not with such advantage as others lower down on the river, who have not such a distance: after clearing, I have planted the land with Indian corn, for three and four years successively, and got from thirty-five to sixty bushels an acre, and at the same time from twenty-five to fifty bushels of Indian pease an acre. Of wheat my crops are not so great; but from thirty to forty bushels an acre is my usual crop. Barley we also sow, usually after wheat or Indian corn; I get the same quantity as of wheat; I have some fields the soil of which is so rich that I have got for six years successively crops of these kinds of grain, and all equally good, and I do not now find that the soil has much abated of its fertility; but in some of my fields, it begins to wear out; but fine grass will come, and soon yield nearly as good profit as middling crops of corn. I do not think our farmers in England grow quite so many successive crops of corn as we do here, yet I imagine our products to be much the largest. I have never laid on any dung or other manure for corn.

My black deep loams, which were covered with wood, yield kitchen plants of very fine flavour and an extraordinary size; I allotted a piece of it near my house for a garden, in which several articles of common product much exceed what I remember seeing in England, and yet I have never manured it: this, however, is much owing to climate. I have raised cabbages of 60 lb. weight, and turneps of 25 lb. Potatoes thrive astonishingly in it; I have had 300 bushels from a bed which in size did not exceed a quarter of an acre; and several of my neighbours having found their great increase in this soil have begun to go pretty much into them as an article of sale: they find a ready market at Savannah for the West Indies. I design taking the same hint, and believe they will be as profitable as any other article.

There is one circumstance in this country which is very valuable in planting; it is the warmth of the climate rendering it unnecessary to house or otherwise attend cattle in winter more than in summer; they find their subsistence in the woods and natural meadows, and return home of nights only for the sake of food given them, not so much through necessity, as to induce them to be regular. Our swine fare yet better, for the woods abound greatly with mast and fruit of various sorts, which they are greedy in finding, and keep themselves fat on; but we use them to come home in the same manner as the kine. The number of hogs kept in this country by every planter is very great; they who begin only with a sow or two, in a few years are masters of fourscore, or an hundred head; I have above three hundred of all sorts and sizes, and in a few years, if the country does not settle very fast, shall have twice or thrice as many. Pork and beef barrelled make a considerable article of our product; and hides are not the most inconsiderable part of the product of our cow kine.

Besides the articles I have mentioned, we cultivate indigo, silk, tobacco, and hemp, but not in such large quantities (silk excepted) as they do in Carolina; I have them all upon my plantations; indigo and tobacco require the same soil, which is the richest and deepest we can give them, but it must be dry; tobacco is but just coming it, but we make as good, if not better than any in Virginia; and I am of opinion, since the price has risen, it will be as beneficial as any article we can go upon. Hemp is sown in the low lands on the rivers and in drained marshes, where the soil is a stiff loam, upon clay: we do not reckon it so profitable as either indigo or tobacco; but as the land which suits it is not the right sort for those crops, it is cultivated in small quantities. I cannot speak with any precision of the products which my neighbours gain of these commodities, but I can tell you pretty accurately what I have done myself. When I had increased my ten negroes to twenty, from that number eight of whom were women (who I should observe do as much field-work as the men), they made me, with the help of five white labourers,

	£.	s.	d.
36 acres of Indian corn, the produce of which sold for in sterling money	146	13	8
26 acres of wheat, the produce of which sold, sold for in ditto	93	8	0
12 acres barley, the product of which sold, yielded	18	10	0
40 barrels of pork at 1£. 12s.	64	0	0
26 ditto of beef at 1£. 2s.	28	12	0
16 acres tobacco yielded 12 hogsheads	96	0	0
33 pounds silk	30	0	0
420 pounds of indigo from 4 acres and a half	52	10	0
Hides, live stock sold, and small articles	47	18	0
£.	577	11	8

This product from 25 hands is above 23£. each but the two following years I had not such good success. You see, by this account, that I made 33 pounds of silk: this is an article which deserves more attention than has been given it, either by the inhabitants of this province, or in encouragement from the mother country: the number of hands who made this 33 lb. in a season was but eleven, which is 3 lb. a head. This appears to be a very considerable object; among them were four of my children (who did it by way of amusement, and indeed a very rational one it is), and three women; they did not employ seven weeks in it, and I need not tell you that in this business it is but a part of the day that is employed. Georgia has, proportioned to its inhabitants, made greater progress in feeding silk-worms than any of the other colonies, but yet her people do not make near the quantities they might; supposing they made but two pounds a head, and less than this I have never made for every person I have employed in it, this would be a vast acquisition for all the women, many of the children, the old men, and disabled persons, with proper assistance from others; and in Carolina, where the people

are so much more numerous, the importance of the object would
in a national light be still greater. This is so favourite a theme
with me that were I to trouble you with all I could say on the
subject I should go near to exhaust your patience.

Hemp has been too inconsiderable an article with me to come
to market, but I hope next year to send two or three tons down
to Savannah. It may be to your satisfaction also to know that I
have made some trials of wine, not yet as an export, but have
used several small casks in my own family, which have proved
better than I expected. Four years ago I planted about a quarter
of an acre of a dry rocky spot of land, hanging on the side of
a hill, to the south of which I thought promised well, I used setts
of our native grapes, having no others; these are so plentiful all
over the country, that you can scarce go an hundred yards without
meeting with numbers. This little plantation, which, for want of
better knowledge than I could gain from one or two treatises on
the vineyard culture, was not managed near so well as it ought,
has turned out much better than I expected. I have made wine
from the same grapes growing wild, and have the satisfaction to
find that the produce of my cultivated ones is beyond comparison
of a finer flavour, which shews that we have much to hope from
attending well to our native vines; were they managed with the
skill that is exerted in the wine countries of Europe, they would
perhaps turn out among the profitable articles of our husbandry.
One of the neighbouring planters, a Frenchman by birth, has
written to France to a relation to send a vigneron,[2] well experienced, with some setts of the Burgundy grape: this is to be done
at my expence, and I have good expectations from the scheme;
though my neighbour is quite of a different opinion, and thinks
that (farther than our own consumption) if I make it succeed,
the culture will not prove near so profitable as indigo: how far
this will prove true, I am not yet a judge. Madeira, which is the
only wine we import, comes very dear to us. If we could make
a sort sufficiently good to be substituted for that, it would be a
great acquisition. I shall give you the account of my sale in a
year since the former, being nearly what my present produce is.

[2] One who cultivates grape-vines.

	£.	s.	d.
50 acres of Indian corn, produce in sterling money	187	14	0
35 acres of wheat produce in ditto	132	0	0
20 acres of barley ditto	35	0	0
50 barrels of pork	82	0	0
40 ditto of beef	50	0	0
Hides	24	10	0
Live stock sold	30	0	0
Lumber	36	0	0
47 pounds of silk	47	0	0
16 acres of tobacco, 11 hogsheads	88	0	0
Indigo	87	10	0
£.	799	14	0

The number of negroes 25, and 5 white labourers, 30 in all; the total divided gives 26£. a head; and this I believe may generally be equalled by those who have any luck in fixing on tolerable land, without possessing great skill in choosing the best.

This, Sir, is a very important part of the information you request me to give, as it explains to you what is to be expected from settling in this country; I have little doubt of your friend being able to make from 20£. to 30£. a head annual produce, sold at market, for all the working hands he employs, besides supplying the plantation with all the provisions consumed, both by the family, slaves, cattle, poultry, &c.; this however is not profit, for negroes cost at present from 40£. to 60£. a head, if good ones are bought. Cloathing, physic, attendance, &c. come to something and distempers will now and then break out among them which prove very destructive, though in general the increase will keep up the number. Implements, tools, furniture, manufactures, &c. &c. are all much dearer than in England, except the articles which are made of wood. Wine, tea, sugar, and spices, are some of them dearer, and none of them cheaper, than in England. Repairs of buildings is an article of some expence. Negroes must have an overseer, at the annual expence of from 40£. to 60£. All these and some other articles are deductions from the planter's profit; nor should I omit to add, Sir, that the nature of the country, as it prevents many of the expences which are common in England, so it brings on us others of which you know nothing. Hospitality, to a degree totally unknown in Europe, is the virtue of all America; and a man can hardly through inclination, but especially from example, be niggardly on any occasions that call for it; his great expence will be wine, rum, and a few other articles of housekeeping; not that this amounts to any thing very considerable.

In general, our planters are very much on the thriving hand, yet few are rich, though I have heard of some large fortunes in Carolina; we have scarce one in the province whose circumstances do not improve. As to making a fortune, I believe no part of the world is better adapted for it, provided the planter is skilled in land, has a good degree of knowledge in matters of agriculture, and is very industrious and attentive to his business: you may easily suppose that all these qualifications are necessary; indeed I know of no business in which money is to be made without knowledge and industry: I must also add, that he ought to have his capital, especially if it is not considerable, free; for interest here is 8, 9, and 10 per cent. and money even on such terms very difficult to be got; he should therefore possess, or raise whatever he wants, in England, for no dependance is to be had on getting any here.

There are very great advantages in the husbandry which is carried on in this country, of a nature not general in others, especially in Europe; the quantity of land to be had by any person that pleases is a circumstance no where else to be met with on the globe, at least in countries where the religious and civil liberty of mankind is secured; and among all our colonies, none has better land or a more favorable climate than the back parts of Georgia. The expences of living are low, and particularly the necessaries of life so very plentiful that subsistence is no where easier gained; on the contrary, the articles of merchandise produced here yield a large price, as it is the nature of mankind to rate luxuries much higher than necessaries, and not to let the value of one depend on that of the other. Thus the planter feeds and subsists himself and family very cheap, while he sells his produce very dear: silk, indigo, wine, hemp, tobacco, &c. are by no means necessaries, but their value is much greater; this is a circumstance of great value to the planter; how far you enjoy in the same in certain articles produced in England, I am not a good judge; luxurious articles may be very dear, but the necessaries which support the planters, and their workmen are dear also.

These extracts, from pretty long correspondence carried on with a view of settling a relation in Georgia (which is since done), I am happy in being allowed to insert: it is true they principally concern only one plantation, but they abound with many valuable circumstances that concern the whole province, and as such could not but be deemed highly worthy of insertion.

The following is a state of the exports of Georgia, upon an average of three years since the peace

	£.
18,000 barrels of rice, at 40s.	36,000
Indigo, 17,000 lb. at 2s.	1,700
Silk, 2,500 lb. at 20s.	2,500
Deer and other skins	17,000
Boards, staves, &c.	11,000
Tortoise-shell, drugs, cattle, &c.	6,000
£.	74,200

But since this account was published the articles are most of them very much increased; the rice is raised to 23,000 barrels, and the price to 3£. 10s. so that this article alone makes more than the whole of the above articles; the indigo is proportionally increased, but the silk is declined: the Indian trade at Augusta is also thriven very much of late.

Before I take my leave of this province it will be proper to mention the large tract of country lately acquired by the government of the Cherokees, containing by estimation about seven millions of acres.[3] This country lies to the westward of Augusta, and is bounded on one side by the Savannah's branches; from the description I have heard of it, I apprehend the plantation described in the above letters very nearly resembles it: the soil is as rich as any part of America; every article of spontaneous vegetation, luxuriant in the highest degree: the climate, like that of the western part of all our southern colonies which bounds upon the Ap[p]alachian mountains, as desirable as any in the world, both for the production of profitable staples and healthiness. It is further said to be as well watered with streams and rivers as can be wished, with three or four of them navigable for large canoes. Many are the people who have given in petitions for grants of land in it, so that it is expected in Georgia the whole tract, large as it is, will be settled in a few years: the articles of culture upon which the planters will go are particularly indigo, hemp, flax, cotton, tobacco, vines, and silk, not to speak of Indian corn, wheat, and other provisions: for all these, it is said, no part of America can be better adapted.

It is very much to be wished that so fine a tract of country may be put to the most advantageous use, particularly in respect of silk, wine, and hemp. These are commodities which we want more than any others from our colonies, but for want of a proper soil and climate the nation has for so many years been disappointed in its expectations; but there can be no

[3] The Cherokee were the largest and most important single Indian tribe in what is now southeastern United States. Their lands included parts of North and South Carolina, Georgia, Alabama, and Tennessee. Culturally they were probably the most advanced of the southern tribes. They practiced agriculture extensively and lived in permanent villages. The cession of territory here referred to was made in 1761. See E. Starr, *History of the Cherokee Indians* (New York, 1921); R. L. Meriwether, *The Expansion of South Carolina, 1729–1765* (Kingsport, Tenn., 1939), chap. i.

doubt of all these articles doing as well in this newly acquired country as in any part of the world, provided the right methods are taken in the culture of them. Planters left entirely to themselves are apt to fall into the articles of husbandry to which they have been most acquainted, and not into those which will pay them the greatest profit, unless they have been before acquainted with them. But their chusing their crops well is a matter of vast importance to this nation, and therefore proper means should be taken to give them all the light and instruction that is wanting in any thing which it would be adviseable for them to undertake. Persons skilled in feeding silk-worms and winding the silk should be distributed through every district of such a country; such might be got in America, and they should teach, gratis, every family that was willing to learn the business. The same thing should be done with vine-dressers from France, or perhaps better from Portugal, Spain, Italy, or Greece; these men should move from plantation to plantation, to shew the planters the culture of vineyards, to assist in planting them and also in dressing the vineyard: it would not be very expensive to procure forty or fifty such; and that number would in a few years be able to train up many pupils, and spread a tolerable knowledge of the vineyard culture through two or three provinces. Hemp is better understood in America, the same means would not therefore be necessary. To these measures, rewards, both honorary and pecuniary, should be added for such planters as produced given quantities of the best wine, of silk, and of hemp: a couple of thousand pounds a year bestowed upon a province in such premiums would be sufficient to introduce, in conjunction with the above mentioned measure, any article of culture the government would have them pursue: and nobody can doubt but the national interest would be far more advanced by such an expenditure of public money than injured by the loss (supposing it such) of a few thousand pounds. There is scarcely any thing in domestic policy but what may be effected, and with profit, by means of premiums judiciously offered and impartially given, provided means be at the same time taken to instruct the people, if the object required be out of their knowledge. Instead of acting thus, the bounty on silk has been suffered to expire.[4]

Bounties and other encouragements of this nature have been of long standing for hemp and other articles without effect; but this proves nothing in general. While the colonists were confined to the coasts of America, by which I mean the flat, poor, sandy tract of country which extends for 100 or 150 miles from the sea, no encouragement would ever make any thing of hemp, silk, or wine, for the soil and climate were equally unfit for all; but now they have spread themselves into the back or hilly country, where both soil and climate are essentially different, the case is different also; and much less encouragement would prove of high utility than before was attended with no effect. For this reason, the old inefficacy of such measures should never be instanced as an argument against them at present.

Very many great and beneficial effects might be made to flow from the settling and planting the internal parts of our

[4] In an effort to build up the silk manufacture Great Britain spent considerable money in trying to induce the colonies to produce raw silk. Moreover, bounties about equivalent to the import duties on raw silk were allowed on the exportation of British manufactured silks. Under these conditions "respectable quantities" of British silks were sold in foreign and open markets. The failure of the colonies to respond sufficiently to these inducements and the opposition in England to continue duties on manufactured silks led to a change of policy as far as this particular commodity was concerned. See G. L. Beer, *British Colonial Policy, 1754–1765* (New York, 1922), pp. 195–96.

maritime colonies. Hemp is an article which costs this nation several hundred thousand pounds annually: it is besides a necessary for our royal navy, which ought not to depend on the good pleasure of any foreign nation, whatever friendship may be between us at present.

Flax is another import which we take from the Baltic, though our colonies would raise it as well, and parts of them perhaps much better.

I have not seen public accounts of what our import of wines of all sorts is, but certainly it amounts to an immense sum; the wealth of the nation would be very different if such an import, chiefly from our own sworn enemies, was transferred to our colonies, and instead of being paid for with cash, as is the case with hemp, to be purchased with our manufactures.

Silk is another article which we import from China, at the expence of more than half a million sterling; yet our silk mills are universal in affirming that what we have had from America is equal to the best we receive elsewhere: surely therefore it much beho[o]ves the government to promote whatever measures have a tendency to render silk an article of consideration in the imports from America, instead of suffering old ones to expire.

Oil is another import which costs this country great sums of money: none is or can be produced at home; but the olive thrives well in the interior part of Georgia, and might be made a valuable article in the products of that province, especially the new acquired district.

Madder we buy of the Dutch, to the amount of more than two hundred thousand pounds a year; those industrious people raise it in the province of Zealand, that is, in a country far inferior in soil to the back parts of Georgia, where are tracts of rich deep black loam that would produce prodigious crops of it: no article of American husbandry would prove a more profitable staple.

Wool we take in large quantities of Spain, because it is of a kind we cannot produce in England:[5] our colonies on the continent of North America, south of New York, produce a wool entirely similar to the Spanish; no staple they could produce would therefore be more advantageous to Great Britain. It is well known that a piece of fine broad cloth cannot be made without Spanish wool; it is also known that the Spaniards have of late years made great efforts to work up their own wool;[6] if they should succeed, or if they should by any other means prevent the export of it, our woollen fabrics, though they might not be stopped, would at least be burthened with a fresh expence and new trouble; all which would be prevented by encouraging the import of wool from America; and at the same time that this good effect was wrought, another would be brought about in cramping the manufactures of the colonies; of which more hereafter.

Cotton we import from Turkey at the expence of above two hundred thousand pounds a year; this commodity agrees well with the soil and climate of Georgia, especially those of the back parts of the province: I am sensible that our West India islands would produce it, but the land which is so occupied there would produce more valuable staples; there we want

[5] Reference here is undoubtedly to the wool of the Spanish merino. As early as 200 B. C. the Romans began to improve their flocks which became the progenitors of the famous Spanish merinos. This breed of sheep is highly esteemed for its fine wool. English wool as well as the wool produced in other parts of the world was improved by crossing the merino with native sheep. See Perry Walton, *The Story of Textiles* (New York, 1929).

[6] These efforts were not very successful. See Herbert Heaton, *Economic History of Europe* (New York, 1936), pp. 263–66.

land, but on the continent is more land than we know what to do with; it is here therefore that it should be produced.

These imports might be enlarged to a greater number, were it necessary, but they are sufficient to shew that the nation takes from foreign countries, and from enemies, commodities to a very great amount, which she might have produced in her colonies. It is at present the opinion of many mercantile gentlemen that the ballance of all our trades, except America and the East Indies, is against us; if so, it must undeniably be owing in a great measure to the great consumption of these articles, many of which are taken from countries that take little from us: if our colonies produced them, we should, on the contrary, pay for them with our manufactures, a circumstance essentially different from having them in any other mode.

A writer who has taken great pains to be well informed, has given the following account of some of these imports.

	£.
Hemp and flax	400,000
Wine and brandy from France alone in 1663, 100,000	
Suppose the total	1,000,000
Ireland alone in one article, claret, takes 150,000£.	
Silk	1,825,000
Cotton	* 300,000
Madder other accounts make	250,000
Let us suppose oil	50,000
And for wool	50,000
Total	3,875,000

* *Political Essays Concerning the Present State of the British Empire,* 1772. [This was one of Arthur Young's many publications. Ed.]

Other imports, which do not concern so immediately our *southern* colonies, as iron, timber, &c. &c. would run this account up to a much greater height: but if the total did not amount to more than half of it, surely the sum is too considerable to take from foreign nations in articles which we might produce generally as well in our own colonies.

CHAPTER XXVI

THE FLORIDAS

*False descriptions of the country—Climate—Soil—Pro-
ductions—Importance of these provinces relative to
situation and commerce—Observations*

IN SUCH a free country as Britain, new acquisitions made
at a peace will not be well understood for some years. The
party who concludes the treaty will in the nature of things
extol the terms they have gained, and for that purpose
magnify the acquisitions they have made: on the other hand,
the party in opposition will be sure to condemn the treaty, and
depreciate the value of the territories acquired; and what is
a great misfortune in such a case, is the almost universal influence of parties: few men that actually go to the countries in
question, but whose judgment or report will be warped by
their connections or political opinions. Most of the people
who frequent such countries are soldiers, sailors, governors,
civil officers, or traders, and if any of these should publish
accounts, not much strict truth is always met with in their
descriptions, either from being fearful to offend their su-
periors, or from motives of interest. It happened thus with
the Floridas.[1] The ministry, upon the conclusion of the

[1] The present chapter heading is somewhat altered from that of the
original double heading, which reads, EAST FLORIDA, False descriptions
of the country—Climate—Soil—Productions—Observations; WEST FLOR-
IDA, Climate—Soil—Importance of these provinces relative to situation and
commerce—Observations. "East Florida" and "West Florida" are now
placed as headings at their logical positions in the text.

peace,[2] sent a physician, who had no business to leave [live] in England, to view and describe East Florida; though upon his return he found his employers out of office, and a new administration, yet as his was an official business, he dedicated his book to the minister of the day:[3] it contained an account of that province which made it appear to be one of the finest countries in the world, and proved it a most valuable acquisition. This was just the report which the world might rationally have expected; for certainly a man on such an errand would take care, first to recommend himself to his patrons, which he could do no ways so effectually as by praising the acquisitions they had made to the skies: in this work, indeed, he did not proceed on those principles of integrity which he ought to have done. An American botanist accompanied him in a part of his journey through the province[4] and kept a

[2] By the Treaty of Paris (1763) England secured Canada and all the French possessions east of the Mississippi River with the exception of two small islands in the mouth of the St. Lawrence. From Spain England got East and West Florida in exchange for Cuba and the Philippines. Louisiana, France handed over to Spain. See C. P. Nettels, *The Roots of American Civilization* (New York, 1938), pp. 590–92.

[3] Dr. William Stork. See above, p. 278, footnote 5. The volume entitled *An Account of East-Florida with a Journal kept by John Bartram of Philadelphia, Botanist to His Majesty for the Floridas; Upon A Journey from St. Augustine up the River St. John's* (London, 1766), was dedicated to George Grenville who at the time of his resignation in 1765 was First Lord of the Treasury and Chancellor of the Exchequer. See G. L. Beer, *British Colonial Policy, 1754–1765* (New York, 1922), p. 230.

[4] John Bartram (1699–1777), pioneer American botanist, was born near Darby, Pennsylvania. Although without formal schooling, he was from boyhood greatly interested in plants. In 1728 he purchased land along the banks of the Schuylkill River, near Philadelphia, and planted there the first botanical garden in what was later to be the United States. He made journeys in the Alleghenies, Catskills, Carolinas, and Florida in search of new plants for his garden. He also received many plants from the Old World and sent many American plants in return. The *Journal* of his Florida trip, to which reference is made in the text, helped to win for him the high praise of being "the greatest natural botanist in the world." See William Darlington, *Memorials of John Bartram and Humphrey Marshall* (London, 1849).

journal; this made a part of the above-mentioned publication; but instead of being published fairly, it was mangled, and the man's general opinion of the country, which was by no means favourable to it, suppressed. Such a conduct, at one stroke, was sufficient to convince the reader that little or no dependance could be placed in what was advanced by a man who could prove, in so material an instance, faithless to the public.

On the other hand, direct contrary accounts were published by others, who were so far from agreeing to the merit of the country set forth by its friends, that they strenuously insisted it had no pretensions to any sort of merit: they totally denied all value to it, ridiculed the title of acquisition, considered the country as a heavy burthen, and condemned the peacemakers with the loudest voice, for accepting such a recompense in exchange for glorious and valuable conquests made in the war.[5] Here therefore were two parties in such direct opposition to each other that a considerable part of what they wrote might fairly be attributed to political prejudice, and this on both sides; the consequence of which was, that the world could form but a very vague guess of the real truth.

Such is the state of public intelligence concerning the Floridas; all the information to be gained concerning them is that of private people who have resided there: I have been as attentive as possible in making numerous enquiries, of planters, agents, officers, &c. who have been any time in those countries; I have compared their accounts, and from the intelligence I have gained, have drawn up the following description, supplying some deficiencies by reasoning from

[5] For an account of this opposition consult *The Cambridge History of the British Empire*, Vol. I (New York, 1929), chap. xvii; and **W. L. Grant**, "Canada *versus* Guadeloupe," *American Historical Review*, Vol. XVII (July, 1912).

analogy of Georgia and Carolina, and others from public accounts, of a date antecedent to our having any connection with Florida, and consequently free from all party prejudice. The account will be incomplete, as the sources from which it is drawn are so; but it had much better be incomplete than otherwise, if, to make it so, bad intelligence or such as was unsatisfactory was taken to render it full. In a few particulars (wherein it would answer little purpose in him to vary from the truth), I follow Dr. Stork.

East Florida

East Florida is situated between latitude 25° and 32° [north]; it extends consequently much to the south of any of our other colonies, which makes the climate hotter. A considerable part of it forms a peninsula, which projects to the south: this circumstance is both an advantage and a disadvantage; in the first place, it makes the air cooler by a regular sea and land breeze than in the maritime part of Georgia; but on the other hand, this benefit is almost preponderated by the increased quantity of rain which falls; it is the mischief of all these southern coasts of America that they are deluged with rain, which, stagnating in the swamps of a flat hot country, poisons the air. The rains that fall in Florida are almost incessant. This in a hot climate must make it very unhealthy, since those are the wholesomest countries, near the tropics, where it seldom rains. Peru is perfectly healthy, and there it never rains at all. Relative to the health and fertility of this country, there is one circumstance that is decisive; all the southern colonies I have elsewhere remarked, consist of a maritime and a back country, the latter of which reaches to the Ap[p]alachian mountains; now the flat sandy coast, full ·of swamps and marshes, is alike in them all, being equally steril[e] and unwholesome; but when this flat country is passed and you arrive at the hilly dry tracts, free from swamps, you then find a country perfectly healthy and very fruitful. Florida, Georgia, the Carolinas, Virginia, and Maryland, are all extremely similar in the appearance of their coasts; the flat sandy tract is the same in them all, except that their small degree of fertility increases as you advance northward, as regularly as the arrangement of the colonies. Now this circumstance is absolutely decisive against East Florida, for unfortunately, that province consists of nothing else but the flat sandy country; it has no back country, for where you should meet with the rising drier tract, you come to the swamps and marshes of West Florida; therefore not a hill is to be met with in the whole province: it consists of marshes after marshes, swamps after swamps, pine barrens upon pine barrens, but no sound good loam like the hickory lands in the back parts of Georgia, &c. Indeed the general spontaneous produce of the province shews us what the soil is. Good lands in this part of America are covered with woods of tall red hickories as high and straight as elms; white, chestnut, and scarlet oaks; tulip trees, black walnuts, locusts, &c. But single trees of these are rare in East Florida, and not a wood of them is to be found in the whole province.

Now these two circumstances are such as can neither be mistaken nor misunderstood—the flat situation of the country, and the spontaneous produce; the one may be in a small degree remedied by the sea and land breezes, and small patches of tolerable (not good) land may be quoted in answer to the other; but as to the country in general, it must be condemned on comparison with very great tracts in our old colonies. This I must own appears to me to be clearly deducible from the circumstances in question; [the] party on either side cannot alter or deceive one in such points, because they are certainly matters of fact, and not opinion; nor could there well be a greater piece of imposition on the public than publishing the direct contrary.

Relative to the soil and face of the country, it resembles, as I before observed, the maritime parts of the other southern colonies: it consists chiefly of swamps and marshes or tracts of sandy white pine ground; the former are covered with the spontaneous growth of the country, live oaks, chinkapins, bays, liquid amber, water oaks, and stunted cypresses. In fertility for the product of rice, there are some of them which it is imagined will answer well, when the swamps more to the north are exhausted or turned to meadow, which, however, is not likely ever to be the case; and therefore the merit of this capability is not of much consequence: the swamps we were in possession of before the acquisition of Florida was made would, if cultivated, produce more rice than half the world consumes.

The rest of the country is in general a pine barren with very small spots of better land which the Indians of Florida formerly grew their maize on: now the pine barren is the worst land of America, but to say that it is absolutely sterile would be asserting an untruth; for no soil can be such in a climate that is very wet and very hot, since those two agents will every where make the worst of land produce something: this pine barren will, when cleared, produce indigo, Indian corn, and some other crops; but then it is not the proper soil for any one of them, and such as no person would move to, from the worst of our colonies, in order to cultivate them. This seems to be the plain fact, when cleared from the attendants which prejudice has given it. The country will produce rice and indigo and a few other unimportant articles;

but the culture will not by any means be so advantageous as the same articles in Carolina.

Several plantations have been formed, stocked with negroes, and set to work on rice, indigo, Indian corn, sugar, cotton, hemp, and cochineal.[6] Among these the plantations of Mr. Rolle, governor Grant, the earl of Egmont, and Mr. Taylor, are the principal; none of these have been able to bring any dubious article of culture into profit, such as sugar, cotton, cochineal, hemp, &c.; on the contrary, had they not depended on rice and indigo they would have lost their whole capital, and with the assistance of those articles which in Carolina are almost uniformly profitable, they have most of them lost such large sums of money as to break up some of the plantations and give no slight languor to them all. The description published of the province induced many to set about planting; they expected returns of sugar, cotton, cochineal, and hemp, and made little doubt of soon acquiring great fortunes: all they met with was disappointment on disappointment; this chagrined them, and perhaps they were then little inclined to do even justice to their own beginnings. But all men who have any ideas of planting in America, whether by going thither themselves, or under the conduct of agents, should consider well the country which they chuse. Had the gentlemen who have laid out large sums in planting Florida considered what the country probably was, from reasoning by analogy with Georgia, Carolina, &c. they would presently have perceived that it would have been more advantageous to settle in the back parts of our colonies, than in our new acquisitions of the Floridas.

[6] Cochineal, a dye, consists of the dried bodies of the insect *Coccus cacti* found on several species of cactus in Mexico, the islands of the Caribbean, and elsewhere.

WEST FLORIDA

In respect to West Florida, we have a little intelligence which can be depended on, as it is principally of an older date than our acquisition of it. The whole coast has been well known ever since the year 1719, and the many accounts the French have given of it, to be nothing but such a sandy desart; "the land is nothing but a fine sand, as white and shining as snow*." This is the account they give of the country from the Mississippi to Mobile; of which last an officer of twenty years experience in the country gives his opinion in these words: "I never could see for what reason this fort was built, or what could be the use of it; although it is 120 leagues from New Orleans, it must be supplied from thence; the soil is so bad, being nothing but sand, that it produces nothing but pine trees, or a little pulse, which is but indifferent of the kind."† They only settled there for the sake of a port in Dauphin isle, and which was choaked up by the shifting of the sands in a gale of wind, and leaves the place without any port above the depth of nine feet. Their other settlements on this coast, they tell us, "only deserved an oblivion as lasting as their duration was short." They then took Pensacola from the Spaniards,[7] but found it only fit to

---

* Du Pratz *Hist. de Louis* [*History of Louisiana*], I, 52. [See page 378, footnote 6. Ed.]

† *Du Mont. Mem. de la Louis.* tom. ii, p. 80. [*Memoires historique sur la Louisana . . . composes sur les memoires de M. Dumont,* 2 vols., Paris, 1753. The author, Georges Marie Butel-Dumont, was a French officer who served in Louisiana for many years. The quotation above is erroneously ascribed to page 80 of the second volume. It is on page 79. Ed.]

---

[7] Pensacola was first settled by the Spanish in 1559, but was abandoned two years later. In 1596 another colony was established on the site. In 1763 the town passed to the English but twenty years later reverted to Spain. See W. E. Dunn, *Spanish and French Rivalry in the Gulf Region* (Austin, 1917).

dismantle and abandon; on which they retired to the Mississippi, as we must do if ever we would hold that country.
The greatest part of Florida was surveyed in 1708 by Captain
Nairn[e][8] from Carolina, who gives this account of it for
about an hundred miles square round Pensacola. "All this
country is a *pine barren* (Sandy desart), without any water in
it"; that is, it has neither earth nor water in it, and must
therefore be very unfit for a *plantation*. All the rest appears
to be the same where it is not swampy and marshy. We may
say of the whole, what Father Charlevoix,[9] who travelled all
over it, says of the next post at St. Joseph's, which lies in the
middle of the country upon the borders of East and West
Florida, "it is a wretched country (*un pays perdu*), and a
mere barren sand, on a flat and bleak sea coast—the last place
on earth where one would expect to meet with any mortal,
and above all with christians*." The following account was
wrote by an officer from Pensacola, and has been confirmed
by other eye-witnesses. "My expectations with regard to this
country and the hopes of every one else are sunk to the lowest pitch. Instead of the finest country in the world (as West
Florida was called), we found the most sandy, barren, and

* *Hist. N. France*, VI, p. 263.

---

[8] Captain Thomas Nairne, ablest southern frontiersman of his day,
played an important role in the Southeast. See V. W. Crane, *The Southern
Frontier, 1670–1732* (Durham, N. C., 1928).

[9] Pierre François Xavier de Charlevoix, French Jesuit and traveler.
From 1705 to 1709 he was in America as professor of rhetoric at the Jesuit
College in Quebec. In 1709 he returned to France only to set out for America again in 1720. He voyaged up the St. Lawrence and through the Great
Lakes, and thence down the Mississippi to New Orleans; after being ship-
wrecked in the Gulf of Mexico he returned to France. In 1744 he published
his *Histoire de la nouvelle France;* an appendix to this work contains a
detailed journal of his travels in America and is the only full account we
have of the interior of North America in the first third of the eighteenth
century. See J. B. Brebner, *The Explorers of North America, 1492–1806*
(New York, 1933), p. 357.

desart land that eyes could see or imagination paint! not capable of producing a single vegetable, nor the least prospect of improving it! as the soil for an hundred miles back is every where the same as the sea-shore, and consists not of earth but of the whitest sand you ever saw"; which agrees with the account of Capt. Nairn[e] above. "In summer it is too hot to go abroad in the day time; the months of July, August, and September are said to be as hot as at Jamaica. The winter is very cold; but as it depends on what wind blows, [and] that is very uncertain. You have often contrary extremes in the same day; a south wind scorches and a north wind freezes, which must be very disagreeable. There is so much sickness at Mobile, that almost all the officers are ill, and only sixty men of a regiment able to do duty"; which was afterwards the case at Pensacola.

This is the first part of North America that was ever attempted to be settled and has been better known than any part of the continent, although it seems now to be almost unknown and forgotten. It was first undertaken to be settled by John Ponce in 1512; Vasquez d'Ayllon [Lucas Vásquez de Ayllón] in 1520 and 1524; Pamphilo [de] Narvaez, who had a grant of it in 1528; Fernando [de] Soto from 1539 to 1541; a company of missionaries in 1549; Pedro de Melendez, who had a grant of all the southern parts of North America in 1562 to 1586; the French under [Jean] Ribault and [René Goulainede] Laudonnière from 1562 to 1567; but they all found the country to be so poor and barren, that they abandoned it, insomuch that it has never been settled as a colony to this day.[10] Soto travelled all over the western

[10] For the activities of these explorers and would-be settlers consult J. B. Brebner, *The Explorers of North America, 1492–1806* (New York, 1933); J. W. Lowery, *The Spanish Settlements within the Present Limits of the United States; Florida, 1502–1574* (New York, 1905).

parts of the peninsula, from the bay of Spirito Santo [Tampa bay], where he landed, and tells us from that to the inland parts of Georgia, "that country which is no less than 350 leagues in extent, is a light and soft sand, full of swamps, and very high and thick bushes, which is very poor and barren"; but where lands bear nothing but bushes or under-woods in America, they are good for nothing. Narvaez again searched all the eastern and inland parts for 280 leagues, "and found it to be all a low flat sand, full of swamps, with a sad and dismal aspect throughout the whole country." "Solum omne quod hactenus lustraverant (secundum ipsorum calculum 280 leucarum) planum erat atque arenosum multis stagnis riguum—Tristem & squallidam regionis faciem re-nuntiavit."*

From all these accounts, and from all the authentic documents with which the council of the Indies in Spain could furnish him, which were numerous, the historian of America again informs us, "Florida is a poor country, without any commodity but a few sorry pearls, and all who ever went to it died in misery."†

* *De Laet.* 1[ib]. iv. c[ap]. 3. *Herrera,* dec. iv. 1[ib]. 4. c[ap]. 4. [The first citation refers to Joannes de Laet, *Novus Orbis sen Descriptionis Indial Occidentalis.* The work of a Dutch scholar, it was first published at Leyden in 1625 as *Nieuvve Wereldt oft Beschrijvinghe van West-Indien.* . . Subsequently revised by the author, it went through several editions and was translated into other languages, including Latin. The work of Antonio de Herrera y Tordesillas, *Descripcion de las Indians ocidentales,* was first published in Madrid in 1601. Translated into several other languages, new editions continued to be published until well into the eighteenth century. In 1725–1726, an English edition, translated by Captain John Stevens, was brought out in London in six volumes as *The General History of the Vast Continent and Islands of America.* The English translation is inaccurate and differs from the original in the decades, books, and chapters by which the original was divided. The citation in the original of *American Husbandry* could refer to any one of the Spanish editions which retained the original division into decades, books, and chapters. Ed.]

† *Present State of Great Britain and North America,* p. 197. *Herrera,* dec. iii. 1[ib]. 8. c[ap]. 8. [See preceding footnote. Ed.]

The bounds of both the Floridas were settled by proclamation in the autumn of 1753: they extend northwards, the east province to the limits of Georgia, and the west to the 31st degree of north latitude: now it is to be remarked that the barren noxious country just described on various authorities extends a very little farther than lat. 31, for when you come to Manchac[11] on the Mississippi the high lands begin, and a country in every respect the reverse of West Florida. Those accounts and writings therefore which represent this country in a favourable light must undoubtedly have reference only to the tract of high country beyond the *new* limits of the province. I shall hereafter shew that that country is one of the finest in the world.

The description here given of the two Floridas may be supposed to carry a strong condemnation of that article in the peace of Paris which gave to Spain an object of vast value[12] in return for a province which apparently was not worth the expence of keeping; but the same impartiality which was my guide in describing the climate and soil, obliges me to declare that this idea would not be so just as it may at first sight appear: if Florida was accepted with a view only for cultivation and colonizing upon the same principles as other colonies, I should agree that the remark would be undeniably just, but the matter may reasonably be put in a quite different light. Florida was an acquisition worth making, upon the principles of removing a dangerous neighbour and acquiring the possession of a coast equally well situated for cramping, in case of war, the commerce of the Spanish colonies or carrying on a clandestine trade with them. When Georgia was settled with a view to rendering it a frontier against the enemy, and when general Oglethorpe executed the expedition against St.

[11] Manchac is now in East Baton Rouge parish of Louisiana.
[12] Cuba and the Philippines.

Augustine, had he succeeded in it, and conquered the whole of the two Floridas, we should then have had pens in plenty to prove the importance of the country: considered in this light it is of importance; at St. Augustine the Spaniards were dangerous enemies, and would have continued so till Georgia became far more populous than it is at present; they also afforded a retreat to runaway negroes, which was a great inconvenience.[13] The point of carrying on a clandestine trade with the Spanish colonies is more important; this may be judged of by the fact of the imports from West Florida, amounting, soon after the peace and notwithstanding Mr. Grenville's preposterous regulations,[14] to the annual sum of 63,000£. in Spanish dollars, a sum superior to what was received from Georgia thirty years after settling at an immense expence, and is an earnest of what may in future be expected if a more politic conduct is pursued.

That the possession of so great an extent of coast, bounding a streight [strait] through which the Spanish galleons have their course, may prove, in case of war, a very valuable acquisition, cannot be denied; for by means of the ports this coast yields us, we may be able to cruize for the enemies ships with much greater probability of success than we ever had before in this part of the world. Nor should it be forgotten that the possession of these provinces renders our dominion

---

[13] This was one of the arguments used later by the many citizens of the United States who desired the acquisition of Florida. See H. J. Carman, *Social and Economic History of the United States* (Boston, 1930), pp. 555–56.

[14] Reference is here made to Grenville's efforts, as Chancellor of the English Exchequer, to tighten the British mercantilistic regulations during the decade of the seventeen-sixties. For the Grenville proposals consult C. M. Andrews, *The Colonial Background of the American Revolution,* (New Haven, 1924); G. L. Beer, *British Colonial Policy, 1754–1765* (New York, 1907).

in North America complete; the whole territory of that continent east of the Mississippi is now entirely ours; the course of that river is now open to us to its mouth, a matter perhaps of more consequence in future than all the other points I have mentioned, and which we could not have had securely without the joint cession of Florida and the eastern Louisiana; there is a roundness now in our continental dominions which will save our posterity, if not ourselves, no slight expences.

That these are circumstances of merit, can be denied by none but men who are determined to judge and condemn compendiously and without the trouble of discrimination; but such general and concise determinations are seldom founded in that degree of accuracy and truth which a candid enquirer will naturally demand. How far the country is adequate to the reasonable expectations of the kingdom—for the great sacrifices made for it—is another enquiry, not fit to be made at present, while the parties who made the peace and those who opposed it are yet living, and their politics yet the signal for arrangement in party matters; nor is such an enquiry so nearly connected with the subject of this work as the objects which I have principally treated of. What I have laid before the reader is sufficient to shew that the rational plan of proceeding with relation to these provinces is to secure the coasts by a few strong and well situated fortresses, that the country may be safe from the attacks of enemies, and that there may be the proper accommodations for shipping, for the views of attack in time of war, and trade in time of peace; as to planting, none should be encouraged but such as was subordinate to the design of supplying the garrisons and shipping. By no encouragement, however, I do not mean restrictions, but avoiding those public means of bringing new settlers which are often put in execution: such people will be employed to far more national purposes in other parts of our colonies, which exceed Florida equally in health and fertility. As the strength of the Spaniards is now collected at New Orleans, and as the navigation of the Mississippi is much the most important object we have in this part of the world, the government should be particularly attentive to keeping all the forts, stations, and fortresses in that part of the province in the best condition, that in case of a rupture with Spain, we might there be secure. When the new colony of the Ohio comes to flourish, in that manner which it certainly will in a few years, the infinite importance of this object will be striking to every one; nor should we forget the noble tract of fertile country we have on the banks of the Mississippi, which will one day or other be among the most important parts of all America, and which will almost entirely depend on the undisturbed enjoyment of the free navigation of that river.

CHAPTER XXVII

EASTERN LOUISIANA

Territory eastward of the Mississippi—Climate—Soil—
Great fertility—Productions—Cattle—Face of the
country—Staples produced here by the French—Pro-
posed colony—Observations

I GIVE the name of Eastern Louisiana to the tract of
country on the east side of the river Mississippi, from the
boundary of West Florida[1] to the forks of that river, formed
by its junction with the Ohio. This country reaches from latitude 31 and ½ to latitude 37 and ½; and from east to west
I extend it to the countries of the Chic[k]asaw, Cherokee,
and Creek Indians, which is about the distance of from 150
to 300 miles;[2] this space being entirely free from the habitations, huntings, and claims of the Indians, having been in
the undisturbed possession of the French till their cession of
it to Great Britain, and settled and planted at various places
according to the inclinations of the individuals, who came
from France or Canada. The country west of the river is that
part of Louisiana which they retained, and afterwards ceded
to the Spaniards.

[1] Following the Treaty of Paris (1763) the British created the province of West Florida, making the Appalachicola River the boundary between East and West Florida. See R. G. Adams, *A History of the Foreign*
Policy of the United States (New York, 1924).

[2] This area embraced what are now the States of Alabama, Mississippi,
and the greater part of Tennessee and Kentucky.

This territory was left as hunting ground for the Indians in the proclamation,[3] which settled the bounds of our colonies, in 1763, an arrangement which has since been justly and severely condemned; since it was in this instance, as well as in that of the Ohio, the giving up the best countries acquired by the late war, at the same time that we planted the worst.[4] But as I conceive that this territory of the Mississippi will come in a few years to be settled and planted, from the same cogent reasons which have at last induced the government to allow the settlement of the Ohio, I think it will be highly proper to give the best description of it that can be procured in those circumstances which relate to agriculture. I am rather induced to do this, as I have it in my power, from the information I have received from an ingenious gentleman of South Carolina, and likewise from two officers, all of whom either travelled through or resided in the country, to lay before the reader a few circumstances not sufficiently known before. Their intelligence also enables me to distinguish, in the accounts that have been published of the country, facts from errors and mistakes.

Relative to the climate of this country it resembles that of the back territories of Carolina near the mountains, but is at the same time generally allowed to be better and more healthy; particularly in the circumstance of not being so hot in summer nor so cold in winter. The whole territory enjoys much such a temperature as the best parts of Spain: the air is clear, dry, and pure, perfectly free from all mists and fogs. This quality is much owing to the country being remarkably

[3] Proclamation of 1763. See William MacDonald, *Documentary Source Book of American History* (New York, 1926), pp. 113–14.

[4] For a detailed treatment of the Proclamation of 1763 and its effect upon public opinion, British and American, see C. W. Alvord, *The Mississippi Valley in British Politics* (Cleveland, 1917).

high and dry; in general from one to two hundred feet higher than the river in its greatest floods; there is not a swamp or a marsh in the whole country; no stinking unhealthy effluvia to thicken and poison the air, which in so considerable a tract of our colonies is destruction to the health of the inhabitants. The heats here are very seldom oppressive, from the dryness of the air; and instead of the incessant and heavy rains which surprise Europeans in Carolina, Georgia, and Florida, it on the contrary seldom rains on the Mississippi, north of the bounds of West Florida, that is, in the high country. This circumstance is very valuable, not upon account of healthiness only, but for several valuable articles of cultivation, particularly silk and wine. The reader cannot attend too much to the climate of this country, because very essential interests will by and by depend on it; whenever the proposition to settle it is made, objections may perhaps arise on account of climate, and new tales in support of Lords of *Trade,* who oppose *plantations;*[5] but let the world then recollect the accounts which have long ago been given of this province, and which in every circumstance of climate has been uniformly described by every person that has been there. Had the countries which have been of late years colonized

---

[5] The Lords of Trade were originally a committee of the British Privy Council. Created in 1675 it was composed of men of high station, influence and wealth. It acted upon royal instructions which embodied the views of the London merchants in carrying out its primary function of making the colonies profitable to the merchants and the Crown. Merchant dissatisfaction with its methods led to its being superseded in 1696 by a new agency—the Lord Commissioners of Trade and Plantations, commonly known as the Board of Trade. This new body of eight active, working members represented the merchant class. Inasmuch as the members of the Board of Trade served continuously and labored diligently, they became the best informed officials in England on colonies and trade, and powerfully influenced imperial policy. See W. T. Root, *The Relations of Pennsylvania with the British Government* (New York, 1912).

(particularly Nova Scotia and the Floridas) been described in a just and true manner in all the circumstances of climate and soil, errors which have been made might not have happened. But with relation to the tracts of country on the Mississippi, all travellers, residents, writers, &c. agree in one general and uniform voice, all describe the climate as being perfectly wholesome, free from excessive and oppressive heats, from fogs, damps, rains, and such intense colds as are felt on the coast of Carolina in the same latitude. In all these respects, no country can be more truly desirable.

The soil of this country is not at all inferior to the climate. Du Pratz,[6] who resided sixteen years in Louisiana, and eight of them at the post at Natchez, and who from his profession of a planter must necessarily be a judge of land, speaks of it on terms that leave one nothing to doubt. From that part of it to the Ohio, which is about 900 miles, the slope of the lands goes off perpendicularly from the Mississippi, being on the banks of that river, from one to two hundred feet high. All these high lands are, besides, surmounted in a good many places by little eminences or small hills and rising grounds, running off lengthwise with gentle slopes. It is only when we go a little way from the Mississippi that we find these high lands are overtopped by little mountains, which appear to be all of earth though steep, without the least gravel or pebble

---

[6] Le Page Du Pratz resided in Louisiana fifteen years. During this time he was not only a successful planter but was interested in the Natchez and other Mississippi Indian tribes. His *History of Louisiana or of the Western Parts of Virginia and Carolina: containing A Description of the Countries that lye on both sides of the River Mississippi, with an Account of the Settlements, Inhabitants, Soil, Climate, and Products* appeared in three volumes in 1758. It was translated from French into English and condensed into two volumes in 1763, and this translation was reprinted in 1774. Although poorly written, it contains a wealth of detail, particularly concerning Indian life.

being perceived on them. The soil, continues he, on these high lands is very good. It is a black light mould, about three feet deep, on the hills or rising grounds: this upper earth lies upon a reddish clay, very strong and stiff; the lowest places between these hills are of the same nature, but there the black earth is between five and six feet deep. The grass growing in the hollows is of the height of a man, and very slender and fine; whereas the grass of the same meadow on the high lands rises scarce knee deep, as it does on the highest eminences. All these lands are either meadows or forests of tall trees, with grass up to the knee; the timber is oak, hickory, mulberry, &c. Even reeds and canes grown on the hill sides, tho' they are found in our maritime colonies only in the richest swamps.

All the accounts we have had, both public and private, agree in these circumstances, and nothing can be more decisive of the excellency of the lands in this country. In the southern parts of this continent grass is very scarce every where but on the richest lands; insomuch that it is no unsatisfactory proof of the soil being good to find a plenty of any grass, much more such a luxuriant product of it as is met with even on the hills of this country. The trees are no less indications of what the nature of the land is, being such as are only found on good soils and of a size and straitness met with alone on the very richest.

Charlevoix, who from the vast extent of his travels was no stranger to these appearances of various kinds which denote good land and in general a fine country, has several particulars which it is proper to transcribe. Speaking of his entrance into this country from the north, he says, "There is not, in my opinion, a place in all Louisiana more proper for a settlement than the fork at the junction of the Mississippi and the Ohio, nor where it is of greater importance to have one; the whole country watered by the Ouabache[7] and Ohio, which runs into it, is extremely fertile, consisting of vast meadows." A later writer, of our own country, makes the same remark:

the most important place in this country, and perhaps in all North America, is at the forks of the Mississippi, where the Ohio falls into that river, which, like another ocean, is the general receptacle of all the rivers that water the interior parts of that vast continent. Here those large and navigable rivers, the Ohio, the Cherokee river, Ilionois, Missouri, and Mississippi, besides many others which spread over that whole continent, from the Ap[p]alachian mountains to the mountains of New Mexico upwards of a thousand miles both north, south, east, and west, all meet together at this spot; and that in the best climate and one of the most fruitful countries of any in all that part of the world, in the latitude 37°, the latitude of the capes of Virginia, and of Sante Fé, the capital of New Mexico.[8] By that means there is a convenient navigation to this place from our present settlements to New Mexico, and from all the inland parts of North America, farther than we are acquainted with it; and all the natives of that continent have by that means a free and ready access to this place. In short, this place is in the center of that vast continent and of all the nations in it, and seems to be intended by nature to command them both; for which reason it ought no longer to be neglected by Britain.

Upon the neighbourhood of the Chisaw[9] river, Charlevoix remarks that the country is delightful; the meadows preserve their verdure in the winter, and a considerable number of well-wooded

[7] The Wabash. That the early explorers and cartographers were not well acquainted with the Ohio region is evident from an examination of their accounts and their maps. *The Novissima Tabula Regiones Ludovicianae* prepared after 1717 for example, which is strikingly accurate in many respects, is faulty in its delineation of the Illinois, the Wabash, and the Ohio. See E. D. Fite and A. Freeman, *A Book of Old Maps* (Cambridge, 1926), pp. 175–77.

[8] An examination of a map of the United States will show at a glance that this statement is not accurate. Santa Fé was a little below the 36th parallel.

[9] Probably the Chickasawhay River.

islands in the Mississippi, some of which are pretty large, form very beautiful canals, through which the largest ships may safely pass; it being affirmed that there is sixty fathom water in the Mississippi above 150 leagues from the sea. As to the forests, which almost entirely cover this immense country, there is nothing perhaps in nature comparable to them, whether we consider the size and height of the trees, or their variety and the advantages which may be drawn from them; for excepting dy[e]ing woods, which require a warmer soil, and are only to be met with between the tropics, there is hardly any sort of trees which can be mentioned that are not to be found here. There are forests of cypress eight or ten leagues in extent, all the trees of which are of a thickness proportioned to their height, surpassing every thing we have of that kind, in France. That sort of ever-green laurel, which we have called the tulip tree on account of the shape of its flower, is now beginning to be known in Europe. This grows to a greater height than the ches[t]nut tree of India, and its leaf is much more beautiful. The canton of Natchez is the finest, more fertile, and best peopled of all Louisiana; it lies at the distance of about forty leagues from the Yazows,[10] upon the same side of the river. Several little hills appear above the fort, which is called Rosalie, and when these are once passed, we see on all sides very large meadows separated from one another by small thickets of wood, which produce a very fine effect. The trees most common in these woods are the oak and those which produce nuts: the soil is every where excellent. The late Mons. d'Iberville,[11] who first entered the Mississippi by its mouth, having penetrated so far up as the Natchez,

[10] *The Yazows constituted one of the important lower Mississippi Indian tribes. See p. 387, footnote 13.*

[11] Pierre Moyne Sieur d'Iberville (1661–1706), French Canadian soldier and colonizer. In 1698 after a series of brilliant campaigns against the English in the North, he was placed in command of four vessels with colonists and supplies, to plant a settlement at the mouth of the Mississippi, a project which La Salle had failed to accomplish thirteen years before. He was the first definitely to ascertain the mouth of the Mississippi from the Gulf approach and to explore its delta. In 1699 he made his settlement at Old Biloxi on the east side of Biloxi Bay. In 1702 the settlement was moved to Mobile. See C. B. Reed, *The First Great Canadian* (New York, 1910).

found the country so delightful and so advantageously situated that he concluded the metropolis of the new colony could no where be better placed. If ever Louisiana becomes a flourishing colony, as it may very well happen, it is my opinion there cannot be a better situation for a capital than this. It is not liable to be overflowed by the river, has a very pure air, and a great extent of country; the soil is well watered, and capable of producing every thing. Nor is it at too great a distance from the sea, and there is nothing to prevent shipping from going up to it. Lastly, it is at a convenient distance from all those places where there can be any design of making settlements.

The reader will remark that these several accounts are perfectly consistent; it is evident from them that all this country, to the east of the Mississippi, is one of the finest in the world in respect of climate and soil; the air is pleasant and healthy, the heats are never oppressive nor the frosts injurious; the atmosphere is clear and dry, and free from the impurities with which it is loaded in countries abounding with marshes and swamps: the circumstance of the face of the country being high, and either hilly or sloping off in gradual ascents, and the soil at the same time deep and rich, is uncommon and particularly valuable; for great fertility in such healthy regions is by no means generally found. The spontaneous productions are also such as give the most perfect satisfaction, whether taken as mere indications of what the soil is, or for their native value. Some of them have been mentioned, but others are equally deserving attention.

Among these I shall first mention the vine, which, says Du Pratz, is so common in Louisiana, that whatever way you walk from the sea coast for 500 leagues northwards, you cannot proceed an hundred steps without meeting with one; but unless the vine shoots should happen to grow in an exposed place, it cannot be expected that their fruit should ever come to perfect maturity. The trees to which they twine are so high and so thick of leaves, and the intervals of underwood are so filled with reeds, that the sun cannot warm the earth or ripen the fruit of this shrub. On the edge of the savannahs or meadows we meet with a grape, the shoots of which resemble those of the Burgundy grape: they make from this a tolerable good wine, if they take care to expose it to the sun in summer and to the cold in winter. I have made this experiment myself, and must say that I could never turn it into vinegar. There is another kind of grape which I make no difficulty of classing with the grapes of Corinth, commonly called currants. If it were planted and cultivated in an open field, I make not the least doubt but it would equal that grape. Muscad[t]ine grapes, of an amber colour, of a very good kind and very sweet, have been found upon declivities of a good exposure, even so far north as the latitude of 31 degrees. There is the greatest probability that they might make excellent wine of these, as it cannot be doubted but the grapes might be brought to great perfection in this country, since in the moist soil of New Orleans the cuttings of the grape, which some of the inhabitants of that city brought from France, have succeeded extremely well and afforded good wine.

Mulberries are found in vast plenty in most parts of the country. They have great numbers and a variety of kinds of walnuts and hickories, and large chestnut trees, which however do not grow in plenty within 100 leagues of the sea. Of the common forest timber, the red cedar is the most valuable; it is found in great plenty. Next to it ranks the cypress: it is reckoned incorruptible; one was found twenty feet deep in the earth, near New Orleans, uncorrupted. Now the lands of Lower Louisiana have been found to be augmented two leagues every century; this tree therefore must have been buried at least twelve centuries. Boats called *pettiaugres* are made of single trunks of this tree, that will carry three or four thousand weight, and sometimes more. Of one of these trees a carpenter made two, one of which carried sixteen ton, and the other fourteen. The pines are only found on the sandy tracts on the sea coast. The sassafras is here a large and tall tree. The myrtle wax tree is found in plenty, and its wax was always one of the principal articles in the exports from New Orleans. The locust (*acacia*) is found on all the higher lands and is a strong sign of a good soil. The mangrove is found in some parts of the country. Among their oaks they have the ever-green one and the red; it is well known that the best ships built in America are those which have their timbers of ever-green oak, and their plank of cedar; and it is asserted that the red oak of Louisiana is as good as the ever-green one. The ash, elm, beech, lime, hornbeam, asp willow, alder, &c. are the same as in Europe. Sarsaparilla grows naturally in Louisiana, and it is not inferior in its qualities to that of Mexico. Hops grow naturally in the gullies in the high lands. The canes or reeds grow to vast height; one kind comes in moist places to eighteen feet, and the thickness of the wrist. The natives make mats, sieves, small boxes, and other works of it. Those that grow in dry places are neither so high nor so thick, but are so hard, that, before the arrival of the French, the natives used splits of these canes to cut their victuals with. After a certain number of years the large canes bear a great abundance of grain, which is somewhat like oats, but about three times as large. The natives carefully gather those grains, and make bread or gruel of them. This flour swells as much as that of wheat. When the reeds have yielded the grain they die, and none appear for a long time after in the same place, especially if fire has been set to the old ones. Hemp grows naturally in this country; the stalks are as thick as one's finger, and about six feet long: they are quite like ours, both in the wood, the leaf, and the rind. The flax which was sown in this country rose three feet high.—The reader cannot well have greater satisfaction relative to the high importance of this country, than the preceding recapitulation of part of its natural produce. The productions of agriculture will not be found to speak less effectually to the same purpose.

Maize was not only cultivated by the Indians in small quantities for their subsistence during a part of the year, but also by the French as an article of considerable exportation to the sugar islands: it was here found to thrive better on a black and light earth than on a strong one. Such as began plantations of it in the woods, thick set with cane, found an advantage in the maize which made amends for the labour of clearing the ground; a labour always more fatiguing than cultivating a spot already cleared. The advantage was this; they began with cutting down the canes for a great extent of ground; the trees they peeled two feet high quite round. This operation they performed the beginning of March, as then the sap is in motion in that country: about fifteen days after, the canes, being dry, were set on fire and burnt, burning or at least killing the trees with them. The following day they sowed the maize, in squares four feet asunder; the roots of the canes which are not quite dead shoot out fresh canes, which are very tender and brittle, and as no other weeds grow in the field that year, it is easy to be weeded of these canes, and as much corn again used to be made in this manner as in a field already cultivated.

Wheat, rye, barley, oats, pease, and beans of many sorts thrive no where in the world better than on the high lands in this country, in every spot where the French planted them, and yielded a produce much greater without manure than can be gained in common lands in Europe with great manuring: the temperature of the climate suits wheat extraordinarily, and no soil can be better adapted to it. But in Lower Louisiana upon the coast, which is the same country as West Florida, the French found that it would not thrive at all.

Indigo was commonly cultivated in this country, than which none more favourable, either in climate or soil, is any where to be found: the high lands produce it naturally. In the islands from the heat of climate they cut it four times; three good cuttings are had in Louisiana, of as good a quality at least, and producing as much as their four. In the particulars before given concerning indigo in Carolina, I shewed that this plant required a rich, deep, black, dry loam, which is scarcely any where to be found in such perfection and plenty as in the country on the east of the Mississippi. No where in all North America will this staple be cultivated with so much success as here: the lands on the Ohio are as rich in many parts, but the climate is not so warm, being hardly warm enough for cultivating this plant with great success. Indigo is highly profitable both to the planter and the nation; it will therefore be found, whenever this noble country is colonized, that it must be one of the chief staples of it, and the crops which will be here raised will certainly induce the people on the barren unhealthy coasts of our old colonies to quit them and settle here, where their profit will prove very different, and they will thereby advance the interests of Britain as much as of themselves.

Hemp, I before observed, grows wild in Louisiana; but upon the eastern banks of the river, for a long way, there are very few tracts of low, marshy, strong land, such as hemp delights in, the lands being in general high and dry; that quantities might be made on the deep black mould, I doubt not, and perhaps if it was tried, it would not be found to require so much moisture; but, as upon the Ohio, hemp is also found spontaneous; and, as the country is more various, having some tracts of low moist land on a strong clay which would do admirably for this plant and in which is found great natural crops, for this reason hemp might be considered as a staple for the Ohio, and the rich dry lands of the Mississippi applied to those crops which will only thrive in such.

Tobacco is another plant indigenous in this part of America; the French colonists cultivated it with such success that had they received any encouragement from their government they might soon have rivalled Virginia and Maryland; but instead of this they were taxed heavily for cultivating it, by duties laid on the trade; what they produced was of so excellent a quality, as to sell some at five shillings a pound. This was raised in the country about Fort Rosalie,[12] and to Yasouz.[13] And there is one advantage in this culture here which ought not to be forgotten: in Louisiana the French planters, after the tobacco was cut, weeded and cleaned the ground on which it grew, the roots push forth fresh shoots, which are managed in the same manner as the first crop. By this means a second crop is made on the same ground, and sometimes a third. These *seconds* indeed, as they are called, do not usually grow so high as the first plant, but notwithstanding they make very good tobacco. Whereas in Virginia

[12] Fort Rosalie was erected by the French just below the Indian town of Natchez.

[13] Yasouz refers to the country of the Yazoo. For location of both Fort Rosalie and the Yazoo see V. W. Crane, *The Southern Frontier, 1670–1732* (Durham, N. C., 1928), map following p. 325.

and Maryland the planters are prohibited by law from cultivating these *seconds,* the summers are there too short to bring
them to maturity; but in Louisiana the summers are two or
three months longer, by which means two or three crops of
tobacco may be made in a year, as easily as one in Virginia.
And a very experienced person in the tobacco trade assures
us, that the fresh lands on the Mississippi will produce thrice
or four times as much per working hand as our old plantations in Virginia and Maryland.[14] This is perfectly consistent
with the best accounts we have received from thence, which
agree in describing the soil as very rich and very deep, of a
black colour, and light and dry; such a soil is of a boundless
fertility from its depth; where there is only a thin stratum,
though the richness may be great for a time, yet successive
crops of exhausting plants will wear it out in no great number of years; but when the soil is, like that on the country on
the east of the Mississippi, the same for three, four, or five
feet deep, the planter has nothing to fear. Every circumstance
that is necessary to success in tobacco planting is found in this
territory. First, the right soil is the greatest plenty. Second,
very extensive tracts of fertile meadow, covered with the
most luxuriant grass for the maintenance of immense herds
of cattle. Third, a navigation close to the tobacco lands, which
admits ships of five hundred tons. Fourth, a climate much
better for this culture than that of our tobacco colonies. If
all these circumstances are duly considered, it will be found
that whenever the tobacco trade declines or threatens a decline, the wise conduct will be to plant it in a country so
highly favourable to the business.

[14] Cf. L. B. Gray, *History of Agriculture in the Southern United States
from 1620 to 1860* (Washington, 1933), I, 213 ff.

Silk may be produced in this country in any quantities that the population will allow of; for the mulberry is found in great plenty all over the high lands. The leaves of the natural mulberry trees of Louisiana are what the silk-worms are very fond of; I mean the more common mulberries with a large leaf, but tender, and the fruit of the colour of Burgundy wine. The province produces also the white mulberry, which has the same quality with the red. Du Pratz has a very just observation on making silk in this country. "The culture," says he, "of indigo, tobacco, cotton, &c. may be carried on without any interruption to the making of silk, as any one of these is no manner of hindrance to the other. In the first place, the work about these three plants does not come on till after the worms have spun their silk: in the second place, the feeding and cleaning the silk-worm requires no great degree of strength; and thus the care employed about them, interrupts no other sort of work either as to time or as to the persons employed therein. It suffices to have for this operation a person who knows how to feed and clean the worms; young negroes of both sexes might assist this person, little skill sufficing for this purpose; the oldest of the young negroes, when taught, might shift the worms and lay the leaves; the other young negroes gather and fetch them; and all this labour, which takes not up the whole day, lasts only for about six weeks. It appears therefore that the profit made of the silk is an additional benefit, so much the more profitable as it diverts not the workmen from their ordinary tasks. If it be objected that buildings are requisite to make silk to advantage, I answer, buildings for the purpose cost very little in a country where wood may be had for taking; I add further, that these buildings may be made and daubed with mud by any persons about the family, and besides may serve for hanging tobacco in, two months after the silk-worms are gone."

There is another circumstance in which the high lands of this country are peculiarly adapted to the culture of silk, which is the dryness of the climate. Upon the maritime parts of our old colonies, the continual rains are very detrimental to this tender worm, which requires a fine healthy climate, as much as a man of a tender constitution: in such the silk is always made in larger quantities, and of a far better quality. This is a point which has not been sufficiently attended to, but whenever we come to plant this country, the great advantage of it will be found in making silk.

Cotton is another article which the French cultivated with success in Louisiana, but which like others never came to be a national object for want of more people, and perhaps for want of encouragement, owing to their fear of rivalling their sugar islands, which also produce it in large quantities. The cotton they cultivated here is a species of the white Siam. This East India and annual cotton has been found to be much better and whiter than what is cultivated in our colonies, which is of the Turkey kind; both of them keep their colour better in washing, and are whiter than the perennial cotton that comes from the islands, although this last is of a longer staple. It is not so long nor so soft as the silk-cotton. It is produced, not from a tree as in the East Indies, but from a plant, and thrives much better in light than in strong and fat land; in the lower lands of Louisiana it never was so fine as on the higher ones. It may be planted on lands newly cleared and not yet proper for tobacco, much less for indigo, which requires a ground well worked like a garden. The seeds are planted three feet asunder, more or less, according to the quality of the soil; the field is weeded at the proper season, in order to clear it of the noxious weeds, and fresh earth laid to the roots of the plant, to secure it against the winds. The cotton requires weeding neither so often nor so carefully as other plants; and the care of gathering is the employment of young people, incapable of harder labour: when the pods burst it is gathered, and the most laborious part of the work is to separate the cotton from the seeds, though it is much lessened since the use of mills was introduced.[15] The high, light, and dry soil in the territory on the east side of the Mississippi is all admirably adapted to this production; and in point of preparation it is not only the fresh that may for the first year be planted with it; after the luxuriance of the soil is abated by tobacco and indigo, it will do exceedingly well for cotton. This article is not mentioned in this or any other case as a proper staple for the sole employment of any colony, but joined with others of greater value it is a good addition to the best settlements in America; for I have often remarked, what should not be forgotten, that no colony should stick to any one staple so much as to neglect others; the inconveniences of such a conduct are to this day and have been long felt in our tobacco colonies, where, for want of other staples such as silk and wine, they have gone too much into common husbandry, which produces nothing wanted in Britain.

The olive tree is common in Louisiana, and very beautiful. The Provençals[16] who were settled here affirmed that its olives yielded as good an oil as those of their own country. The crop is always very abundant. This is an article which would prove of great advantage to Britain, and of profit to

[15] The first successful device for separating cotton seed from the lint was the cotton-gin invented by Eli Whitney in 1793. Prior to this date crude "machines" had been tried but the results were unsatisfactory.

[16] Peoples from an old province in southeastern France called Provence.

the planters; and no produce would be a staple more proper for a colony. In Carolina, on the coast, the frosts sometimes kill large olive trees, but such extremes of weather are never met with in the high dry territories of this country.

These are the principal staples which should be attended to when this country is planted; wine, silk, indigo, tobacco, and cotton; they are valuable commodities, come truly within the definition of a colony *staple;* [and are] commodities which this nation either consumes herself or could command a ready market for, and which are of such value as to enable the planters to purchase negroes in great numbers, so as to enter largely and effectually into their culture. I before shewed that the climate, in respect of health and pleasantness, possessed every advantage that could promote the interests of every branch of agriculture, an object which is of great importance and in which the British colonies upon the coast, through all that part which is flat and sandy, are greatly deficient. In other respects, the advantages attending this country are equally valuable.

Among these the plenty of wild cattle is not the least, since they not only indicate the fertility of the land, but will afford, for many generations, immense supplies of meat and hides: the principal kinds are deer and buffaloes. All Louisiana contains prodigious tracts, almost boundless they might be called, of rich meadows, covered with a luxuriant growth of very fine grass; tracts that have scarce any interruptions of forest, hills, or vallies extend from five to ten and twenty leagues. Such immense pastures of the richest land, in a warm and fine climate, where the winters yield a plenty of food as well as the summers, could scarcely be free from herds of cattle; and accordingly they are found in such prodigious numbers, as to astonish all travellers that go through the country.

This beast is about the size of one of our largest oxen, but he appears rather bigger on account of his long curled wool, which makes him appear to the eye much larger than he really is. This wool is very fine and very thick. A pretty large bunch rises on his shoulders, in the place where they join to the neck. He is the chief food of the natives, and was the same with the French from the beginning of the colony. The quantity of tallow they yield is very great, and their skins are an object of no small consideration. The natives dress them with their wool on, as Du Pratz informs us, to such great perfection as to render them more pliable than our buff.

The plenty of deer in all parts of this country is very great, notwithstanding the numbers that are constantly killed; they are much the same as the deer of Europe: their skins form one of the most valuable articles of commerce in all the southern colonies of America, and in this country the plenty is yet greater from the immense space of uncultivated land which they have to spread over. Nor is it only in these two articles, which are native to the country, that a great plenty is found; for all the animals which have been brought from France and the English colonies have multiplied exceedingly; horses, cows, hogs, sheep, &c. are, I apprehend, cheaper than in any of our colonies; this is not to be wondered at, for in no part of America are there found such plenty of natural meadows. The fruits of this country are in the same plenty as Carolina, but of a finer relish from the dryness of the climate; they have, besides grapes, plums, papaws, peaches, oranges, citrons, figs, apples, &c. The French colonists planted the peach stones about the end of February, and suffer the trees to grow exposed to all weathers. In the third year they will gather from one tree at least two hundred peaches, and double that number for six or seven years more when the tree dies. As new ones are so easily produced, the loss of the old ones is not in the least regretted. Upon the whole, there is the greatest reason to conclude that the territory on the east of the Mississippi, which is at present in our possession, is one of the most valuable countries in all America, and one which will pay admirably for colonizing, whenever the measure is thought proper by [the] government to be embraced. It appears on respectable authority, not only of able writers, but gentlemen now living who have travelled through it: that the climate is as fine as any in the world, equally favourable to the production of many valuable staples and to the health and pleasure of life; that the soil is as fertile as any in the world, though high and dry, circumstances almost invaluable; that the country abounds in an immense plenty of food for cattle, and is spread with vast herds of buffaloes and deer; that fruits, of various kinds, are superior in plenty and flavour to those of any other part of the continent; that indigo, tobacco, hemp, flax, vines, silk, olives, and other valuable staples may be cultivated here with much greater success than in most of the other parts of America. To this if we add navigation of the Mississippi and the rivers which fall into it we shall find the territory to be deficient in no one circumstance that can contribute to render it a flourishing and wealthy colony.

As such, I think there can be no objections rationally made to settling it. The establishment of a new colony on the Ohio might be thought at first sight to supersede it, but if better considered it will not be found so. There is one circumstance in which this territory is much superior to the Ohio, which is that of navigation: the latter has a land-carriage across the mountains of forty miles, which will lay a heavy burthen on those commodities that are not very valuable, so as to make it necessary, perhaps, to send them down the Mississippi, in which case the same commodities may be sent to market from this country upon cheaper terms. Nor should we forget to add that the greater degree of heat on the Mississippi would prove more favourable to several of the staples than the climate of the Ohio, which is not so hot—and we may in general conclude that the value of the staples of all colonies that are healthy will be found to increase in proportion to their proximity to the line. This comparison of the two climates concerns only certain articles, for instance, indigo, cotton, and olives, which require for a perfect culture a hotter climate than the Ohio, though indigo may be produced there with profit. But in the case of tobacco, hemp, flax, silk, wine, &c. the Ohio is fully equal; and in all the productions of common husbandry, except Indian corn, perhaps superior. But in another case there is found a strong propriety, at least, in settling the Mississippi, which is the forming a chain of settlements along the banks of that river to the junction with the Ohio colony, in order for strengthening the country on one side against the Spaniards, and on the other against the Indians. The Creeks, Cha[o]ctaws, Cherokees, and Chic[k]asaws would then be entirely surrounded, and we should never more have any thing to dread from their resentments: the scheme long ago proposed by several gentlemen of America, well versed in Indian affairs, to stop all supplies of gunpowder for them in case of a war, would then be practicable; and without doing them any injury, we should lay the foundation for a perfect security.[17]

[17] The selling of guns and ammunition to the Indians was forbidden in many parts of colonial America. In Netherlands, for example, such trade was prohibited by edict of the Dutch West India Company. Cf. C. M. Andrews, *The Colonial Period of American History*, Vol. III (New Haven, 1937), pp. 87–88.

In case of such a settlement being made, the whole valuable part of that continent, the southern division of it, would then be in the desirable state of improvement: the population, from being so spread round a great extent of frontier, would increase without giving the least cause of jealousy to Britain, land would not only be plentiful, but plentiful where our people wanted it; whereas at present, the population of our colonies, especially the central ones, is confined; they have spread over all the space between the sea and the mountains, the consequence of which is that land is become scarce, that which is good having been all planted or patented; the people therefore find themselves too numerous for their agriculture, which is the first step to be [i.e., toward] manufactures, that step which Britain has so much reason to dread. Nothing therefore can be more political than to provide a superabundance of colonies to take off all those people that find a want of land in our old settlements; and it may not be one or two tracts of country that will answer this purpose; provision should be made for the convenience of some, the inclinations of others, and every measure taken to inform the people of the colonies that were growing too populous that land was plentiful in other places, and granted on the easiest terms; and if such inducements were not found sufficient for thinning the country considerably, government should by all means be at a part of the expence of transporting them. Notice should be given that sloops should always be ready at Fort Pit[t], or as much higher on the Ohio as it is navigable, for carrying all families, without expence, to whatever settlements they chuse on the Ohio or the Mississippi. Such measures, or similar ones, would carry off that surplus of population in the central and northern colonies, which has been and will every day be more and more the foundation of their manufactures. They never could establish such fabrics, while the plenty of good land in a good climate was so great as to afford every man an opportunity of settling; for while that was the case, none would let themselves as workmen in a manufacture. Consistent with these ideas, we see that [in] those colonies where the good land is most plentiful in a good climate, the manufactures are trifling, or none to be found, which is the case with the tobacco colonies and with the southern ones; but in the northern settlements, where these circumstances are different, we there find many fabrics.

Nothing can be more fortunate than the navigation of the Ohio quite to the Ap[p]alachian mountains, at the back of the center of all our colonies, since by that means people may, with only a small or a moderate journey, arrive at a navigation that will carry them through all that immense tract which we may in future colonize, a part of which we are now about to settle, and yet more of which I am urging the propriety of likewise settling. Were it not for this vast navigation, to the very spot almost that one would wish to have it, there would be difficulties in the people getting to the countries we wanted them to settle in; but as we possess this great advantage, it would be unpardonable not to make effectual use of it, in case the establishment of new colonies did not of itself draw the whole surplus of population away from those provinces the numbers in which want so much to be thinned.

Nor is the advantage of drawing off people from the northern colonies confined to the prevention of manufactures; it is further of vast consequence to take them from countries that produce nothing valuable in a British market, and fix them in others abounding with staples of high importance to the commerce and manufactures of the mother country:

this single idea ought to be the corner-stone of all the regulations and measures adopted by this country in her transactions
with America; and if it is well pursued in future, will keep
off the dangerous rivalship, which there is so much reason
to fear, from the manufactures and commerce of the northern
colonies.

If the country on the east bank of the Mississippi was
settled, and that to the south of the Ohio also, there would
be such a variety of land, climate, and productions, that every
new comer, either from Europe or our own colonies, would
have it in his power to chuse the culture with which he was
best acquainted or by which he expected to make the most
considerable profits: they might fix on the climate most agreeable to their constitutions, and in all other respects have such
a variety of circumstances to select from, that the temptation
to move would be very great. At the same time that they
suited themselves, they could not fail, fix where they would,
of promoting the interest of the mother country in a very
sensible degree. By not delaying such a measure, there would
be a population, and with it, a power, fixed in the most important part of all this continent, upon this immense inland
navigation, which spreads far and near from the Atlantic
Ocean to the South Sea, and from the Gulph of Mexico to
Hudson's Bay: the river Mississippi with its branches spread
over most of it, and the lakes, with the St. Laurence, which
are nearly connected with the former, go through the rest.
It is of prodigious future consequence to be masters of this
navigation, and to have early a power fixed on it, in order to
over-awe and keep the Spaniards from designs against our
colonies. We ought not to forget their jealousy of us in this
country, and that they have at present a much greater military force there than ever was possessed by the French. It

is a mistake to imagine that the Spaniards have been inattentive to the *security* of their American colonies; as backward as they have always been in their improvement, they have been far enough from negligence with relation to a military power; I mean since the last peace, for upon the conclusion of it, their whole army was dispatched from Old to New Spain, and the arrangement of the former left entircly to new levies. This was a very bold and decisive measure, and which shewed a resolution to be stronger in America than ever was experienced before: it is for this reason that we ought to be particularly attentive to the strength of our territories on the Mississippi, and to give them it effectually must be done by peopling them, instead of keeping the whole country in as desolate a condition as it was a century before the French discovered it.

General O'Reilly,[18] when he took possession of New Orleans, had a force of five thousand regular troops, with a good train of artillery, and every requisite for a small but well appointed army. This force they have maintained here; it is much superior to any thing we have in West Florida and upon the Mississippi; our government therefore ought certainly to be upon their guard in this part of the world, and not only to have a sufficient military force in the forts and armed sloops upon the river, but a chain of populous settlements to cut off all possibility of communication between the Spaniards and the Indians to the east of the Mississippi; a point which may in future prove of very great consequence.

[18] Alexander O'Reilly, a Spanish general of Irish descent, took possession of Louisiana in 1768. He subsequently commanded an expedition against Algiers.

CHAPTER XXVIII

THE ILLINOIS

Country of the Illinois—Climate—Soil—Productions—
Importance of this territory—Observations

B Y THE country of the Illinois, I mean all that territory
to the north-west of the Ohio, extending on both sides
the river Illinois quite to Lake Michigan and the river St.
Joseph, the settlements made by the French on the river
My[i]amis; but in particular the country east of the Mississippi, between the Ohio and Illinois river, to the distance of
about an hundred miles from the former. This territory
went among the French by the general name of the country
of the Illinois. It claims attention in this work, first because
we are in possession of all the settlements made by the
French in it, and notwithstanding its being deficient in all
government but that of the commanding officers of our forts,
they have increased considerably by the wandering settlers
from our colonies: and secondly, because the great richness
of the soil and fertility of the climate will hereafter attract
so many inhabitants as to make the establishment of some
civil government highly necessary. The public accounts given
of this country are not numerous, but what there are, are
very consistent with each other and also with the private
information I have received from the officers with whom I
have conversed, that made a considerable residence here.

Charlevoix, who passed through this country, has given

some slight descriptions of different parts, which will afford
a pretty good idea of it: he entered it by Lake Erie,
the country upon which, though not included in it, yet is so
near as to deserve our attention here. Of the tract on the very
southern point of that lake, he speaks as follows. "I coasted
along a charming country, hid at times by very disagreeable
prospects, which however are of no great extent. Wherever
I went ashore, I was quite enchanted by the beauty and variety of a landscape, which was terminated by the noblest
forests in the whole world. Add to this that every part of it
swarms with water-fowl; I cannot say whether the woods
afford game in equal profusion; but I well know that there
is a prodigious quantity of buffaloes. Were we always to sail,
as I then did, with a serene sky, in a most charming climate,
and on water as clear as that of the purest fountain; were we
sure of finding every where secure and agreeable places to
pass the night in, where we might enjoy the pleasure of
hunting at a small expence, breathe at our ease the purest
air, and enjoy the prospect of the finest countries in the universe, we might possibly be tempted to travel to the end of
our days."

Of the country between Lakes Erie and Huron, he says,
"It is pretended that this is the finest part of all Canada;
and really, if we may judge by appearances, nature seems to
have refused it nothing that can contribute to make a country
delightful; hills, meadows, fields, lofty forests, rivulets,
fountains, rivers, and all of them so excellent in their kind,
and so happily blended, as to equal the most romantic wishes;
the lands, however, are not all equally proper for every sort
of grain, but most are of a wonderful fertility, and I have
known some [to] produce good wheat for eighteen years
running, without any manure; and besides, all of them are

proper for some particular use. The islands in the channel, between the two lakes, seemed placed on purpose for the pleasure of the prospect; the river and lake abound in fish, the air is pure, and the climate temperate and extremely wholesome. There grow here citron trees[1] in the open fields, the fruit of which, in shape and colour, resemble those of Portugal, but they are smaller and of a disagreeable flavour. On both sides of the channel the country is said to preserve its beauty for ten leagues up; after which you meet with a smaller number of fruit trees and fewer meadows; but after travelling five or six leagues further, inclining to Lake Erie towards the south-west, you discover immense meadows, extending above a hundred leagues every where, and which feed an immense quantity of those buffaloes, whereof I have more than once made mention. Twelve leagues off this channel, before you come to Lake Huron, is a village of Missisaguy Indians,[2] seated on a fertile soil, at the entry of three magnificent meadows, and in the most charming situation that can be, the country for the whole twelve leagues continuing always most delightful. This is a noble channel, as strait as a line, and bordered with lofty forests, interspersed with fine meadows, with many islands scattered up and down in it, some of which are considerably large."

Of the territory on the river St. Joseph, he speaks as follows. "The river St. Joseph has more than an hundred leagues of course, its source being at no great distance from Lake Erie; it is navigable for fourscore leagues, and as I was sailing up towards the fort, I saw nothing but excellent lands, covered with trees of a prodigious height. Tobacco grows

[1] An ovate, acid, juicy fruit, larger, less sour, and thicker in rind than the lemon.

[2] A branch of the Ojibwa or Chippewa Indians.

well here, and by making a proper choice of soil, we might raise a most excellent sort of it."

Proceeding to the south by the river Huakiki[3] which falls into the Illinois, he observes, that

at about fifty leagues from the source the country becomes beautiful, consisting of unbounded meadows, where buffaloes are to be seen grazing in herds of two or three hundred. Where the Huakika joins the Ilionois, the latter becomes a fine river; it does not yield in largeness to any of our rivers in France, and I can assure you, it is not possible to behold a finer and a better country than this which it waters. Before we came to Lake Pimiteouy,[4] we crossed a charming country, and at the end of that lake came to a village of the Ilionois; than which nothing can be more delightful than its situation: opposite to it is the prospect of a most beautiful forest, which was then adorned with all the variety of colours, and behind it is a plain of an immense extent, skirted with woods. The lake and river swarm with fish, and the banks of both with game. From the lake to the Mississippi the river Ilionois, both in breadth and depth, is equal to any of the greatest rivers of Europe. After sailing five leagues on the Mississippi, we arrived at the mouth of the Missouri. Here is the finest confluence of two rivers that I believe is to be met with in the whole world, each of them being about half a league in breadth; but the Missouri is by far the most rapid of the two, and seems to enter the Mississippi like a conqueror, carrying its white waters, unmixed, across its channel quite to the opposite side; this colour it afterwards communicates to the Mississippi, which henceforth it never loses, but hurls with precipitation to the sea itself.

About Fort Chartres[5] the French have several settlements, and

---

[3] Kankakee.

[4] Peoria Lake in North Central Illinois.

[5] Fort Chartres was located on the east bank of the Mississippi, about twenty miles above the point where the Kaskaskia River empties into that stream. See "A Plan of the Several Villages in the Illinois Country with Part of the River Mississippi &c." by Thomas Hutchins, reproduced in E. D. Fite and A. Freeman, *A Book of Old Maps* (Cambridge, 1926).

live pretty much at their ease: they sow wheat, which succeeds very well; and they have black cattle and poultry. The banks of the river are extremely high, so that though the waters sometimes rise five and twenty feet, they seldom overflow their channel. All this country is open, consisting of vast meadows to the extent of five and twenty leagues, which are interspersed with small copses of very valuable wood. White mulberries especially are very common here; but I am surprised that the inhabitants should be suffered to cut them down for the building of their houses, especially as there is a sufficient quantity of other trees equally proper for that purpose. The whole country, from hence to Kascasquias [Kaskaskia], and around the latter, is very fertile; it is capable of becoming the grainery of Louisiana, which it is able to furnish with corn in abundance, even should it be peopled quite to the sea. The soil is not only extremely proper for wheat, but besides, refuses nothing necessary or useful for human life. The climate is extremely temperate, lying in 38 degrees 39 minutes north latitude. Cattle and sheep would multiply here wonderfully, even the wild buffaloes might be tamed and great advantages drawn from a trade of their wool and hides and from their supplying the inhabitants with food. The air is very wholesome. Frosts are sometimes felt that are very severe; the river last winter was frozen over in such a manner that people crossed it in carriages, notwithstanding it is at that place half a league broad, and more rapid than the Rhone. This is the more surprising, as for the most part, excepting a few slight frosts occasioned by the north and north-west winds, the winter is in this country hardly sensible; the leaves fall sooner in this place than in France, and do not begin to bud till about the end of May, notwithstanding that it snows very seldom here, and although, as I have already observed, the winters are exceeding temperate. What then can be the reason of this backwardness of the spring? For my part I can see no other than the thickness of the forests, which prevents the earth from being warmed by the sun soon enough to cause the sap to ascend. At Cape St. Anthony I saw the first canes.

I have been led to make these long extracts from Charlevoix, because his authority has always been justly esteemed, and he gave this account long before the country became subject to Britain: although he only touches upon certain circumstances of the soil and climate, as a traveller and not a resident, yet may we gather from it that both are excellent, that the soil is fertile in yielding tobacco and the articles of common husbandry, particularly wheat; that the forests are among the finest in the world; the meadows of an unbounded extent, and full of buffaloes; that the air is pure and healthy, and the climate in every respect temperate and agreeable; and lastly, that the beauty of many tracts of this country is as great as the finest assemblage of wood, water, hill, and dale can make it.

Much later accounts confirm these particulars. When Charlevoix was there, in 1721, the French had but begun to cultivate it, but since that period they have made a great progress; so that at the peace of 1762[6] they had a fine and well settled colony about Kascasquias [Kaskaskia] and Fort Chartres, and also many settlements on the river My[i]amis, principally inhabited by emigrants from Canada: some of these sold their effects, and retired upon the conclusion of the peace, but the major part remained under the British government; nor has the country declined since, notwithstanding the only government established in it is that of the commanding officers of the garrisoned forts.

Mr. Pownall,[7] in his *Administration of the Colonies*, gives,

---

[6] Peace of 1763 (Treaty of Paris).

[7] Thomas Pownall, English statesman and colonial governor, aided the English attempt to expel the French from North America. He became governor of Massachusetts in 1757 and of South Carolina, for a short period, in 1759. He returned to England in 1760 and four years later published his famous work, *The Administration of the Colonies*, in which he urged a closer union between the Colonies and Great Britain. In 1767 he became a member of Parliament. He opposed Edmund Burke's move for

from very good authority, a few particulars concerning the country of the Illinois. "This country, says Charlevoix, in 1721 will become the grainery of Louisiana; and in 1746 we find it actually becoming so, for in that year it sent down to New Orleans fifty ton of flour; in 1747 we find it well furnished with provisions, and having fine crops; and in a letter of Mons. Vandreuil's [sic],[8] in 1748, we have an account of its produce and exports—flour, corn, bacon, hams both of bears and hogs, corned pork, and wild beef, myrtle-wax, cotton, tallow, leather, tobacco, lead, copper, some small quantity of buffalo wool, venison, poultry, bear's grease, oil, skins, and some coarse furs; and we find a regular communication settled with New Orleans, by convoys, which come down annually the latter end of December, and return at latest by the middle of February."

The private accounts I have had of this country confirm the preceding articles of intelligence, and give the greatest reason for determining that it ranks among the best and most agreeable of America; especially in every circumstance that concerns the plenty and agreeableness of living, and all the

conciliation but subsequently realizing the hopelessness of the English cause, introduced a peace bill in 1780. He spent the latter part of his life in travel. See A. W. Pownall, *The Life of Thomas Pownall* (New York, 1908).

[8] Pierre François Vaudreuil to whom reference is made in this passage was the son of the Marquis de Vaudreuil, last governor of New France, from 1703 to 1725. Pierre François, who inherited his father's title, was born at Quebec in 1698 and died in France in 1764. Like his father, he was a soldier in the French army. In 1733 he became governor of Three Rivers and ten years later of Louisiana. In 1755 he became governor of Canada, but was regarded with contempt by Montcalm, whose friends, after the surrender of Montreal and the return of Vaudreuil to France, made charges which caused the ex-governor's imprisonment in the Bastile. He was exonerated from all blame and released, but was stripped of nearly all his possessions. See Francis Parkman, *Montcalm and Wolfe* (Boston, 1884).

productions of common husbandry, in which I believe it yields to no part of the world. As to staples in a British market, it will be by no means deficient in them, whenever the advantages of the climate are any ways seconded in these respects by the skill and industry of the planters. Tobacco may undoubtedly be produced here in any quantity, and of a quality equal to any other: the country, most of it, in the same latitude as Virginia and Maryland, with the advantage of a much more regular climate, and winters less severe. Charlevoix expressly says that in general the winters are exceedingly temperate; whereas in Virginia extreme sharp frosts are common: but through all our southern and central colonies the maritime parts are exposed to greater degrees of heat and cold than the internal country. The navigation of the Mississippi will make the culture of tobacco very profitable. Wine may also be a most beneficial staple to this country, the climate is perfectly agreeable to it, and high, dry, and hilly tracts common throughout the whole territory: the navigation will be equally favourable to the product of this country. Silk is another which will undoubtedly be made in considerable quantities whenever the territory is peopled, since the healthiness and temperature of the climate cannot in this latitude but agree admirably with the worm, and mulberries are plentifully spread over the whole of it. In a word, it is deficient in no article that can tend to render it a valuable colony, and whenever it is settled will be found of that importance to this kingdom, of which we have already experienced those to be that possess staple productions.

CHAPTER XXIX

JAMAICA

*Climate—Soil—Productions—The culture of sugar—
Expences — Produce — Profit — Observations — Other
staples—Settlements—Remarkable instances of beneficial improvements—Observations*

THE amazing importance which has attended the culture
of the sugar cane, is perhaps one of the most extraordinary instances of the effect of agriculture that the world has
produced, and it shews clearer than any other circumstance
wherein consists the true and beneficial nature of colonies:
the profit which this nation reaps from her islands in the
West Indies ought above all other things to make her attentive to every particular in the culture of the sugar cane. As
Jamaica is our principal colony for this production, I shall
be more minute in my account than in the description of
other islands, as they will call only for the circumstances
wherein they differ from that island.

Jamaica lies between 17 and 19 degrees north latitude,
from whence it is easy to judge that the climate is extremely
hot: indeed the sun passes directly over their heads, and
would, in the height of summer, render the air too suffocating to breathe, were it not for the trade wind and land breeze
which refresh and cool the air. Yet with this advantage which
Jamaica enjoys in common with the rest of the islands, the
climate is in general pernicious to European constitutions.

The extreme heat is not so great an enemy as the dampness and moisture which attend it: and we may in general remark that this is the circumstance which in all latitudes, but especially hot ones, decides the healthiness of a country. A dry and pure air, such as is found on hilly or mountainous sea coasts, free from marshes or swamps, is always healthy, though under the line; but when a meridian sun unites with a marshy rotten soil, in which the heavy rains stagnate, then it is impossible for a country to be tolerably healthy. The people of Jamaica lament their thunders and lightnings, their tempests and hurricanes—the last are indeed very fatal to their profit; but if health was only considered, a low marshy tract of land, in parts of which the rains stagnated, should be considered as a much more fatal circumstance. The great evil of the climate is its moisture, which, united with heat, brings that numerous list of fatal distempers which are common in this island; which renders caution in diet and living remarkably necessary, and which is worse than fatal in causing that extreme languor of the body and oppression of the spirits, which make the inhabitants suffer worse than death through half their existence. In a word, the climate of Jamaica is such an one as nothing but the hope of wealth could induce an Englishman to live in. With an exception, however, of the hilly tracts, which, and the mountains, are by no means unhealthy for a hot climate.

The island is entirely out of the reach of frost and snow, nor have they ever any weather that can be denominated cold: they have properly neither winter nor summer, for the trees never lose their leaves; the only distinction of season is that of the rains, which fall in July, August, and September, but principally in August. They also have heavy ones in May and October, and sometimes a season (that is, a rain) happens in January. Their hurricanes are extremely dreadful; in some of them the wind is so furious, and rises to such a pitch in a few minutes, that every obstacle flies before it; trees of an immense size are torn up by the roots, and blown away like chaff—whole groves disappear in an instant—buildings, however solidly constructed of stone, and the walls, many feet thick, purposely constructed to withstand these terrible blasts, are destroyed in a moment; in a word, the surface of the earth is truly bared, every thing is swept from it with irresistible violence: it may easily be imagined, that, in such a situation, the canes and other objects of culture are the first to be blown away. These storms of wind are not all of equal violence, nor do they spread [over] a large tract of country at once; buildings very strongly built sometimes escape, at others every thing gives way.

Jamaica is about one hundred and forty miles long by sixty broad, and contains about four millions of acres. But much the greater part is not patented to any owners, and a very small portion of it is cultivated. The face of the country is extremely various. Along the middle of the island, from east to west, runs a vast chain of mountains, called the Blue Mountains: these occupy above half the island, for they spread in various ridges, some higher than others, with deep furrowed glens between them; and in some places flat vales of amazing fertility are found, quite surrounded with rock and precipice. The hills are all either rock or stiff tenacious clay; every thing else is washed down into the vales by torrents, cascades, and waterfalls, which are numerous, or by the heavy rains in general; thus all the lower lands are found to be a loose friable mould, prodigiously fertile—as the want of roads and navigation prevent their being cultivated, they are generally covered with fine grass, but some are forest. Most of the hills and even the rocks, though apparently without earth, are covered with large and strai[gh]t timber trees of various sorts: so that nothing can be seen more romantic or noble to behold than the mountainous scenes, which are usually formed of a great intermixture of rocks, mountains, woods, and waterfalls, with gleams of vale of the finest verdure. The country from the sea coast to the hills is various, but generally consists of woods, marshes, swamps, savannahs, or meadows, and cultivated plantations; many tracts are sandy, but there are none but what produce some article or other spontaneously, which adds to the wealth of the owners, except indeed some of the undrained swamps, which are totally useless.

Among the productions of this island we may reckon sugar, cocoa, indigo, pimento, wild cinnamon, coffee, cotton, tobacco, fustic, red wood, logwood, guaiacum, china root, sarsaparilla, caffia [coffee], tamarinds, venilloes [vanilla], chochineal, mahogany, manchineal, &c. Among these articles, what chiefly claims our notice at present, is the culture of sugar.

The sugar cane is a reed, smooth and jointed, of a shining, greenish, yellow colour. Their size varies according to soil, culture, &c. but the height is generally from four to eight feet, but in some soils they do not rise above two or three feet; in others we sometimes see them nine, ten, or more. In the French islands we are told by Labat,[1] that canes have been known four and twenty feet in length, exclusive of the top and lower joint, and each weighed twenty-four pounds. The largest canes are three or four inches thick, but generally not above an inch.

[1] Jean Baptiste Labat (1663–1738), a French Dominican missionary, was sent to the West Indies which he explored extensively. His several volumes describing his American travels are authoritative sources of information.

They are propagated by cuttings; pieces from fifteen to eighteen inches long are cut from the tops of the canes, a little below the upper leaves: the more knots or eyes there are, the better. The season of planting is principally August, being the height of the rainy season; but it is a work which is done also in September and October, and even quite to January and February, but not later. Before we proceed with the culture, I shall describe the soils usually chosen for a plantation.

In Jamaica the best soil for sugar is the red brick earth, strong, but not clayey; black mould on clay is excellent; all loose friable lands, not very sandy, will do very well, and are of a value proportioned to their moisture; drained swamps, marshes, and bogs, from which the water is carried clean off, frequently do well. But let me in general remark, that a sugar planter's choice of soil is very similar to that of a good English farmer; so that good land is the same in all countries; the mere stiff clay is not good with either; but all loams are excellent; brushy wet gravels are rejected by both; light sands in a hot climate are worse than in England; black mould is every where excellent; and drained bogs and marshes, wherever found, are generally fertile: thus is there not that mystery in judging of soils in different climates that many would persuade us. Poorer lands in Jamaica, as well as in England, require the assistance of dunging and other manuring, and the best yield crops proportioned to such management. The richest soils are fresh woodlands, which when cleared from the wood, and much of the rubbish burnt upon the land, prove for many years an inexhaustible fund of fertility and wealth to the planter; but those woodlands in Jamaica, which are near enough to water-carriage, are mostly taken up and cleared, for if this requisite is wanting, the richest soils will not pay for culture.

Respecting the preparation of the ground, it is brought into tillage and rendered clear of weeds; the former is effected by hand-hoeing, and is repeated till the weeds are all destroyed: the worst is the *withe*,[2] which like couch grass in England has such a vegetative property that the least bit left in the ground grows and multiplies very fast; it climbs up and strangles the canes. The roots of trees must also be destroyed if they are of a kind that sends up suckers or shoots; this is done by burning or scorching them: but other roots they are not attentive to destroy, for as the tillage is given with hoes, it is not necessary to extract such obstructions as would stop the plough. If the land to be planted is fresh or in great heart, they do not manure, but if it has been long under canes or out of order, ample manuring is necessary. In raising dung, they rank among the best farmers in the world, and this I take to be owing to the difficulty of procuring it; in England, where the winters enable good husbandmen to raise almost any quantity they please, it is much neglected; but in Jamaica, where they have no winter, and where the heat of the sun is in general a great hindrance to the work, they are forced to be indefatigable in the work, or they would never effect it.

The refuse of the sugar canes assists them as litter and food for the cattle; the cane tops and leaves of Guinea corn are given the cattle plentifully in pens, where they waste enough to make litter; the pen is first spread thickly with marle or earth, generally the former, and by feeding many

[2] A tropical American weedy herb, the stems of which are used for making baskets and hats.

horses, asses, mules, cows, oxen, and swine in them, by their dung and urine and waste of food they add a layer upon the marle, and prodigiously enrich the whole compost. Then more marle is carted in, and the cattle fed upon that in the same manner; and so in succession till it is wanted for the plantation, when the cattle are moved into other pens, and the compost is turned over and mixed well together, after which it will in a little time be ready for carrying out. This management of cattle lasts through the whole year.

I must observe upon it that it is a system which deserves universal imitation in all countries, how far feeding fat cattle in pens would do in summer is not clear, but as to all lean stock, such as draught oxen, horses, cows, young cattle, swine, &c. it would beyond all doubt answer extremely well: marle, chalk, clay, turf, or earth, should, as in Jamaica, be carted into the farm yards and spread in an even layer about them; upon this should be all the foddering which the farmers bestow upon their cattle; and in summer the system should be continued, by feeding them with grass or clover, &c. mown and given fresh in racks; upon this plan their food would go infinitely farther than in the common way, and they would make four times the quantity of dung they do at present. Necessity obliges the planters in Jamaica to pursue a method, which, if the farmers of Britain would pursue, they would certainly find the same great advantages from.

When the plantations are upon a clay or a stiff soil, they mix sand with the compost, by carrying it in and forming a layer in the pens in the same manner as marle; and the good effects have been often experienced. Ashes of all burnt vegetables are used with care, and their effects said to be great.

After the field has been sufficiently prepared it is marked out, and holes made in regular rows to receive the dung, upon which the canes are planted. This work is called *holing:* the methods used are not all the same, nor the distances. Some make the holes four or five feet asunder, or four by five, and put two or three sets in a hole; but the most common method is to make trenches from four to eight inches deep, according to the weather, in which they lay the canes and cover them; these trenches are sometimes laid out by lines, and ought always to be. The distance between the rows and betwixt the plants in each row may in good ground be about three feet and a half; in poor worn-out grounds two feet are sufficient.

But let it here be remarked that this way of regularly disposing the canes is only followed by the best planters; there are more that plant promiscuously, but it is a very erroneous method, which ought to be exploded. The land planted in either case is in squares, formed by intervals fifteen feet wide, which cross the field at right angles, and are of great use in several instances; they admit carts to be loaded in harvest with the canes, without going over the ploughed ground, which is very mischievous to the crop; and they prevent the spreading of fires, made on purpose to burn trash, or accidental ones; they give a free path to the planter to view the state of the canes, and the negroes when employed in hoeing them; nor is the land occupied by such intervals lost, as pease, beans, potatoes, and other plants may be cultivated in them, that come off before the sugar canes are cut.

When the canes are about eighteen inches high, which will be in a fortnight or three weeks after planting, they are cleared from weeds, and the soil about them loosened by hand-hoeing; and this operation is repeated two or three times, as it happens, till the plants are arrived at such a growth and thickness as to kill all weeds by their thick shade.

The canes are cut when in full maturity, which in dry loose soils is generally at the end of fourteen or fifteen months after being planted; but in cold clay soils not till sixteen or seventeen months. They are cut with hand-bills,[3] as close to the ground as possible, then cleared from their leaves, &c. and cut into shorter pieces, from two feet and a half to four feet in length. The chief precaution here is that the cane be cut off smooth, without hacking the root, which in the dry season is of great prejudice to it. The top of the cane, to the distance of three or four inches below the flag, should be cut off along with the leaves: some are accustomed to save this part, and endeavour to turn the whole of the cane to advantage; but this is a piece of ill-judged frugality: the top of the cane is always green, and contains only a crude, unripe juice, which, mingling with the rest, will greatly debase it.

On cutting the canes they are immediately carried to the mill, usually a windmill, in which, being ground between iron cylinders, the juice is pressed out, and flows through a tube into a vat; thence it is conducted through a pipe into another vat, and after that to the cauldron in the boiling house; it is then boiled, and as fast as any scum arises it is taken off; it runs from this boiler through four or five more, smaller and smaller, in all which it is likewise boiled till it becomes a thick glutinous consistence: when boiling can be carried on no farther, a fermentation is raised by lime water, which is subsided by a small piece of butter, after which it is taken into coolers, where it dries and granulates. In this operation of boiling, the fires are kept in night and day, and the boilers filled in succession, as fast as empty, with fresh juice; the fewel [fuel] is dried cane trash stacked ready for use, and

[3] A small pruning hook or knife.

faggots cut from copses[4] planted on purpose, or from logwood hedges, which are of a very quick growth.

After the sugar is dried and granulated, it is put into pots
of a sugarloaf form, open at the point, through which aperture the dregs of the sugar falls; these dregs are melasses,
or treacle, when it has sufficiently purified itself, it is called
muscovado sugar, being then in order to be put into the hogshead and shipped off. Some planters chusing to refine it yet
farther, cover the sugar in the pots with white tobacco-pipe
clay kneaded with water, which, sinking through the sugar
carries down more of the melasses than will go off without
it, leaving the sugar much whiter than the muscovado: and
at the discretion of the planter the work is repeated once or
twice more, the quality each time increasing in value, but the
quantity diminishing. After this operation it is called *clayed*
sugar.

From the melasses rum is distilled, by means of fermentation in the common method of gaining all other spirits; they
gain in this island from a puncheon[5] to 65 hogsheads of rum
to every hogshead of sugar, but much of their melasses are
sold to New England to be distilled there.

In the continuation of the culture it is to be observed, that
after the canes are cut the land is hoed quite clean, and mis-
carriages among the canes replanted: the shoots that are sent
forth by the stools are called rattoons [rattan], which in due
time yield a second crop nearly as luxuriant as the first, but
not always so, the management of which is exactly the same
as of the first crop. The duration of the plants, however,
depends upon the soil; in poor or worn out ones they will

---

[4] Underbrush, saplings, small trees.
[5] A large cask of varying capacity.

have only one rattoon crop, but in very rich and fresh soils they cut several. Labat says that in some of the French islands they will continue yielding for fifteen or twenty years; but no such thing happens generally.

Upon the system of cutting a crop but twice the planters divide their cane land into three parts. One is fallow, prepared either with the plough or the hoe for planting; the second is the crop in its first year; the third is the crop in its second year. By this means a third is planted new, and two thirds cut in every period of the growth of the crop; that part which this year (of fifteen or sixteen months) is fallow, next year is the crop of the first growth; that part which this year is the crop of the first growth will next year be the rattoon crop; and that part which this year is the rattoon crop, will next year be fallow. Cane grounds are in general from ten to twenty-five acres each piece. The whole system is transferred continually from old ground to new, according to circumstances.

The buildings upon a plantation are very considerable and expensive; they consist principally of a mansion-house, windmill, boiling-house, furnaces, store-houses, sheds, &c. the furniture of which, such as cylinders, vats, coppers, pipes, tubes, reservoirs, coolers, &c. are costly.

Before I give any account of the expences and profit of the culture, I shall make some observations on the essential faults with which their agriculture in this article abounds. First, the preparation of the ground, which is generally fallowed with hoes, though ploughs are used by a few planters, yet the number is inconsiderable. In clearing a piece of fresh ground, they destroy the wood in the manner practiced in the colonies, that is, saw it off and leave the stump to rot in the ground: this effectually precludes the plough. The hoeing culture is more trivial than can easily be credited; for in strength and efficacy it is not comparable to the same operation given by the farmers in England to several crops. Three, four, or five hundred negroes have been seen hoeing a piece of forty acres; they cut about an inch deep, sometimes if the soil is loose a little deeper, and at others not half an inch; if the planter attains any depth that approaches that of ploughing, the expence he is at to get it is enormous. Now it should not be forgotten, that the cane roots at a depth proportioned to the loosened mould upon soils that have any tenacity, indeed in very friable sandy loams, or loose hazel mould, the roots strike much deeper than the hoe has been, or they would not thrive at all; and to remedy these evils it is that holing is practiced, in which they dig small holes where the canes are to be set, to receive the dung and cane set: but such methods in every article of husbandry throughout the world are bad: the roots of all crops should be encouraged to spread over the whole land, instead of being confined to spots where the dung is put, which is always the consequence of not dunging the whole land. Then comes the planting, in which the planters exclude every thing but the hand-hoe, by setting the canes promiscuously; those that plant in rows, use no other tool; the consequence of which is, that the keeping the spaces between the plants loose, in good order, and free from weeds, is all performed by the negroes with their hand-hoes, which is just such management as to use no other tool between the rows of a field of cabbages in England, planted wide enough to admit of horse-hoeing; which in this country would be an expence of ten or twelve shillings for very badly performing an operation which might be very well done for half a crown.

The two errors I have here disclosed are very essential

ones, and in the conduct of them render such prodigious stocks of negroes necessary, as eat amazingly into the profit of the planter. Hence therefore arises the necessity of pointing out methods whereby they may escape such expences, and at the same time execute their work in a much superior manner.

In the preparation of my ground, I would carry the ideas of the improved husbandry of England into that of sugar in Jamaica; I would, in clearing my fresh land, remove all obstacles which might stop the plough, such as roots or large stones; this expence would be well repaid by my successive advantages. I would then plough the fallow of a depth proportioned to that of the soil; in rich deep lands I would go a foot, but in shallower soils eight inches: before the last ploughing I would spread the dung or compost all over the land; and immediately turn it in by the last ploughing, leaving the surface, when the work was completed, flat on dry soils, and ridged on wet ones.

In the next place, my ploughman should draw furrows by the eye, as strait as an arrow, at the distance of three, four, or five feet, according to the distance of the rows of canes, which should be regulated by the fertility of the soil: the richer the land the greater the distance. In these furrows I would lay the cane sets, and cover them by drawing mould over them by negroes with hand-hoes; let us suppose the rows equally distant four feet asunder. As soon as the plants were a foot high, I would run a Berkshire shim,[6] the cutting plate three feet wide, through the intervals; it should cut about two inches deep, in order to cut down the weeds and loosen the surface of the land: at the same time the rows should be hand-weeded. But if the soil was stoney, instead of

---

[6] A horizontal knife attachment to a cultivator for surface scraping between crop rows; used principally for weed removal.

the Berkshire, the Kentish shim should be used, which has three triangular shares instead of one flat one in the other.

These operations should be repeated often enough to keep the soil loose: when the plants were come to that point of growth that made earthing proper, I would run a double-winged plough, the mould-board of which extends or contracts at pleasure, through each interval, the wings so extended as just to throw a surge of mould along the roots of the plants. Such a plough will perform that work better than any hand-hoe; and by thus earthing once or twice after other operations of horse-hoeing, the well tilled earth of the intervals—after being well mixed and intimately united with the dung—would be thrown to the roots to supply them with nourishment as their growth demanded it.

After a trench was thus opened in the middle of each interval, I should go in with shims that took a narrower cut, in order to keep pulverizing the interval till the growth of the canes shut out the horses. After the crop was cut in the usual manner, another great advantage would arise; by laying them in bundles on the top of every third or fourth ridge, carts constructed so as the wheels should spread eight feet, and go each in a trench with the horses in that between them, the carts would be admitted to every part of the plantation without doing the least injury to the stools or roots of the cane: it is upon this system that farmers in England carry cabbages, &c. from off wet lands in winter without poaching.[7] Another benefit arising from this mode of culture, would be the following operation. After the plantation was cleared, I should widen the wings of the double plough, and passing it through every interval, throw a ridge of mould over the cane stools, covering them up, which with such an implement is

[7] As used here "poaching" means "sinking."

very easily performed, and very completely in the effect: this practice, performed with hoes at a great expence, has in several of our islands been found excellent; consequently this compendious way would do it in a manner much superior, and at a twentieth of the expence.

If any considerate person reflects upon this system, in comparison of the method of hand-work now in use—which is certainly the most expensive conduct that is known in any part of the world—he will, I am confident, allow that the saving of expence would be prodigious, and the culture at the same time performed in a manner far superior. The objections that will be made to it (for what plan was ever thought of, against which objections could not be started?) I can easily suppose may be numerous. Those which I have heard, that carry any appearance of reason with them, are the following.

First, that the number of mules, &c. which would be necessary, could not be kept without a greater expence than the present number of negroes. I must be allowed to deny this, as a circumstance perfectly incredible: let it be remembered that most of the planters are obliged to keep very large herds of cattle merely for the purpose of making dung, why not therefore let a large proportion of them be draught cattle for the purpose of tillage? A well-fed beast that works will make as good dung as a beast that does not work; but granting that a larger stock of cattle would be necessary, the quantity of dung raised would be proportioned, and that advantage, where dung is so valuable, would go far to pay the extra expence. But why not appropriate a larger part of the estate to the production of food for cattle? I do not apprehend there is any part of the world in which cattle pays so well, and the want of food is rather owing to the negligence of the cultivator than denied by the climate. Cane tops at one season afford the most luxuriant supply in the world—and stacks of them are made by way of hay, which yield a plenty through some months: the leaves of Indian corn are also made the same use of, and found of high advantage: but the returns made in Jamaica by Scotch grass,[8] as they commonly call it, the greater panic grass, is prodigious. The quantity of its produce exceeds that of any other fodder whatsoever, and yields in value a produce to the amount sometimes of fifty or sixty pounds an acre. When such ample products are to be had, with the assistance in many parts of Jamaica of large savannahs or meadows, and barley, pease, and beans imported from North America at a very moderate price, it must surely be evident enough that any quantity of cattle might be kept for the advantageous purpose of substituting horse or mule tillage for that of hand-work; and the profit attending the practice would certainly be immense.

But let us suppose the expence of attending cattle greater than it really is, are we to be allowed nothing in the saving of negroes, that most expensive mode of labour? Two mules or oxen and one man with a shim will do more work in a day than twenty good negroes; but who will be so hardy as to assert that the former can possibly cost the planter as much as the latter: in the earthing up the plants, three mules or oxen, a double mould-board plough, and two men will do more work than thirty-five negroes. In the preparation of the field a plough, two, three, or four mules, and one or two men will, supposing the depth of tillage the same, perform more work than an hundred negroes; but they will not be able to go the depth at all, and therefore the superiority is the greater: if a less depth is stirred, the plough, or a wide shim of four feet, would do a proportionate quantity of land.

[8] A variety of broom grass.

Now can any persons be so senseless or prejudiced, as to suppose that the saving in negroes would not infinitely more than pay for the increase of expence in cattle?

Secondly, it is objected that the nature of the climate is such as will not admit of the tillage and horse-hoeing I have recommended; that the rains are so amazingly impetuous and the successive sun-shine so powerful as to bind many soils into a hard cement, which could not be wrought by the tools I have described: but in answer to this, I appeal to the common sense of every understanding person, whether horse-work will not prove more effectual than the weak exertion of the negroes hoes? The harder the soil is bound, the less able are they to make an impression on it: if the land was like a baked hard trodden path, the hoes would be useless: but no turnpike road in England is too hard to be torn in pieces by horse-work. But the assertion is not true; cane grounds so hard as to be difficultly worked by horse-hoes would be in such order as none but a sloven could bear; the crop would be nothing; it is a plant that requires as loose friable a soil as any other, and always in that condition; stiff soils must be rendered open with much dung and compost; and a soil that is well manured can never bind in any climate. As to such degrees of baking as really happen, small variations in the horse-hoeing would answer: I would, for instance, be provided with a scarificator or plough of coulters alone to spread two or three feet of ground and cut it into stripes, which would destroy all that caking of the surface which the objection supposes, and which would prepare it for the other operations I have proposed. Another tool proper to be provided with is a spiky roller, weighing several tons, about eight feet long, for working the fallow; and also a small globular one to work in the trenches of the intervals between the rows of canes; these three instruments would effectually answer all such objections as this.

Thirdly, it is answered that the distances of the rows necessary for the admission of the horse-hoes I have described would be too great for the production of a full crop of canes. I am sensible that the majority of planters set their canes in the promiscuous method, at nearer distances than I have supposed; but let me observe, that supposing such practice judicious and necessary, yet is it no objection to my system, since I could horse-hoe wherever the negroes could hand-hoe. English farmers, upon much the same principles, assert that four or five bushels of beans should be sown broad cast over an acre, and the men afterwards to hoe amongst them as well as they can; this assertion, in opposition to the Kentish culture of that vegetable, is like quoting the ideas of the common Jamaica planters in answer to my argument. The moment the growth of a vegetable is known, every person, the least conversant in the different modes of husbandry, must be able to decide at once whether the horse-hoeing mode is well calculated for its culture; and when the sugar-cane is described, that is a strong reed, an inch diameter, and from four to eight feet high, will they not laugh at promiscuous planting and hand-hoeing which, comparatively speaking, is like hand-hoeing a grove of oaks. The article of culture known in England which most resembles sugar is beans, and all our farmers who cultivate that crop to considerable profit agree that the drill and horse-hoe is the only mode which can be attended with great success.

And here I shall make a few remarks on the conduct of the Jamaica planters in the management of their negroes, which may very justly be ranked among the errors of their husbandry.

In the account I gave of the culture of tobacco and rice by negroes, I had occasion to observe that the stock of Blacks was there kept by natural increase; and that the planters were all in the method of tasking their slaves; that is, they allotted them a portion of work every day, which the overseers attended to see well done, but never exacted a larger portion of labour. The management of Jamaica is very different: no task is there set, consequently the men know no end of their labour; they are followed throughout their work by the lower overseers with whips, exactly in the same manner as horses are in England, or if there is a difference, it is that the negroes are more hardly used. The consequence of this system is seen in the decrease of the stock; so that a plantation in Jamaica which employs one hundred slaves requires an annual supply of seven to keep up the number. This destruction cannot be owing to climate, because the coast of Guinea is very similar, and the heat is never oppressive to them; it is owing merely to excessive work and bad usage. Nothing can be clearer to common sense than the evidence of this fact.

The expences, profit and loss of the sugar culture in this island have never been laid before the public with the least degree of accuracy; I have, by making repeated enquiries among Jamaica planters and agents, gained many particulars, which will enable me to give a very satisfactory estimate, and such as, I am clear, will yield more information than has by any other person been published.

Calculation of a considerable plantation in Jamaica

	£.
6,000 acres of land purchased at 11£. per acre	6,600
Two windmills 1,000	
Reservoir, &c. 260	
Boiling-house, coppers, &c. 1,350	
Curing-house 460	

		£.
The stove, &c.	180	
The still-house, &c.	180	
Sheds	90	
Stables, cattle-pens, &c.	230	
Mansion and three other houses	1,600	5,350
Implements of all sorts exclusive of fixtures		500
10 negroes at an average of 120£.		1,200
167 negroes at 50£.		8,350
100 head of cattle, 15£.		1,500
100 ditto at 10£.		1,000
30 mules at 25£.		750
100 swine, 15s.		75
	£.	25,325

One year's expence.

Overseer, managers, drivers, clerks, agents, carrier, &c.	650	
9 negroes	450	
Expences on 177 ditto at 3£.	531	
Repairs of buildings	200	
Wear and tear	100	
Cattle	150	
Lumber	200	
Taxes	100	
Sundries	119	
		2,500
	£.	27,825
Interest at 5 per cent.		1,391
	£.	29,216

If borrowed in Jamaica, the interest will be 8 per cent.

Product

400 hogsheads of sugar of various sizes, but at an average of 15£.	6,000
Rum, 270 hhds.	2,434
	8,434

	Expence	£.
Sundries as above		2,500
Profit,		
which is 20£. 6s. per cent on 29,216£.		5,934

This upon a very moderate average: the interest per cent. will vibrate from 15 to 30; and the planter, if he is very skilful, will carry this 20 to 25 at least; but he must in either case reside on the spot. And here it is necessary to remark that less interest for a capital cannot be supposed in a climate highly insalubrious to European constitutions, and which is exposed to the most dreadful accidents of earthquakes and hurricanes: some allowance, indeed, is made for these in the preceding calculations, but such cannot be adequate, and excludes articles of entire destruction: that the interest is not less, we may also judge from the planters residing in England, leaving their estates to the management of agents, &c. and yet making from four to ten per cent. of their capital, according to their conduct and sagacity, which, all things considered, is a great proof that the culture must be very profitable. And I should further observe that if more enlightened ideas were introduced into the modes of cultivating the cane, the profit would be far more considerable; I have no doubt but 40 per cent. on the capital might be made with as much or more ease than 25 at present. And the reader should note in this case of the sugar culture in Jamaica, as well as in all the branches of husbandry on the continent, that the part of the capital employed in the purchase of the estate pays as great interest as the rest of it which is employed in the cultivation; an advantage no where to be met with in Europe. If a person engages in husbandry in England he may make a good profit on his farming, but as to the purchase of his estate he will not make above 2½ or 3 per cent. by it. Upon

the whole I am inclined to believe that the agriculture of
sugar might be, of all other branches, the most profitable;
and so it ought, for men who sacrifice themselves with such
fortunes, in such a climate, ought surely to make a larger
interest of their money than if they were employed in their
native, or some wholesome climate.*

Besides sugar, this island produces some other staples which
are or might be of very great importance. Among these cotton
is a considerable article, the export amounting to about 2,000
bags; coffee, but nothing like what the French make in their
islands; pimento; mahogany; cocoa was once a very great
article, but it has much declined; indigo was once the staple
of the island, but the attention now given to sugar has rendered all other articles of but small comparative account.

The following is an account of their exports	£.
48,515 hogsheads of sugar at 15£.	727,825
Rum and melasses	433,591
Cotton 1,626 bags at 10£. 5s.	17,479
Coffee 220 casks	2,342
Pimento 438,000 lb.	15,632
Mahogany	17,858
Sundries, as logwood nicarago, fustic, lignum vitae, cocoa, ginger, canella, or winter's bark, peruvian bark, balsams, indigo, aloes, hides, staves, dry goods, bullion, &c.	32,140
Total†	1,246,868

* Since this was written a New History of Jamaica has appeared, which
makes the interest 10 per cent. that is, 6 for interest paid and 4 for the
planter; but that this is very inadequate, every person, on reflection, must
allow, for the planter must very soon be in gaol: if the circumstance of
planters residing in England and making 6 per cent. be considered, it will
certainly be allowed, that on the spot it ought to be 20. [The *History of
Jamaica* mentioned in this note was published in London in 1774. Its author
was Edward Long. It contains much of permanent historical value. Ed.]

† *Political Essays*, p. 286. [See Arthur Young, *Political Essays Concerning the Present State of the British Empire* (London, 1772). Ed.]

This is a prodigious sum for an island to produce, the cultivated part of which does not exceed three or four hundred thousand acres; but as the whole contains four millions, it ought to be a spur to our government to remedy the monstrous evil of such a proportion of it remaining waste: much is certainly incapable of culture, but the tracts of fine soil which would yield sugar, and yet the greater tracts which might be most profitably applied to the culture of other staples, are so many nuisances to the public, which deserve the most serious consideration: the monopolies of wastes are infinitely detrimental, and ought not only to be guarded against in future, but even remedied in past.

Settlements might be made most advantageously upon the lands in this island not yet granted away, if not for the culture of sugar, at least for those of other staples, such as cotton, indigo, cocoa, &c. which require small capitals, and would prove very profitable. A little management in government would bring such culture into more repute, and spread it through those waste tracts which are such a reproach to the nation.

There have of late years been a few very important improvements made in particular spots; but these, though reflecting great honour on individuals, are not of such extent as to remedy the evil of so large a portion of the island remaining uncultivated. Among these one deserves particular attention; it is the improvement Mr. K—— wrought.

That gentleman purchased a swamp for a thousand pounds, which was at the time of his purchase reckoned a very large price for it: his first work was to survey it carefully in order to mark out the drains that would be necessary to lay it dry. Having performed this with as much accuracy as possible, he cut a main drain, through the center of the swamp, into a navigable river, wide enough for canoes to pass and repass; by properly directing this drain, he found so much immediate service from it as to give him the greatest hope of success; this was a very heavy and expensive work to him, for at the time that he first planned the design of a drain, he had his eye on the convenience of a navigation in the future cultivation of the land.

When this main cut was finished, he began cross cuts, through the swamp on each side the main drain and communicating with it; these were of a something less dimension, but yet sufficient for navigating, and as fast as they were finished the swamp became nearly dry, and to appearance sound land: but this was rather deceitful, for upon the subsidence of the surface of the swamp he found it necessary to sink all his drains, which was a work of much trouble and expence.

Having completed a considerable part of the draining, he erected sugar works, with all the necessary buildings, upon the most convenient spot for that part of the swamp which was first dry, purchased negroes, and all things necessary, among which, however, cattle made but a small article. In this respect he made a wonderful use of his navigable cross cuts; by multiplying them from cross to cross he made them fully answer all the purpose of roads and intervals between the divisions of the cane grounds: thus every article of *carriage* in the plantation was by this means transferred from negroes and mules to boats, even to that of the bundles of canes to the mills, &c. This contrivance rendered very few cattle necessary: respecting the object of raising manure, for which so many planters are obliged to sacrifice many other interests, this gentleman, from examining the soil of the swamp accurately, found it of so fertile and promising an appearance, that none would be necessary for many years, as the land looked as if the canes would be rather too luxuriant in their growth than not enough so. But as he also knew that such a quality is continually on the decrease after the land becomes cultivated, he made an ample provision for cattle, by bringing into tillage with the plough some of the larger divisions, and sowing them with Scotch grass (panic), and other plants, so that the profitable part of cattle-keeping might at any time be practiced, without the expence of supporting them merely for their work and dung; there is no part of the world in which cattle for provisions answer better than in Jamaica: this system therefore was answering every beneficial purpose that could be wished. It was executed by degrees as the other works went on.

When drained, the soil of the swamp was found to be a light hazel mould inclining to a peat, about eighteen inches deep, on a bed of stiff loam five feet deep, and under that a white clay: nothing could shew greater signs of inexhaustible fertility than the experiments made with several plants on the first division that was completely drained.

The first establishment for the purpose of planting was that of 100 negroes, with all the buildings requisite, and which was began before the first work of draining was in all parts finished. Nothing could exceed the crop which was reaped, and contrary to expectation the sugars proved of a very fine grain. Every working hand made three hogsheads, which was a produce that is but rarely met with. Every year, for six successive ones, Mr. K—— increased his stock of negroes considerably, and the produce did not fail him in any one of them; so that the immense receipts from his plantation repaid him part of the expence of his drainage; when it was finished, three hundred negroes more were thrown to planting, and the sugars they made were supposed to exceed in quantity per head those of any other plantation on the island.

Upon this great success attending the undertaking, many persons were desirous of purchasing parts of the swamp in order to convert them in like manner into sugar plantations; but Mr. K—— was desirous of having only one trouble with the whole, and offered it to sale to any person or persons that would bargain for the whole purchase. The event of the affair is perhaps the most extraordinary instance of improvement that was ever known: the whole, that is land, buildings, negroes, &c. were sold for ONE HUNDRED THOUSAND POUNDS.

This vast sum was to be paid by installments, bearing interest 8 per cent. till paid. In the valuation the land was reckoned at 60£. each one with another. The following account is not absolutely accurate, but the particulars are not far from the truth.

		£.
Produce of the sale		100,000
Profit on the planting, after the improvement, during seven years		32,000
	Total receipt £.	132,000

Purchase .... £.	1,000	
Drainage, expence in negroes, &c.	27,500	
Buildings	13,000	
Negroes	14,700	
Implements	2,080	
Cattle and sundries	7,500	65,780
Clear profit		66,220

It is very much to the honour of this sensible gentleman that he had sagacity enough to understand the advantages which might be made by draining such a swamp: his plan, before the execution, was treated as a visionary scheme by all the old planters, who laughed at the project and foretold the ruin of the undertaker. The work turning out so successfully will have most beneficial consequences: there are other swamps in the island equally accessible, of the same soil, and as easily to be drained; all which circumstances are clear from the almost immediate rise in the price of such lands upon the success of Mr. K——; and some other undertakings of the same kind have been begun, from which there is reason to expect a similar success.

Improvements of this and other kinds are more wanting in Jamaica than in any of our other islands, for here we have the largest territory we possess in the West Indies. Not above a fourth of this island being patented, and not a fourth of that fourth under any sort of culture, ought to instigate men to more activity and a more acute examination of the districts in this island, which have been hitherto rejected or neglected. Doubtless there are many extensive tracts among them, which might be applied to sugar, if planters would, like the gentleman who executed the above improvement, apply to raising that commodity in new methods, varied and adapted to circumstances in the soil and situation not usual in the old plantations.

CHAPTER XXX

BARBADOES

Climate—Soil—Productions—Exports—Observations on the culture of sugar in Barbadoes

THIS little island, deservedly one of the most famous in the world, is situated in 13 degrees north latitude: it is about twenty-five miles in length, and in breadth fourteen, containing one hundred and forty square miles, and by supposition 100,000 acres.[1] The climate is in some respects preferable to that of Jamaica, and in others inferior: the face of the country on the coast is higher and more free from low grounds and swamps, much of it being quite walled with rocks; this makes the air drier, and consequently healthier; but the nights are hotter from the want of the land breeze, which in Jamaica is owing to the mountains, and Barbadoes having none cannot possess this advantage; but upon the whole, the climate is reckoned superior to that of the other island.

The soil is generally a light hazel loam of a dark or reddish colour, with exceptions for stiffer tracts; it is in every spot of the island capable of bearing some valuable product or other; contrary to Jamaica, every inch being under cultivation. Of their products, sugar is the grand article; indigo they

[1] Barbados is the most easterly of the West Indies. Its area is 166 square miles. It has never been under any flag other than the English; it is sometimes called "Little England." See V. T. Harlow, *A History of Barbados, 1625–1685* (Oxford, 1926).

still cultivate; ginger is a very good article; they have some cotton and pimento. Among their other products they reckon oranges, lemons, citrons, pomegranates, pine apples, guavas, plantains, cocoa nuts, Indian figs, prickly pears, melons, &c. In general, the produce of the island is as rich as any other in the West Indies.[2]

The great value of it to this country will appear clearly from the progress of its trade and export. In 1650, which was only twenty years after its first settlement, it contained between 30 [30,000] and 40,000 white inhabitants, and a yet larger number of blacks. Upon the Restoration the colony granted 4½ per cent. duty on its exports towards maintaining the forts and fortifications, but which has been shamefully misapplied to other purposes.

It is very remarkable that the people of this island spent forty years in raising indigo, ginger, cotton, and tobacco, and then learnt of the Portuguese at Brazil the art of planting the sugar cane, and this acquisition in no longer space than ten years totally changed the face of affairs in the island: the planters who were before in but low circumstances, became remarkably wealthy.

In 1676 the island was at its meridian; by a calculation that was made with great exactness there were then found in it 50,000 white people of all sorts, and 80,000 negroes: this was a degree of population truly amazing. The author of the *European Settlements in America*[3] justly observes that Holland itself, or perhaps even the best inhabited parts of China, were never peopled to the same proportion; and Dr. Campbell remarks, with equal truth, that never any

[2] Its climate is reputed to be the finest in the West Indies.
[3] The authorship of this document has been attributed to Edmund Burke and his cousin William Burke. See p. 29.

colony of ours, or any other nation, was so populous as this: and to make this still clearer to an English reader, we shall observe that Barbadoes is rather less than the county of Rutland, the smallest county in England, and that according to the highest computation, the number of people in that county in 1676 did not exceed 20,000. But this may be made still clearer by comparing that whole island with this in point of extent; for if England and Wales taken together consist of nearly forty millions of acres, then if they were as populous as Barbadoes, they ought to contain fifty millions of people—whereas Sir William Petty,[4] who was a very able man in computation, and is thought not to have undervalued this country, but rather the contrary, never reckoned the people higher than eight millions, which shews what a vast disproportion there is between the peopling of the two countries. But to proceed farther still; the same great man asserts that in Holland and Zealand, which are looked upon to be the best peopled countries in Europe, there are a million of souls inhabiting about as many acres; and consequently it appears from hence that even this country was not so well peopled as Barbadoes.

At present the number of whites are computed to be near 30,000 but the slaves amount to about 100,000. About the same time that the population was at its height, so also was its wealth. In the year 1661 King Charles II created on the same day thirteen baronets in Barbadoes, none of them having less than one thousand pounds, and some of them ten thousand pounds a year. At this time their trade actually main-

---

[4] Sir William Petty (1623–1687), English statistician, was one of the founders of the Royal Society. With Captain John Graunt he compiled the *Natural and Political Observations Made upon the Bills of Mortality* (London, 1662), the first volume published on vital statistics. He also rated as a political economist of high standing.

tained four hundred sail of ships, one with another of [i.e., averaging] 150 tons; their annual exported produce in sugar, indigo, ginger, cotton, &c. amounted to upwards of 350,000£. and their circulation cash at home was 200,000£. These are facts that may be depended upon, that deserve in every respect the greatest consideration, and that plainly demonstrate at once the great value of this island and the prodigious consequence of our plantations in general.*

Let us exclude all that accrued from Barbadoes to the people of England before the Restoration, and estimate its produce from 1660 to 1760 at 16,000 hogsheads of sugar, which make 12,000 ton annually, and omitting entirely the rum or spirits, melasses, cotton, ginger, aloes, and all the other commodities of the island, estimating this at 20£. a ton, it will amount to 240,000£. per ann. or 24,000,000£. in the course of the century either gained or saved to this nation, which, considering that Barbadoes is not bigger than the *Isle of Wight,* must appear a most amazing sum; and yet in proof of the modesty of this computation it would be easy to name a very intelligent author, who before the close of the last century affirmed that no less than thirty millions had been gained by our possession of Barbadoes at the time he wrote. But though his zeal might possibly carry him a little too far then, there is not now the least room to question that the very best judges, by which is to be understood those who are best versed in these kind of things, and who also best understand this trade, would more readily concur in fixing

---

* *Harris's Voyages,* II, 256. [This two-volume document was prepared at the request of London booksellers by John Harris in 1705. A second revised edition, with large additions by Dr. John Campbell, appeared in 1744 ff. A third edition was published in 1764. See the article on Harris in the *Dictionary of National Biography* (London, 1917), Vol. V, pp. 13–14. Ed.]

the amount of our profits during the period before assigned, at thirty than at twenty-four millions.*

As to the present produce of this island, the following is the best account we have had.

	£.
Sugar, 20,266 hogsheads, at 15£.	303,990
Rum and molasses	203,992
Sundry articles, such as ginger, cotton, indigo, sweetmeats, aloes, caffia	30,000
£.	537,982

But in this account is included all the rum that can be made from the total of melasses: I think that article too high: if 100,000£. is allowed for rum, the total will amount to above 400,000£. a year. The custom-house books for 1763 make the British imports from this island above 300,000£.; if to this North America is added, the total, probably, would be as large as above mentioned.

Considering that the export of only 400,000£. a year amounts to 4£. annually for every acre in the whole island, and as towns, roads, water, rocks, &c. which yield no produce must necessarily reduce the 100,000 acres considerably, it would amount probably to 4£. 10s. upon the cultivated part of the soil: and considering further that a large portion of the food of the people, both whites and blacks, is raised upon the island, and also that the planters are obliged to keep many cattle, the principal part of whose subsistence grows

---

* *Considerations on the Sugar Trade*, p. 27. [The author of this volume was Dr. John Campbell. It was written at the request of Lord Bute in order to show the value of the islands ceded by the French at the close of the Seven Years War. Its full title was as follows: *Candid and Impartial Considerations on the Nature of the Sugar Trade; the Comparative Importance of the British and French Islands in the West Indies: With the Value and Consequences of St. Lucia and Granada, Truly Stated* (London, 1763). Ed.]

there, it will be evident that a large part of it is applied to other uses besides yielding the exported produce: further considering that a third part of all the cane grounds is fallow every year, and it will then appear that the part of the island actually yielding exportable produce is small in comparison of the whole; I should not imagine that more than 25,000 acres [is] in that situation, consequently the produce per acre is 15£. But whatever produce is taken, most certainly agriculture never flourished in any country in the world equally with what it has done here: for many years it has been on the decline, not in the value of its produce, for that is as great as ever, but in the *quantity* of it: in the last century they made, it has been asserted, more sugar than at present, consequently the real product of the island was once greater even than the above account: it is the rise in the prices of their commodities that has kept up the total value of their products. But let me slightly remark that I recollect no particular account of the exports in the last century which shews any decline at present even in the quantity.

Relative to the culture of the sugar cane in this island, there is no material difference between their method and that described under the last article. But the Barbadoes planter labours under greater difficulties and larger expences. The soil of the island has been so long employed in yielding crops that it requires more dung than the fresh grounds in Jamaica; it is not worn out, as many superficial writers have asserted, for a good soil never wears out; bad management in the culture of sugar, as well as in any other branch of culture, will exhaust the soil, and it will be inferior till good management restores it. But as long as the planters conduct themselves upon rational principles they will find the produce of their island great as ever. As to the fertility of fresh lands, it is exhausted much sooner than commonly imagined: planters are too apt to take liberties with such land, and pour in a succession of crops in haste to reap the benefit of the goodness of the land, without giving it sufficient rest or changing their system: when this is the case, the fertility of new lands is gone in ten or a dozen years, and they will be even inferior to neighboring tracts that have been in culture a century, but managed upon good principles.

In these there is nothing of greater importance than manuring; this they understand very well in Barbadoes, where every planter keeps considerable stocks of cattle merely with a view to the dung they raise him. They confine them to pens, in which they are fed, that all their dung, urine, and waste of food may be retained in a bed of marle, which they spread in each pen; at certain seasons they mix the heap well together, and find it a mass of manure admirably calculated for the improvement of their land; superior even to what a similar quantity of dung alone would be. This I attribute to the marle retaining the juices of the dung, and parting with them gradually to the roots of the successive crops. Nor has the sun (which in this hot climate is a material point) near such power to exhale the beneficial parts of the manure when united with an absorbent earth, as it has upon dung alone.

The great difficulty of the planters is in supporting cattle sufficient for the purpose of raising the requisite body of manure: the smallness of the island, which is so crammed with people, denies them the extensive savannahs or meadows which they possess in Jamaica; their crops of Scotch grass are not near so great, nor have they the land to spare for it of the right sort; their dependance therefore is principally on cane-tops and the leaves of Indian corn, both which they feed with green, and also make into large ricks in hay. But if they would be persuaded to cultivate lucerne, they would surely reap great benefit from it in the support of their cattle, than which they have no object more essential. The length of the root would secure the plant from the sun, probably when its beams were most violent, and afford, through the heats of summer, fresh crops of green food every month regularly for the cattle: this is what they most want, for at that season all their grass is burnt up, and contrary to the practice of colder climates, the summer is the season for feeding with dry fodder, and the winter that for green. Lucerne therefore would prove of the highest advantage to them.

Another article in their management which might be much improved is the arrangement of their grounds for crops: the cane grounds they keep under canes for ever, with only the assistance of fallow and dung. But on the contrary, the canes should be planted by turns on all the lands of a plantation: sometimes yams, plantains, garden plants, cotton, indigo, &c. &c. at others fallow; and at others under canes, &c. This change of crops would be of great service; the canes would in the succession have the advantage of what may, to them, be called fresh land; and less dung would do than when they are planted always in the same spot.

Nothing hardly is more profitable to a planter than yams, potatoes, and plantains; and these three crops have the same effect in meliorating the soil and preparing it by their shade, for exhausting crops, as potatoes, clover, pease, &c. have in England: nothing therefore can be better management than to make a change of product the foundation for sugar. Let grass lands, when of a proper age, be broken up for those roots, &c. and let the roots be succeeded by canes; after canes, other staples, corn, &c. then fallow, and upon that canes

again, then grasses, &c. By means of such a system the food
for cattle would be much increased, all the lands of an estate
kept in good order, the grasses superior to the common ones,
and the canes from such a change would yield more plentifully.

CHAPTER XXXI

LEEWARD ISLANDS

Antigua—St. Christopher's—Nevis—Montserrat—Barbuda—Anguilla—Climate—Soil—Products—Exports—Agriculture—Observations

ANTIGUA, or Antego, as it is sometimes written, lies in 16 degrees 11 minutes north latitude. It is circular in its form, being about twenty miles in diameter and sixty in circumference, containing about 70,000 acres of land. The climate is inferior to that of Barbadoes, being hotter, and is reckoned more subject to hurricanes. Only a part of it is yet cleared, being in many places covered with its original woods; a circumstance to the benefit of the present planters in many respects. The face of the country in one respect is very singular; there is neither a brook, rivulet, or spring in the whole island, which obliges the inhabitants to depend on artificial ponds, cisterns, and reservoirs of water for all their uses. Threatening as this was originally, experience has removed the difficulties which flowed from it, and they have been able to supply themselves very regularly with this necessary of life.

The soil of the island is generally sandy, but not therefore infertile; on the contrary, there are nowhere more flourishing sugar plantations to be met with than in this island; for there is a loamy mixture in the sand which keeps it from burning; and the reddish earths, though sandy, are found excellent cane lands. The produce of the island has been thus stated:

£.

15,500 hhds. sugar at 15£. 232,500
Rum 63,933
Sundry articles 10,000

306,433

These sundry articles are ginger, a little indigo and tobacco, fruits and other things, common in all the islands; but the quantities are but small, and I should rather think 10,000£. too great an allowance for them. We have no island in the West Indies, Jamaica and the ceded ones excepted, that is capable of such improvement as Antigua: indeed the industry of its owners has carried their agriculture to a much greater height than it was ever expected they would attain; for the time was when Antigua sugars could find no market in Britain, but were sold at low prices to Hamburgh and the North. A very great change has been made since, for at present we do not often see finer muscovado sugar than comes from this island. The improvements to be made are principally those of bringing into culture the lands yet waste or underwood; most of which, it is not doubted, but will produce good sugar, perhaps from freshness superior to the old plantations; if this measure was well effected, we should annually receive from Antigua 20,000 hogsheads of sugar, and a much greater quantity of rum would be made than is at present, proportionably to the quantity of sugar.

St. Christopher's

St. Christopher's [St. Kitts] is situated in 17 degrees 25 minutes north latitude; it is about seventy-five miles in circuit, yet are there not in it above 24,000 acres of land that can ever be brought to yield sugar, for part of it is covered with very high mountains. The soil is remarkable for producing the finest sugars in the West Indies; it is a light, hazel mould on brick earth, of a surprising fertility, which soil is justly supposed to be of all others the best for producing sugar. The climate is as agreeable and temperate as any other island in that hot latitude. The products are

	£.
10,000 hhds. of sugar at 15£. a hhd.	150,000
Rum	41,250
Sundries	7,000
Total £.	198,250

I have had an account of a small plantation in this island given me, which it is proper to introduce here. It is as follows. One hundred and ten acres of land, only part of which is fit for sugar, with a small mansion, one mill, and a proportioned sett of buildings, coppers, &c. were purchased about five years ago for the sum of

	£.
	3,200
Paid for the implements, &c. at the same time ..	113
For 47 seasoned negroes at 62£. a head	2,914
For cattle, &c.	640
£.	6,867

The gentleman who made the purchase left it to the management of an agent, who also had the care of some other plantations. He has generally shipped him 60 hogsheads of sugar a year, and 26 hogsheads of rum.

	£.	s.	d.
60 hhds. sugar at 15£.	900	0	0
26 rum at 9£...	234	0	0
Total receipt	1,134	0	0

	£.	s.	d.		£.	s.	d.
Deduct							
Interest of 6867£. at 5 per cent.	343	0	0				
Agent's bill of charges	655	10	0	998	10	0
Neat proceeds				135	10	0

Hence it appears that the planter in England gains only 2 per cent. for his money more than he may be supposed to pay for it, or 7 per cent. which for a security any ways hazardous, and that of every plantation is much so, must be reckoned miserable interest for his money. This, however, is not owing to the fault of sugar, but of agency: plantations that are left to the conduct of agents and overseers generally turn out so. There is reason to believe from this instance, as well as many others, that greater extortioners are hardly to be met with than West India agents, attornies, and overseers, who generally take such advantage of the distant residence of their employers as to make those estates carry the worst aspect which ought in fact to be highly valued. But it is farther curious to see the profit they allow their masters, which is just calculated to prevent their selling their estates, when themselves shall borrow money in the islands at 8 and even 9 per cent. to throw into a business, from which they remit the owners no more than 7! The truth is, planting sugar upon the fine soil of St. Christopher's will, with proper management, pay from 25 to 35 per cent. for the money employed; but then residence is necessary; for as to living in London by agriculture in the West Indies, it is an impracticable scheme to unite such contraries with profit.

St. Christopher's was many years ago in a very thriving condition; as may be gathered from [the fact that] the sale of the French lands in the island, after the cession of their part of it at the peace of Utrecht, produced so large a sum that the princess of Orange's marriage portion of eighty thousand pounds was paid out of it.

NEVIS

Nevis is situated so near St. Christopher's as to be separated from it only by a narrow channel; it is about six miles across, and near twenty in circumference; for want of the high lands of St. Kitt's, the climate is not so good, nor is the soil reckoned quite equal to it; yet is this small island inhabited by 5,000 whites and 12,000 blacks; a great number for so little a spot, and shows how completely cultivated most of it must be. Its produce is

	£.
6,000 hogsheads of sugar at 15£.	90,000
2,000 hogsheads rum at 9£.	18,000
Sundries	3,000
Total £.	111,000

MONTSERRAT

The island of Montserrat lies in 17° north latitude; it is about nine miles long, and nearly of the same breadth. There is no part of the West Indies that is more healthy or agreeable than this little island. There are some high mountains in it which cool and refresh the air by a land-breeze; and these being at the same time well covered with tall cedar and other wood, the shade afforded is delicious, as well as the prospect it yields lovely. The valleys are extremely fertile, yielding all the West Indian productions in perfection; and they are at the same time well watered. The number of white inhabitants in the island is about 4,500, and the slaves 12,000. The product is about 3,500 hogheads of sugar;

but it is on the improving hand both in population and product.

		£.
3,500 hogsheads at 15£.	....	52,500
1,110 hogsheads rum at 9£.	....	9,900
Sundries	....	1,500
	Total £.	63,900

BARBUDA

Barbuda lies in 17 degrees 30 minutes north latitude; it is about fifteen miles long. The climate is not equal to that of Montserrat, from the lowness of the lands. The soil is very fertile, yet the inhabitants have not gone upon sugar; this has not been from any defect in the soil, climate, or situation, but has been owing to that degree of custom and habit which are so apt to govern mankind. Long after our first settling this island the native Caribbees remained in it, and more than once burnt and plundered the new settlements; this deterred every body from erecting and establishing such expensive and hazardous works as those for sugar; but after the natives were carried off the island, this motive ceased and the conduct should have ceased likewise; but the people being got into the course of common husbandry, they knew not how to quit it: the best part of the island was in hands who, from their ease and comfort of their life, would not part with their farms, which excluded newcomers from introducing sugar; and thus has the island continued to the present time applied almost entirely to raising corn and provisions, principally the breeding of cattle. The neighborhood of the sugar islands, with whom alone they have any connection, affords them a certain and good market for everything they have to sell. The number of people in the island is about 1,500, among whom are very few negroes. The property of the island is in the Codrington family,[1] the head of which puts in a governor at Barbuda, having the same prerogatives the other lords proprietors in their several jurisdictions in America. Their ancestor, colonel Christopher Codrington, governor of Barbadoes, who, dying in 1710, gave two plantations in Barbadoes and part of this island (valued in the whole at 2,000£. per ann.) to the society for the propagation of the Gospel,[2] for the instruction of the negroes in Barbadoes and the rest of the Carribbee islands in the Christian religion, and for erecting and endowing a

[1] The Codrington family was one of the few English families with large estates in the West Indies which resided on its domains and not in England. See F. W. Pitman, *The Development of the British West Indies, 1700-1763* (New Haven, 1917), p. 3.

[2] Christopher Codrington (1688-1710), soldier, wit, scholar, and landed proprietor, was born in the Barbados. Educated at Oxford, he succeeded his father in 1699 as governor of the Leeward Islands. His rule does not seem to have been entirely popular. He spent the last years of his life in seclusion and study, chiefly of Church history and metaphysics. By his will he left two of his Barbados estates, consisting of 762 acres, three windmills and buildings, 315 negroes, and 100 cattle to the Society for the Propagation of the Gospel in Foreign Parts as a foundation for a college in the Barbados in which a convenient number of professors and scholars were to be maintained, "all of them to be under the vows of poverty, chastity, and obedience; who shall be obliged to study and practice physic and chirurgery, as well as divinity; that by the apparent usefulness of the former to all mankind, they may both endear themselves to the people and have the better opportunities of doing good to men's souls, whilst they are taking care of their bodies." The net income of £2,000 a year derived from the estates at this time was sufficient to start Codrington College in 1716. The most flourishing period for the college was from 1740 to 1750. It was the only notable school in the West Indies in the eighteenth century. See F. W. Pitman, *op. cit.*, pp. 9-10; consult also, Sir Robert H. Schomburgh, *History of Barbados* (London, 1848). "The Society for the Propagation of the Gospell in Forreigne Parts" was incorporated by Royal Charter granted by William the Third, June 16, 1701. For the founding and general work of the Society consult C. F. Pasco, *Two Hundred Years of the S. P. G.: An Historical Account of the Society for the Propagation of the Gospel in Foreign Parts* (London, 1901).

college in Barbadoes. This great man was a native of Barbadoes, and, as has been well observed, for a great number of amiable and useful qualities both in public and private life, for his courage and his zeal for the good of his country, his humanity, his knowledge, and love of literature, was far the richest production and most shining ornament Barbadoes ever had.

I before observed that the people of Barbuda addicted themselves to breeding and feeding cattle, and raising corn. Their meadows are some of them very fine ones, abounding plentifully with those grasses which in the West Indies are found most profitable: their herds are not large, from the division of property, but very numerous: having many cows and young cattle, horses and asses, for breeding mules, some sheep, and particularly swine; the products of America are peculiarly adapted for rearing and feeding hogs; most of the trees yield plenty of mast; the leaves of many of their succulent vegetables do well for them, and the products of roots much exceed any thing in Europe. An acre of potatoes and yams in Barbuda will yield as much as three or four acres of potatoes in England. Their method of planting them in this island is thus: they plough the land three times, and then carrying on such manure as they have, mark the field by line into stripes of five feet broad; on each side the line, at the distance of eight inches from it, they lay a row of potatoe setts, and as they proceed cover them with earth, taken with shovels from the spaces between the lines. Planters less attentive will do the same work without lines, but then their land is far from having any neat appearance. As the crop grows they keep earthing it up in the same manner, quite through the summer; and when they take up their roots, they do it with spades or forks; as to produce, I have been assured they sometimes get from one acre of land up to fifty-three or fifty-four tons, and that from thirty-five to forty are common crops. It is easy to conceive what a source of profit such products must be, where potatoes bear a constant price, as they do all over the West Indies; and to what advantage the people of this island may breed swine upon the very offal of such crops.

The way of life among the farmers of Barbuda resembles that of the little freeholders in New England; these also having the property of their farms, seldom renting them from others. Each man has his comfortable dwelling, and his well inclosed fields around it, a fine grove of trees for shelter, his orchard and garden filled with delicious fruits, his meadows for his herds, some lands for Indian, called here Guinea, corn, and others for roots, &c. Considering the vast plenty which husbandry in such a climate yields of almost every thing, it may truly be said these little farmers lead a life very much superior to that of their little brethren in Europe.

ANGUILLA

Anguilla is situated in 18 degrees 12 minutes north latitude; it is thirty miles long by ten broad, and is in every respect too fine an island to be left in the condition we see it. There are not above 800 people in it, who are to be divided into two classes; one a set of industrious farmers (like those of Barbuda), among whom there was a few years ago one or two sugar works, and the other a set of lazy people who live like Indians, pursuing no other occupation than that of tending a few herds, and living on them and the spontaneous fruits of the island. It is very remarkable, and indeed is a circumstance of curiosity, that there is no government in this island, every head of a family being truly a sovereign, and yet the settled part of the inhabitants live in peace and security, notwithstanding the wandering class, who know neither law nor gospel. This seems a great contradiction; but so it is.

The farmers in this island principally follow the planting Indian corn, in which they have good success, and sell considerable quantities of it to the sugar islands: their crops are reckoned very good: they also plant some tobacco, which, after neglecting for many years, they have lately taken up again, but the quantity is not considerable. Great improvements might be made, if a deputy governor was fixed here with a regular civil government; which it has been apprehended would draw people of property to make purchases in the island, with a view to plant sugar; for there are large tracts of land in it of a fine sandy loam, of a reddish colo[u]r, which resembles the brick earth of Jamaica, and which in its fertility in the production of such crops as the people plant, shows how excellently it would do for sugar. The scarcity and dearness of land in our islands make it the more surprising that this has never been done.

CHAPTER XXXII

CEDED ISLANDS

Dominica—St. Vincent—Granada—Tobago—Importance of these islands—Their produce—Improvements—Observations

BY THE peace of Paris we procured the cession, or rather the confirmation, of our right to these islands; the degree of merit that treaty possesses on this account does not turn on the value of these acquisitions, but on our degree of right to them before; and as that enquiry is not connected with the subject of this work, I shall dismiss the idea of it; but proceed to describe them, as well as the imperfect accounts we have had will allow, with the assistance of such private information as I have been able to gain, some of which has been valuable.

DOMINICA

Dominica lies in 15° 30′ north latitude between Martinico and Guadalupe; it is twenty-eight miles long by thirteen broad, and in circumference about ninety: it is supposed to be about twice as large as Barbadoes. The air, except in some places that are marshy and overgrown with wood, is generally reputed wholesome. There is no doubt but when the island is cleared it will, like the rest, become still more healthy, or at least more agreeable to European constitutions. The face of the country is rough and mountainous, more especially towards the sea side, but within land [inland], there are many rich and fine valle[y]s, and some large and fair plains. The declivities of the hills are commonly gentle, so as to facilitate their cultivation, and the soil almost everywhere a deep black mould, and thence highly commended for its fertility by the Spanish, English, and French. It is excellently well watered by at least thirty rivers, some, and particularly one, of them is very large and navigable for several miles, and the rest very commodious for all the purposes of planting. Hogs, both wild and tame, are here in great abundance, as well as all sorts of fowls, and ground provisions, such as bananas, potatoes, manioc; none of the islands produce better. Their fruits also are excellent, and the settlements, which however were not numerous, flourished very much, and produced sugar, cotton, coffee, cocoa, and most of the articles common in the West Indies.*

Since it has come into our possession, a considerable progress has been made in cultivating it: many tracts of lands have been purchased, and sugar-works erected on them. Insomuch that in 1763, only a year after the peace, the export from the island to Great Britain amounted to 46,211£. 17s. 9d. a very considerable sum for so short a time after the possession. Since that time the products have increased considerably, so that at present it is one of the most beneficial islands we have; insomuch that last year its exports amounted to above two hundred thousand pounds.

St. Vincent

St. Vincent lies in the same latitude as Barbadoes, at the distance of only thirty leagues. It is from north to south

* *Considerations on the Nature of the Sugar Trade.* [John Campbell. See the editor's note, page 439. Ed.]

twenty miles long, and in breadth about twelve, the circumference being about sixty miles. It is something larger than Antigua. The warmth of the climate is so tempered with the sea breezes, that it is looked upon as very healthy and agreeable, and on the eminences, which are numerous, the air is rather cool. The soil is wonderfully fertile, though the country is hilly, and in some places mountainous. But amongst the former, there are some pleasant valle[y]s, and at the bottom of the latter, some spacious and luxuriant plains. No island of the same extent is better watered with rivers and streams, yet are there no marshes nor stagnant waters. There are here great quantities of fine timber, and excellent fruit trees, some peculiar to this island. It abounds with wild sugar canes, corn, rice, and all sorts of ground provisions. In the south part of the island, where the French have raised some spacious and flourishing settlements, they have coffee, indigo, cocoa, anatto,[1] and some very fine tobacco. They have likewise abundance of cattle and poultry, and send from thence *lignum vitae* and other kinds of timber to Martinico, where they were employed in building houses and in their fortifications. We may collect,[2] that if this country was thoroughly and regularly cultivated, it would, in respect of its produce, be very little if at all inferior to any of the islands that we already possess.

But there is one circumstance very capitally in disfavour of this otherwise excellent island, which must not be overlooked; it is the number of native Indians and free negroes that are in possession of it. In the year 1735 it appeared, by an authentic report that was then made to the government of Barbadoes, that according to the best information which

---

[1] The annatto is a tropical tree whose seeds are useful for dye purposes.
[2] That is, infer or deduce.

could be at that juncture obtained there were about six hundred French, four thousand Indians, and six thousand negroes in St. Vincent's: it is, however, said, that the numbers have since been much decreased, owing to a cruel war breaking out between the Indians and negroes, which lasted for many years.*

Several reasons have been brought to shew that so far from esteeming these prior inhabitants a disadvantage we ought to reckon them a valuable acquisition. But such arguments are far enough from being founded in fact or experience. The author of the *Considerations* says as much on this head as can be said; but in spite of all that can be advanced, practical men know well enough, that till an island is clear of Indians and free negroes, no sugar can be planted to advantage. The instance of the Jamaica negroes proves this, rather than contradicts it, as may be seen by any person who reflects on the immense losses, expen[c]es, and trouble it cost that island not to extirpate, but make a peace with a handful of men; and the example of the French proves the same thing, for though no island can be more favourable in soil and climate to sugar than St. Vincent's, yet they did not, though at peace with both Indians and negroes, venture upon that culture; confining themselves to provisions and other articles that required little expence. But if this reasoning should not be satisfactory, what are we to think of the transactions now going on in this island, which in the violation of the natural rights of mankind are of such a hue, as to have brought on the enquiry now before parliament?† It shows plainly

---

* *Considerations on the Nature of the Sugar Trade.*

† This was written at the time of the enquiry into the affair of St. Vincent's. [In 1763 the population of St. Vincent numbered approximately 2,000, nearly all black Caribs. Attempts to survey the land of the island and to settle questions of ownership were resisted by the blacks who claimed

enough, that the island was of no worth while possessed even in part by the natives, and that, in order to render it valuable, means had been taken which it is to be feared will make but a bad appearance in the face of day.

GRENADA

The island of Grenada lies in 11 degrees 30 minutes north latitude, the farthest to the south of any of the Antilles. It is upwards of thirty miles long, and about half as many broad, being seventy-five in circumference. It is twice as large as Barbadoes, and contains one-third as much land fit for culture as is to be found in Martinico. The climate, as may be supposed from the latitude, is very hot, yet is it refreshed by the sea breeze; it is well known to be as wholesome as any other island in these parts; notwithstanding the fever which has gone under the name of this island, but which is owing to the thickness of the woods, and of course declines every day. The seasons as they are styled in the West Indies, are remarkably regular; the blast[3] is not hitherto known; the inhabitants are not liable to many diseases that are epidemic in Martinico and Guadalupe; and, which is the happiest circumstance of all, it lies out of the tract of the hurricanes, which, with respect to the safety of the settlements on shore, and the security of navigation, is almost an inestimable benefit.

---

that they were the rightful owners and that they were as a people independent. As a consequence English troops were sent to the island in 1772 to compel obedience. After some desultory fighting which was adversely commented on in Parliament, a treaty was concluded in 1773 by which the Caribs acknowledged the supremacy of the English Crown and were assigned land reserves in the northern portion of the island. See C. P. Lucas, *A Historical Geography of the British Colonies* (Oxford, 1897), II, 209. Ed.]

[3] A hot wind.

There are in Grenada some very high mountains, but the number is small, and the eminences scattered through it are in general rather hills, gentle in their ascent, of no great height, fertile, and very capable of cultivation. But exclusive of these, there are on both sides [of] the island large tracts of level ground, very fit for improvement, the soil being almost every where deep, rich, mellow, and fertile in the highest degree, so as to be equal in all respects, if not superior, to that of any of the islands in the West Indies, if the concurrent testimonies both of French and British planters may be relied upon. The former indeed have constantly, in their applications to the French ministry, insisted that this might be very easily made one of the most valuable, though hitherto it has remained the weakest and the worst settled of all their colonies. It is perfectly well watered by many streams of different sizes; there are also smaller brooks running from most of the hills. The great produce of the country before our cultivation in it, and indeed partly since, is a prodigious variety of all the different sorts of timber that are to be met with in any of the West India islands, and all these excellent in their respective kinds; so that whenever it comes to be tolerably cleared, vast profits will arise from the timber that may be cut down, and for which markets will not be wanting. Cattle, fowls, and provisions, are in the utmost plenty. But the distinguishing excellency of Grenada does not lie simply in its great fertility, or in its fitness for a vast variety of valuable commodities, but in the peculiar quality of its soil, which gives a surprising and incontestible perfection to all its several productions. The sugar of Grenada is of a fine grain, and of course more valuable than that either of Martinico or Guadaloupe. The indigo is the finest in all the West Indies. While tobacco remained the staple commodity, as once it was of these islands, one pound of Grenada tobacco was worth two or three that grew in any of the rest. The cocoa and cotton have an equal degree of pre-eminence. For some years before it came into our hands, the French planters in this island sent home twelve thousand hogsheads of sugar annually, besides coffee, cocoa, and a large quantity of excellent cotton. Yet it is generally allowed that never one-half of the country was properly settled that might have been obtained, if the inhabitants had been better planters, and had been also better supplied with slaves. An English gentleman, who has had great opportunities of knowing, thinks as much sugar is raised here as in Barbadoes, which is not at all impossible, though it did not find a regular passage to France. The Grenadines run from the southern extremity of the isle of Grenada; there are twenty-three small islands, capable of cultivation, the soil being remarkably rich, the climate pleasant, and all the necessaries of life, as fast as they are settled, easily obtained. According to the sentiments of the best judges, large quantities of indigo, coffee, and cotton may be raised upon them, nor are they at all unfit for sugar. Besides these, there are five larger islands, generally comprehended under the title of the Grenadines, *Cariouacou, Union, Cannouan, Moskito* island, and *Bequia,* called by the French Little Martinico. The first is of a circular figure, six or seven leagues in compass; it has been represented, by those who have visited it, as one of the finest and most fruitful spots in America; the soil remarkably fertile, and from its being pervaded by the sea breeze, the climate equally wholesome and pleasant. It is covered with valuable timber, interspersed with rich fruit trees, and when settled and cultivated is capable of all kinds of improvement; and it has also the advantage of as deep, capacious, and commodious an harbor as any in the West Indies. *Union* is three leagues long. *Cannouan* is three leagues long, and one and a half broad. *Moskito* is three long and one broad. All of them very pleasant and fertile islands. *Bequia* is the largest, being thirty-six miles in circumference, consequently larger than Montserrat: the soil is equal, if not superior to any of the rest, but it has little fresh water, and abounds with venomous reptiles.*

As a strong proof that these representations were well founded, I shall remark, that Grenada and its dependencies sent home in 1763, to the British market, only sugar and other commodities to the amount of 206,889£. which tallies extremely well with the above mentioned product of 12,000 hogsheads of sugar. St. Kitt's produces 10,000, and its total export 198,250£. consequently 12,000 must at least be equal to 206,889£. Since that time our people have made a wonderful progress in planting this island: many very capital plantations have been established by gentlemen in England of the largest property, and the success which has attended, and is daily attending, such as reside on their estates in this island, and at the same time understand the business of planting, shows clearly that in a few years this will be one of the most valuable settlements we have in the West Indies. I have been favored with an account of one plantation, which I shall lay before the reader, as in several points it is very satisfactory.

	£.
Purchase of 350 acres of land for canes (200 cleared) and 95 of woodland in the hills for raising provisions, &c.	2,560
Mansion and one set of buildings	2,600
Utensils	480
200 negroes at 56£. on an average	11,200
Cattle	320
£.	17,160

* *Considerations on the Nature of the Sugar Trade.*

One year's expence

Expences on 200 negroes, including over-seers, 4£. a head	800
Repairs of buildings	90
Wear and tear	100
Cattle	40
Taxes	32
Extra charges	86
Supply of negroes	460
	1,608
.. £.	18,768

Product

89 hogsheads sugar, at 19£.	1,691
70 at 18£.	1,260
276 at 15£.	4,140
	7,091
200 hhds. of rum	1,800
Timber and sundry articles	75
Total £.	8,966
Annual expence	1,608
Annual profit	7,358

This is near 39 per cent. interest of the capital, but it was drawn up from the particulars of an extraordinary year: while the possessor was on the plantation himself, he made near 27 per cent.; since he has been in England, his neat [net] produce is only 9 per cent., a fresh instance of the loss attending any person possessing estates in the West India islands without living upon them.

There is a very great error in the culture of the new lands in this island, which is the clearing them of wood in such a manner as to exclude the use of the plough: this has been the case with all our islands, but the new settlers in Grenada have, through an eagerness for profit, left the stumps so thick that no plough can be used; and even for hoes, by the accounts I have received, the inconvenience must be great. It is much to be regretted that they will not bestow a little extra expence upon this article in their first undertaking, and at the same time determine upon introducing horse-culture in every branch of their agriculture where it is practicable. Another circumstance of consequence, and which demands equal attention, is their making free with the fertility of the fresh lands so much as our planters are too apt to do; the consequence of which will be exhausting them in a few years, and then they will be in a worse state than if the soil under good management had not been of a comparable richness.

TOBAGO

Tobago[4] lies a little to the south-east of Grenada; it is thirty-two miles long, and about nine broad, being seventy miles in circumference; it is rather larger than Barbadoes. The climate, though it lies only eleven degrees and ten minutes north from the equator, is not near so hot as might be expected, the force of the sun's rays being tempered by the coolness of the sea breeze. When it was first inhabited, it was thought unhealthy, but as soon as it was a little cleared and cultivated, it was found to be equally pleasant and wholesome, which the Dutch ascribed, in a great measure, to the odoriferous smell exhaled from the spice and rich gum trees, a notion borrowed from their countrymen in the East Indies, who are persuaded that cutting down the clove trees in the Moluccas has rendered those islands very unhealthy. Another circumstance which may recommend the climate is the

[4] Tobago was one of the islands acquired by Great Britain from France in 1763.

island's lying out of the track of the hurricanes. There are many rising grounds over all the island, but it cannot be properly styled mountainous. The soil is very finely diversified, being in some places light and sandy, in others mixed with gravel and small flints, but in general it is a deep, rich, black mould. Hardly any country can be better watered than Tobago, for besides springs that are found in plenty all over the island, there are not fewer than eighteen rivulets that run from the hills into the sea; but there are very few or no morasses or marshes, or any lakes, pools, or collections of standing waters, which of course must render it more healthy. It is covered with all that vast variety of timber that is to be found in most countries in the West Indies, and many of these as extraordinary in size as excellent in their nature. The same may be said with respect to fruit trees, and amongst these there are some that are peculiar to Tobago; such, for instance, as the true nutmeg tree, which the Dutch, who of all nations could not in that respect be deceived, affirm to have found here. It is true, they say, it is a wild nutmeg, that the mace is less florid, and the taste of the nut itself more pungent, though larger and fairer to the eye than the spice of the same kind brought by them from the East Indies. The cinnamon tree grows likewise in this island, though the bark is said to have a taste of cloves as well as cinnamon. Here likewise grows the tree that produces the true *gum copal*,[5] resembling that brought from the continent of America, and very different from what goes by the same name in the rest of the West India islands. All ground provisions are produced here in the utmost abundance, as well as in the highest perfection. There is likewise plenty of wild hogs

---

[5] A resinous substance exuding from various tropical trees. Used chiefly in making varnishes, lacquers, and plastics.

and other animals, together with great quantities of fowl, and an amazing variety both of sea and river fish. In the time the Dutch were in possession of this island, which was not many years, they exported large quantities of tobacco, sugar, caffia, ginger, cinnamon, sassafras, gum copal, cocoa, rocou,[6] indigo, and cotton; besides rich woods, materials for dy[e]ing, drugs of different kinds, and several sorts of delicious sweetmeats. We shall here take the liberty of observing that there is at least the highest probability of our being able to produce all the valuable spices of the East Indies in this island. Cinnamon is said to grow in some of the other West India islands, and general Codrington had once an intention to try how much it might be improved by a regular cultivation in his island of Barbuda. It is universally allowed, that the bark of what is called the wild cinnamon tree in Tobago is beyond comparison the best in all the West Indies, and even in its present state may be made an article of great value. The bark when cured with care differs from that in the East Indies by being stronger and more acrid while it is fresh; and when it has been kept for sometime it loses that pungency, and acquires the flavour of cloves. This is precisely the spice for which there is a very considerable sale at Lisbon, Paris, and over all Italy. This kind of spice is drawn principally from Brazil, and the Portugueze believe that their cinnamon trees were originally brought from Ceylon, while it was in their possession, but that through the alteration of soil and climate they are degenerated into this kind of spice, and this may very probably be true: however, from their size and number it seems to admit of no doubt that the common trees actually growing in Tobago are the natural pro-

[6] A cruciferous annual belonging to the cabbage family, and used for salads.

duction of that island, and the point with us is to know what improvement may be made with respect to these. The nutmeg tree as well as the cinnamon, is a native of this island: we cannot doubt of the fact, that is, of the nutmeg's growing here; because we find it asserted in a book addressed to M. de Beveren, then governor of Tobago. A man who had invented a falsehood would hardly have had the boldness to repeat it, not only to a respectable person, but to the person in the world who must have the clearest knowledge of its being a falsehood. The nutmeg tree that naturally grows in Tobago is in all probability as true, and may, by due care and pains, be rendered as valuable a nutmeg as those that grow anywhere else; for the fact really is, that wherever there are nutmegs, there are wild nutmegs, or, as some style them, mountain nutmegs, which are longer and larger but much inferior in the flavour to the true nutmeg, and are very liable to be worm-eaten; the point is to know how these defects may be remedied, or, in other words, wherein the difference consists between the wild, tasteless, and useless nutmeg, and that which is true, aromatic, and of course a valuable spice.*

This idea with [and] other arguments to inforce it, too cogent to be overturned, are to be met with in the same work, which it must be confessed by every one is very well reflected, and drawn up with much candour and judgment: but unfortunately for the interests of this country, they have met with no more attention than if the author had wrote concerning raising spices in the moon: it is near ten years since he composed his treatise, yet has not there been the least step taken towards making the experiment, though nothing can be more obvious than the design, nor (more easy than the execution), of taking plants wild from the forest, and trying what change

* *Considerations on the Sugar Trade.*

a regular cultivation will make in their flavour and nature. Our ministers have attended enough to *selling* the lands in these ceded islands, but as to the national improvement of them, they have neither thought nor cared about. Very much is it to be regretted that something at the public expence has not been done towards ascertaining the degree of improvement which the native productions of these islands are capable of receiving. A very small public plantation for this purpose, under the conduct of an able botanist, would be sufficient for the experiment; nor can I see any good objections to such a scheme, upon the score of an expence which could hardly amount to more than a few hundred pounds a year.

Dropping the idea of improvements, which we may be certain will, for want of public virtue, never be executed, it remains for us to remark that the ceded islands of St. Vincent, Dominica, Grenada, and Tobago, are among the few principal acquisitions made by the late glorious war. Before the successes of that war took place, it was a common complaint in our islands that good sugar-land was so scarce that the product of that commodity was entirely at a stand, while our rivals, the French, were making an amazing progress, owing to the great plenty of excellent land at their command: but the acquisition of these islands has at least lifted us from that stagnant situation in which nothing but a decline could be expected; the purchase of land in these territories, and their cultivation, has animated our people since the last peace, and given them some of that activity which ever attends advance: in commerce and politics no enemy is more to be dreaded than standing still. Had we not secured these islands, our ruin in the West Indies must soon have followed, without the greatest dexterity of management, for France has made a much greater acquisition by gaining the Spanish half of Hispaniola in exchange for Louisiana; which is such an acquisition of valuable territory in the West Indies, as we can never hope again to make.[7]

But while our rivals have such an advantage of territory, be it our aim to gain the ascendancy in industry; and that is principally to be done in the quick and thorough cultivation of these islands. Public arrangements ought to co-operate with private endeavors; encouragement should be given to settlers to plant those parts of the island which do not sell, which will of course be all the parts that do not possess every requisite for cane-grounds; but the climate is highly propitious to commodities as valuable as sugar: encouragement should be given to such settlers to go upon coffee, indigo, cocoa, cotton, cochineal, and other articles, so that every part of the islands, except those which it would be proper to leave in wood from ruggedness of situation, might be brought into some kind or other of profitable culture. With respect to spices, which certainly our India company might long ago have secured in some of their settlements, small plantations of the native growths should be made, in spots selected for that purpose, to see what perfection culture would bring them to; we should probably, by this means, gain at least some articles that would be useful and profitable in certain branches of our commerce. The expence would be small, the benefit might be great.

[7] The importance of the acquisition of the French West Indies by England is discussed at some length in G. L. Beer, *British Colonial Policy, 1754–1765* (New York, 1922), chap. viii. See also Kate Hotblack, *Chatham's Colonial Policy* (London, 1917).

CHAPTER XXXIII

BAHAMA ISLANDS

Climate — Soil — Productions — Observations on their state—Proposals for their improvement

THE LUCAYOS, or Bahama islands, are some hundreds in number, some of them many miles in length, and others little better than rocks or knoles [knolls] rising above the water, which render navigation among them remarkably dangerous. They are seated in the finest climate of the world, between 21 and 27 degrees north latitude, which, though very hot on the continent, is in these islands but another word for an almost perpetual spring. The isle of Bahama is in latitude 26 degrees 30 minutes, being about 50 miles long, but very narrow. Providence is in 25 degrees, it is 28 miles long, and 11 broad. Some of them are of much larger sizes than these, but not above three or four inhabited: Providence is the seat of government. In 1763, the imports to Great Britain were above four thousand pounds from Providence.

I before remarked, that the climate is excellent in most of them; of this I have been assured by a gentleman who spent some time among them during the late war:[1] he added that the heats were temperated in the very hottest months by the sea breezes, and the number of the islands surrounding, gave them more than an equivalent to the land breezes,

[1] Seven Years War.

by generally fanning them with eddies and gales of wind. Nothing of that suffocating heat which renders the West Indies so pernicious to European constitutions, and which strictly confines the inhabitants to their houses during the best part of the day; on the contrary, in July and August you may be out about any kind of rural sports or business without the least inconvenience. The healthiness of the islands is owing greatly to the dryness of their soil: there is not a swamp, a marsh, or a bog in any one that has been examined; they are high, dry, hilly, or rocky spots admirably watered with streams, being in the exemption from bad water, and in the possession of good, equal to any country in the known world.

While the heats in summer are so little oppressive, the spring is a season too delicious to admit description, and the winter is entirely free from snow or frost; the tenderest fruits of the West Indies flourish throughout them, and are of flavour equal to what is tasted in much hotter climates. The uncommon healthiness of the few inhabitants proves how just this representation of the climate is.

Respecting the soil, it is in most of the larger islands various, but every where excellent. It consists generally of a loamy sand, in some places mixed with flints, and in others free from them: very considerable tracts are of a black rich mould, light, but of a putrid appearance, and of a good depth; this is not found only in the vallies, but along the slopes of the hills to a great tract of country through many of the islands. The extraordinary growth to which all vegetables, cultivated and spontaneous, arrive, is proof sufficient of the great fertility of this land. Among its productions are to be reckoned sugar, cotton, indigo of a remarkable fine quality, cocoa, ginger, pimento, wild cinnamon, pine apples, guavas, bananas, plantains, oranges, lemons, citrons, etc., these valuable articles are either wild, or cultivated in gardens; for the quantity in regular culture by way of plantation is very small, as may be judged by the whole product of all the islands at the British market being under five thousand pounds, and in that small sum their cedar and other valuable timber make a considerable portion.

If the fineness of the climate and the richness of the soil be considered, it will appear self-evident that every article usually cultivated in our West India isles might with a certainty of success be raised here. Is it not therefore astonishing that they should be left in so neglected a state? That so few enterprising minds should be found to undertake plantations in them: tracts of land might here be chosen and had for no other expence than paying the usual fees of office; whereas 60£. per acre for land not better, is a common price in our sugar islands. That commodity might beyond all doubt be cultivated to no small advantage, for it thrives luxuriantly in much more northerly climates; and if the advantage of plenty of land, with all sorts of lumber on the spot, with a profusion of provisions of all kinds, both for the slaves and cattle of a plantation; if these circumstances are considered, with the difference of having the land almost for nothing, or paying 60£. an acre for it—if these points are considered, it will be sufficiently plain that considerable estates might be made by sugar planting in these islands, as it is most certain that less crops than the produce of Jamaica and Barbadoes would pay better interest for a capital here, than large ones there, all expences carried to account.

But supposing that equal profit by sugar could not be made, which is much more than there is any necessity to grant, why should they not be applied to indigo, cotton, vines, tobacco, &c. [?] In these articles there has never been a doubt of the climate being hot enough—nor can any person doubt but they would yield larger crops than are gained of them on the continent. And a beneficial culture of these commodities, in such of the islands as are capable of cultivation, would bring into this nation an annual profit of one or two hundred thousand pounds a year, without reckoning anything for sugar: but if the most was made of them that they are capable of, knowing people well acquainted with them have thought they would be worth half a million a year to Britain, instead of producing not five thousand pounds.

The navigation, I am sensible, of these islands has always been reckoned very hazardous, but this notion must not be adopted in general; when ships have been driven in storms among their rocks and shoals, several have been wrecked, but as to those that have steered regularly thither as their course, the navigation has never proved dangerous: there is a regular communication open by ships often passing to and fro between Providence and Charlestown in Carolina, Philadelphia, &c. and also to the Leeward Islands, not to speak of those which pass between England and that island. And if the navigation is frequented for the small concerns of these islands at present, and the few commodities of value they export, surely by a parity of reasoning we may suppose that if more valuable products were raised, and in much greater abundance, the navigation would not then be objected to: if it is sufficiently safe to induce shipping now to frequent it, most certainly they would then. Nor should I omit to remark that the inhabitants on the few islands that are at all peopled are the most dextrous seamen in all America; one principal branch of their employment is building sloops and other small vessels, with which they carry on a traffic be-

tween the northern colonies and the sugar islands, and export
their own provisions in tolerable quantities to those islands;
this makes them able navigators, and gives plenty of pilots
for most of the passages and channels of their own Archi-
pelago.

But there is another view in which these islands may be
considered, which though not essential, yet deserves mention:
it is that of affording perhaps the most agreeable and eligible
retreat for men whose active or variegated lives have taken
off that relish for the world which once actuated them; and
to whom nothing appears with such charms as a prospect of
a safe, easy, and agreeable retreat. Or to men who from
failures, losses, disappointments, or a general want of income
for living agreeably in a wealthy, luxurious, and expensive
country, are desirous of spending, at least, some years of their
life in a retirement where their little fortunes may be sufficient for providing them with such enjoyment as their own
country denies them: to any such these islands could hardly
appear in any other light but that of a paradise upon earth,
which will plainly appear from considering them with this
view.

In the first place, here is an air and climate perfectly unexceptionable, as healthy to an European constitution as almost any other part of America; where the heats are never
excessive, and where severe cold was never known: a clear
serene sky, and an atmosphere free from every species of
damps and fogs; a soil as fertile as any in the world in the
production of all the articles that form the necessaries and
superfluities of life, from bread to pine apples, and that in a
profusion which scarcely any other country experiences. In
addition to these circumstances, here is further to be met with
a plenty as remarkable of both sea and river fish, with vari-

ous sorts of wild fowl and game: timber in every island for all the purposes of building whether houses, or sloops and boats. And in point of agreeableness, many of the islands abound in situations which are equally pleasing and romantic. There are in Mogane and some others of them the finest slopes of country that can be imagined. A wave of gentle but varied declivities from the tops of very high hills, shelving down to a bold sea shore; in some places spread with open lawn, in others scattered with open groves of tall trees, rivers winding in slopes, and in other places falling down the hills in cascades, the whole bounded generally by thick woods: some of these scenes take in the space of three, four, or six hundred acres, and have from the shipping the noblest effect imaginable.

Where now can such persons as I have mentioned, find a more eligible retreat than in such scenes as these! Much more so than the Bermudas Islands, where there is a confined society, which in the nature of things must be full of all the jars and bickerings of the world; and where the people are in too low a sphere of life to afford conversation of pleasing or satisfactory [nature] to a man of any ideas. But the Bahamas are so circumstanced that a man may live in just that degree of retirement he likes—that is, he may live entirely to himself, and come again into the world whenever he wishes for it.

CHAPTER XXXIV

IMPORTANCE OF THE AMERICAN COLONIES TO BRITAIN

Principles upon which colonies are established—How far answered by those of Britain—Wherein their importance consists—Depends on Climate—Observations

IN CONDUCTING the reader [on] the tour of all our colonies, I have laid before him every circumstance that was necessary for giving a complete idea of their agriculture; little has been said of their commerce or of their manufactures, because it was conceived that it is upon the culture of their lands that the interest of this country in America chiefly depends; and because the channels, through which my intelligence came, principally afforded communications relative to agriculture. Upon the general importance of the colonies there has been much wrote, and by able pens; but from the extravagance to which certain arguments have been carried of late, we may reasonably conclude that clear ideas are not yet entertained, not so much upon the importance in general, as the points upon which that importance principally depends. A very little discrimination is sufficient to convince us, that however well our best writers agree in that general circumstance, they are far from attributing effects to the same causes. What I shall chiefly attend to therefore in this chapter, will be to point out in what manner Britain reaps such great advantages by her colonies—in what degree it depends on their agriculture—what variations there are in husbandry, which are attended with corresponding variations in the interest of the mother country. In making this enquiry, I shall be naturally led to clear up some apparent difficulties which the reader might remark in his progress through the preceding pages.

There are three grand reasons for a country's planting colonies. *First,* affording a *national* retreat to such persons as will emigrate. *Secondly,* affording a retreat to the emigrants of foreign countries. *Thirdly,* raising the productions of climates different from their own, and thereby saving the purchase of such productions.

As to the first reason, every one must know that there is a certain degree of emigration at all times going on from all nations; necessity or private inclination will carry many people from one country to another, and very many of the number are indifferent where they go, provided it is from home—or to a country in which they can maintain themselves better than at home; if they go from Britain to France or Spain, those countries are proportionably strengthened, and we are weakened; it is therefore of particular importance to provide a colony for such persons, that they may not, by their emigration, add to the population of an enemy's country, or that of a rival. For the same reason that makes this rule of conduct adviseable, it is also to be wished that the emigrants from our enemies and rivals may make choice of our colonies, by which means, at the same time that they weaken them, they strengthen us. From the many favours nature has showered down upon some of our American settlements, we see them resorted to by numbers of French, Dutch, Germans, Danes, Swedes, and Switzers, adding thereby greatly to the populousness of the country, and enriching Britain by their labour. The third reason for forming colonies is no less cogent; countries in a northern latitude, like Britain, cannot raise either sugar, tea, coffee, wine, silk, tobacco, indigo, cochineal, and many other articles; nor can their own territories yield a sufficiency of hemp, flax, iron, timber, &c.; all such commodities must therefore be purchased in the way of trade from other nations; but if the import is large, the country is under a necessity of exporting other commodities or manufactures in great quantities, or a considerable ballance must be paid in bullion, to the impoverishment of the country: and in proportion to the import of such commodities, is the industry and wealth of other nations increased at the expence of Britain. Hence the value of colonies that will provide us with such commodities—which spares our taking them from foreign nations, which sell them to us not for bullion but for manufactures—and [the] whole increase in people and wealth is so much added to the scale of Britain, instead of that material deduction which the increase of some of our neighbors makes from us. This is so evident that it can scarcely be contradicted with propriety.

Here therefore we deduce that the population of the colonies is an increasing weight in the scale of Britain, and that their producing those commodities which the climate of Britain refuses, or which we cannot raise in sufficient quantity, is an advantage of the first magnitude. The excess to which the first may be carried in time will be more properly examined when I come to consider the probability of their independence.

In the production of such staples as Britain cannot produce herself, there are some circumstances which demand distinctions; for the policy of colonization is one of the most curious speculations that can be made in general politics. When the products are raised, should they be brought to Britain in British or American vessels? Should the same products be sold to other nations, and in what manner? Should the colonies pursue other employments, such as commerce, manufactures, or fisheries? How are they to be restrained? And in these queries it is not to be supposed merely what a mother country would wish for—but what she would command, from the nature of her superiority.

A wide field for discussion here opens itself, but having been so much discussed by others, the less will suffice from me.

Two circumstances require equal attention; first, preserving the natural and political rights of the Americans; and secondly, the interest of Britain: it is not necessary that either should be sacrificed to the other, but then a sensible and attentive conduct is essential: things must not be left to their own progress, but thrown by artificial means into that train which is necessary for both. Colonies may naturally think themselves entitled to the common privileges of raising what commodities they please—selling them to whom they please —navigating their vessels how and where they please—and, in a word, acting to all purposes as a mother country. But on the other hand, if all this is indulged, instead of being colonies they are independent states, and a country can never have any interest in planting and supporting such.

That a strong distinction must be made here is evidently necessary: the mother country discovers, founds, peoples, and supports the people for some ages; does not this lay them under an obligation different from what is experienced by any original and independant people? Does it not, upon the very face of it, imply a dependance, or an agreement to certain conditions? Is it to be supposed that any people would plant colonies with any other idea? And is it not clear that the people who go to them do in that action, and in accepting the protection of the mother country, tacitly acknowledge and agree to a submission to those reciprocal terms of agreement which are supposed to bind them? These *supposed* terms (for no absolute expression can be given to so uncertain an idea) are a general obedience to the acts of the British legislature, when legally, and according to the laws of nations, exerted. In the establishment and progress of all our colonies they invariably obeyed the authority of the British parliament, and in many instances even that of the crown; and what is of consequence, they received perpetual accessions of new settlers during the whole period of their submission to such authority. All this proves sufficiently, that the mother country has an undoubted right so to regulate the pursuits of the colonies, as to render them consistent with her own interest.

It has been found, for instance, necessary to prevent the colonies from trading immediately with foreign nations; a point of policy necessary in the management of all the colonies which the European nations have settled in America; for if this was allowed, they would to all useful purposes be the colonies of other powers as much as of our own. It has also been enacted that no law passed in the American assemblies shall have force till assented to by king and council in England. Various other instances might be given, but these are sufficient to shew a restraining and superior power. And in the exertions of this power we see nothing to shock the political liberty and freedom of the colonists, any more than in distant countries of England being governed by laws passed at Westminster, and to which perhaps not a five hundredth part of the inhabitants ever gave a direct or virtual assent.

Having premised these circumstances, which prove that the mother country had a right, and must always enjoy it, of regulating the pursuits of the colonies so as to turn them to their own advantage, it remains to be considered how far this conduct has been pursued by Britain, in which enquiry will be seen those errors which have brought on the differences that have lately happened between her and her American plantations.

I have observed that one great benefit resulting from colonies was the production of such commodities as the climate of the mother country will not yield; this advantage Britain has experienced in an high degree. Her islands in the West Indies produce that great modern luxury, sugar, in larger quantities than she can consume; so that after satisfying her own consumption, there remains a surplus which is re-exported to other nations of Europe that have not sugar islands. We have shewn in the preceding pages what a considerable sum this total amount of sugar, &c. is, which, being in this age a necessary of life, must have been bought of France, had we not possessed our West India islands. The amount of these commodities is between two and three millions sterling, a sum sufficient to drain any nation, and would at this day, while the trade of the kingdom is in a most flourishing situation, give such a balance against her, as to bring on every evil that can accrue from the impoverishment of a people.

If it be said that the West Indies and England are not the same country, and that these commodities, at least as much of them as are consumed, cost the nation as much as if bought of foreigners, I reply, that supposing this was true, which is not the case, still there is this essential difference, that in the transaction with our own islands we pay in manufactures, but in our transaction with a foreign country, we must pay in whatever the ballance of the commerce between the two nations is paid in, which, with such a vast import added, would certainly be bullion. We already pay a considerable annual ballance to France; but what would that ballance be if our import of West Indies commodities was added to it? Importation of any thing, and in almost any quantity, is harmless, or perhaps beneficial, as long as paid for with manufactures; for such importation is then the means of feeding our poor, and supporting our population. But this is not the only advantage resulting from our islands: in the cultivation and sale of the commodity, there is a great profit made by the planter, as we every day see by the large estates made in that part of the world: all these estates come at last to Britain—every great fortune made enables the possessor to come over and live here, and he leaves his plantation to overseers. The overseers in their turn make fortunes, and do the same; and fresh overseers are left for the same purpose: but the end of the whole is the same, all the money that is made in considerable sums is sure to send its owners to England. What the amount of such incomes spent by absentees is, cannot be discovered, but every one's knowledge must tell him that it must be very considerable. This circumstance is clear profit, from having sugar colonies of our own, instead of buying our sugar, &c. from France or other countries.

Nor is the employment of shipping and seamen to be forgotten, which are of the very first importance to a maritime and commercial power: the navigation to the West Indies breeds and employs many seaman, all of which would be lost to the nation if she was to lose her sugar colonies; or, what would be worse than lost, they might be added to the navigation of France and other countries, than which nothing could be more highly detrimental. The freight alone of our West India staples amounts to above half a million sterling, whereas the share we should have in the freight of the same commodities from European countries would be very insignificant in its amount.

I have entered particularly into this enquiry concerning the sugar colonies, because they are more immediately applicable to every circumstance of the argument than most of our other settlements: and the instance is strong to shew us the great importance of planting colonies in such climates as produce commodities totally different from those of the mother country; in a luxurious age the products of one zone are necessaries of life in another; in order therefore to have as many commodities as possible without purchasing them of foreign nations, the mother country should be in one zone and the colonies in another, which is the case with Britain and her West India islands. It is these principles which have proved so fortunate in the colonization we have carried on in this part of the world; and whether we consider wealth, employment of our poor, of our seamen, shipping, and all the attendants of navigation, we must decide that our West India islands are in every respect as valuable settlements as any the world can boast. France possesses others in the same region, which are superior only in proportion as they are superior in numbers and quantity; the qualities of one are equal to those of the other.

While we reap such immense advantages from these islands, it is necessary to observe two circumstances, first, that they [were] gained without laying any violence or constraint upon them, which is contrary to the common principles of all colonies, or the natural liberties and rights of mankind; and secondly, that the benefits we receive from them are greatly owing to their attending to agriculture alone. The first shews, that the national advantage made by colonies does not result from oppression, but from a fair communication of reciprocal benefits. On the second I must observe, that it is the case to a very extraordinary degree: the West India islands are, I apprehend, more free from manufactures than any other territories in the world. In all our continental plantations there are either manufactories or numerous families who spin, weave, and do other works of *manufacture* for the cloathing or answering other wants of themselves or a part of themselves. But in the islands there is hardly to be found a man, woman, or child, that has a single article of dress, furniture, or implement of business, but what is imported: this shews that husbandry is the most profitable employment they can follow. While a man was taken up in weaving a peace of cloth, or making hose or any other manufacture which brought him in five pounds for his labour, he would, in working upon the land or at those trades dependant on the land, earn three times that sum; from whence it follows, that manufactures cannot be introduced into such a country, since, in order to make them, such wages must be given as would render the fabric vastly dearer than the same made in England, with all the additional charges of sending it to the West Indies, which would bring ruin to all such undertakings. Neither do the inhabitants of these islands apply themselves to commerce, except it be to the illicit trade with the Spaniards, in which very great profits are made; and even in this many more North American vessels are found than West Indian, for it much deserves attention that these islands possess very few ships, or, more properly speaking, scarcely any; their trade is carried on in North American or British vessels—even when the planters turn merchants, as most of them do, in shipping their own products, still they do it all in vessels belonging to other people. All this is owing to the profit of their business; when their husbandry is so beneficial, as to pay, we will suppose, 25, 30 or 35 per cent. it would ill answer to have money in shipping at 8 to 10 per cent.

Here therefore is an example of colonies going of themselves into the pursuit which the mother country has the greatest reason to approve and promote: every circumstance attending colonization in the West Indies is precisely in the train best calculated for the interest of Britain, and at the same time for the profit of the planters. This is not the case with all our colonies; to what therefore is it owing here? The answer to this is ready enough; it is owing to *the profit of their husbandry*. Every people will give their application to that branch of industry which they will find most advantageous; if the soil and climate of a colony are such as will produce *valuable* commodities, it is to the production of such commodities they will apply. Why is not Barbadoes filled with merchants, fishermen, manufactures, and farmers, like New England? Because planting sugar is there a more profitable employment. Why is not New England filled with planters? Because trade, fishing, manufacturing, and farming are more profitable employments. This distinction is that of climate, and it gives a lesson of all others the most important in the politics of colonization, which is to plant them in climates the reverse of the mother country. This is the principle upon which depends the immense consequence of our West Indian possessions. Britain and those islands are similar in none of their products: the latter wants every thing produced by the former; the former wants every thing produced by the latter; thus it is impossible the one should ever rival the other, as the communication between them consists of a regular exchange of good offices, the one yields upon the ballance profit to the other; protection and a ready market are dispensed in return.

If from the West Indies we proceed northward to the southern continental colonies, we shall find as we go continued reasons to shew the great importance of colonies to Britain: by that title I mean the settlements to the south of the tobacco colonies; these produce rice, indigo, cotton, silk, wine, and other commodities which are of great value in a British market, and which Britain cannot produce herself: the same reasons that make the sugar colonies of so much value to us, render these the same; and though some writers have calculated that these settlements are not so valuable as the islands proportioned to the numbers of their people; yet we are to remember that this is not owing to a want of value in their products (some of which, silk and indigo, are far more costly than sugar), but to the country being more agreeable and healthy to live, which induces many persons to reside in their back parts, and cultivate common provisions to supply the rest with—and also to the ease with which any man who has five or ten pounds, may get a grant of land, build a hut, buy a cow or two, and turn farmer; such people, though they reckon in the numbers of the province, produce perhaps none of the staples of it: whereas, if only those were reckoned who are employed on the staples and the trades dependant, they would be found to raise as great an amount per head as the planters of the sugar colonies. This circumstance does not act in the islands from two causes, first the want of land, which is so far from being given to whoever will have it, that it is sold at considerable prices; secondly, the unwholesomeness of the climate, which is in general such that no person would chuse to make it their residence for small profits, or with any other view than to make money enough to be able to live elsewhere. These circumstances cannot but have the effect of fixing far more people in the continental colonies, proportioned to the production of staples, than in the West Indies.

This kingdom enjoys a very considerable trade by means of these colonies; out of above an hundred thousand barrels of rice which they export, we do not consume ourselves above four or five thousand; the rest goes to Spain, Portugal, Germany, Holland, and the North. Indigo is an article of the first consequence to our manufactures, silk is the same, raw hides the same; so that these commodities are in fact equally valuable to us with sugar; they are not bought with money, but with manufactures; the navigation occasioned by them is all our own, so that they add to our strength and wealth in the same manner as sugar, cocoa, coffee, ginger, &c. The southern colonies have no manufactures among them, they are without fisheries, and their commerce consists in nothing but sending lumber to the West Indies, and shipping their staples for a British market in British bottoms.

Objections indeed would have been raised against the production of rice, upon the principle of its being a grain which in the European markets rivals the exportation of British corn. This has an appearance of truth, and in some years in a small degree may be so: but it is not to be supposed that if we had sold no rice we should have added a proportional quantity to the export of corn: nothing can be farther from truth. Rice is purchased by very many people who would not lay the money out in corn if they could not get the rice:

it is used for soup and other different purposes from corn; and if consumed to save wheat by some, it may be a matter of choice rather than economy. Nor should we forget that our corn exportation is quite another thing from the export of rice from Carolina, it is uncertain, depends upon the crop; prohibitions have of late been common and continual; and in several years we have imported instead of exported: now it would certainly have been very absurd to have restrained or wish to have restrained the culture of rice, because it is possible that it may rival us to the amount of two or three thousand pounds worth that is sold. Besides, the export of rice is regular; it is a grain that depends very little on the seasons, and being made not for the consumption of the country where grown, but in order all to be exported, the money gained by the trade comes as regularly as the year; and is, in a word, the very contrary of our corn trade for some years past. For these reasons we may determine rice to be a very proper staple for a colony, and may look on its increase of culture with satisfaction, instead of being jealous of it. If it increases in future, as it has done of late years, it will soon bring more money into the kingdom than any other commodity.

If we advance yet farther northward, and take in the tobacco colonies, those of Virginia and Maryland, we shall find the same reasons to congratulate ourselves upon the great value they are of. Tobacco is the grand staple of these settlements, a staple as proper as possible for a colony, and than which none is more valuable to this kingdom. Out of 96,000 hogsheads made, only 13,500 are consumed in Britain, and the duty alone of these is 26£. 1s. per hogshead, or 351,675£. The rest is re-exported to the other parts of Europe, paying also a duty, though not so heavy, and bringing a flood of wealth into this kingdom.

Every circumstance that can concur to render a colony valuable to a mother country unites in this product, tobacco. Much the larger part of it is consumed by foreign nations—it could not be profitably raised in Britain—it is a bulky commodity, which employs many ships and seamen belonging to the ports of Britain—it is so profitable an article of husbandry as to preclude all other employments like sugar, as long as good land is to be had to plant. All these circumstances are of vast importance, and should make us as solicitous to increase and improve the tobacco culture as any other article of our American produce.

The excellency of this staple is seen in its enabling the planter to buy every necessary of life except food, and without his attending to any other object. These colonies, so far from rivalling us in fisheries, manufactories, or commerce, have none of the three among them, insomuch that people have found so little profit in herding together that there has never yet arose a single town of any consequence in either Maryland or Virginia; a strong proof of the advantage they find in spreading over the country as planters, rather than fixing in towns as merchants and manufacturers. These colonies, from the health and fertility of the climate and soil, are grown very populous, and in proportion as their numbers have increased, there has not been an increase of fresh land for their tobacco planting: this has been owing, first, to the confinement which the war gave their settlements, and afterwards to the extreme ill-judged proclamation of 1763, which forbid all settlements beyond the rivers which fall into the Atlantic ocean: this has driven many of their people to common husbandry, to which the soil and climate are equally well adapted. The consequence of this was that when the export of tobacco is divided among the population of the provinces the people seem to earn by it but a small sum, compared to those of the islands and the southern colonies. But we are not from thence to conclude that the staple is deficient in value; on the contrary, I am of the opinion that if the amount of it was divided only among the people actually employed by it, and depending upon it, it would then be found more valuable even than sugar, or at least as valuable. A part of the population applying, for want of fresh land, to the culture of wheat and provisions, is no fault in tobacco.

But of as great importance as this plant is, yet we are to remember that it is not the only staple of this colony; it has some other very promising ones.

	£.
Hemp, 1,000 tons, 21£.	21,000
30 sail of ships	30,000
Masts, planks, &c.	55,000
Iron	35,000
Skins	25,000
Flax-seed	14,000
Ginseng and drugs	7,000
£.	187,000

Besides 4,000 tons more of hemp worked into the uses of their ships, &c. all these articles are true staples, being such as Britain either buys of foreign countries or can sell to them in any quantities: they are articles also which promise a considerable increase, and which may be carried to a height as the population of these provinces increases, which, with the help of silk and wine, may by and by be as valuable as tobacco.

It may not be improper here to review the staples of these

colonies, the southern ones, and the islands, as they all unite in the circumstance of having such valuable staples as render them in every respect highly valuable to Great Britain, and more so than other settlements more to the north can prove. The commodities chiefly produced in all our settlements, from Maryland to Grenada, are such as we cannot have at home, of which we consume great quantities, which must be purchased of foreigners, and perhaps of enemies, if we had not colonies that produced them. This advantage renders the consumption of those commodities, not to speak of the re-exportation of many, a benefit to the kingdom rather than an evil; for as the purchase is made with our manufactures, the wealthy part of the nation, in proportion as they consume American luxuries, find employment for their poor neighbors; instead of which, if we had no colonies, the rental of their estates would go for the employment of poor Frenchmen and Germans; the immense difference of which is obvious at first sight. A late writer, from whom however I have had reason in the preceding pages to differ in certain articles, gives the following table of the tobacco and southern colonies.

	Ships	Seamen
Virginia and Maryland	330	3,960
North Carolina	34	408
South Carolina	140	1,680
Georgia	24	240
St. Augustine	2	24
Pensacola	10	120
	* 540	6,432
Sugar islands†		3,600
		10,032

* *American Traveller.* [The statistics are derived from a table on p. 121 of the Cluny volume described in the editor's note on p. 91, above.]
† Editor of Du Pratz.

	Exports from Britain	Exports from Colonies
Virginia and Maryland	865,000	1,040,000
North Carolina	18,000	68,350
	883,000	1,108,350
South Carolina	365,000	395,666
Georgia	49,000	74,200
St. Augustine	7,000	
Pensacola	97,000	63,000
	* 1,401,000	1,641,216
West Indies†		2,702,060
		4,343,276

These accounts are not the newest, and I have corrected some of the particulars from whence they are drawn, elsewhere, as I observed before; the real totals at present, could they be all known, probably would not be found less than 13,000 seamen, 650 ships, and colony exports of 5,000,000£. but whether something more, or something less, the conclusions to be drawn are the same: the possession of colonies that produce staples which cause such a prodigious commerce of the most advantageous sort in the world, which is entirely carried on in our own products and manufactures, the balance of which is ours—the profit of which, on both sides, is ours— the ships ours—the seamen ours—the freight ours—a flourishing revenue raised on them, ours—the population of the countries which support this trade, of our brethren and subjects of the same crown—when all these circumstances are considered, they will be found to involve a magnitude of interests

* *American Traveller.* [The statistics are derived from a table on p. 121 of the Cluny volume. See the editor's note, p. 91, above.]

† Political Essays. [Arthur Young, *Political Essays Concerning the Present State of the British Empire* (London, 1772). Ed.]

which have long supported the greatness of Britain; which now is the most firm support of it; and which, by a prudent and political conduct in future, can hardly fail of being an increasing and improving support.

These therefore are colonies that it much beho[o]ves this country to give every degree of encouragements to that it is possible they should receive; for by encouraging them, she in fact encourages herself. I shall hereafter endeavour to shew, wherein such encouragement ought to consist: but I shall at present observe, that we ought to be very tender of increasing one branch of their value to us, that of *duties*, for therein we cramp instead of extending their products. Upon tobacco the duties are near three times the value, which is carrying that taxation to a degree which hardly any other commodity knows. Cases may happen which may make it very adviseable to lower such burthens, though I believe not unless our government is very ill advised in American affairs: but if (which however is hardly to be expected) the governments of those countries which produce either at home or in colonies the same commodities should take political steps for greatly encouraging such products, such a rivalship would render counter-operations necessary; in which that of lowering duties would be found essential.

As to the northern colonies, all [those] to the north of the tobacco ones may with propriety be classed together, since neither Pennsylvania, New Jersey, New England, Nova Scotia, nor Canada, have any staple product of agriculture; the consequence of which is their flying to all other employments; the culture of the soil is common husbandry, like that of Britain herself; the employment of their towns, which are numerous and large, is manufactures, commerce, and fisheries. It is impossible they should be so employed, and at the same time be the occasion of Britain's prosperity, like the colonies to the south. But some writers have carried this deficiency of the northern colonies too far, in allowing under 100,000£. for all their staples: that this matter may be set in a clear light, I shall transcribe here the totals of several articles before inserted in the tables of their exports, by extracting those articles which may be called staples.

Skins	£.	
Hudson's Bay	29,340	
Canada	76,000	
New York	35,000	
Pennsylvania	50,000	
		190,340
Ginseng and drugs		
Canada		3,000
Timber		
Canada	11,000	
Nova Scotia	4,000	
New England	75,000	
New York	25,000	
Pennsylvania	35,000	
		150,000
Ships		
New England 70	49,000	
New York 20	14,000	
Pennsylvania 25	17,500	
		80,500
Pitch, &c.		
New England		600
Pot-ash		
New England	35,000	
New York	14,000	
		49,000

Flax seed
   New York   14,000
   Pennsylvania   30,000

                                           44,000
Copper and iron
   New York   20,000
   Pennsylvania   35,000

                                         55,000

                    Total   £. 572,440

The tobacco of Virginia alone amounts to more money than all these staples of all these colonies, which contain thrice the people of those to the south: but at the same time [that] we must acknowledge these to be staples, to every intent and purpose, doubts have been conceived about timber and ship-building; but when it is considered that there is scarcely any commodity that Britain wants more—witness her imports from the Baltic, and building even men of war with fir—there will not be found any reasons for rejecting them.

The reader will at once recollect that the exports of these colonies amount to far greater sums in fish, oil, wheat, &c. but these are certainly to be rejected, because, in proportion as they increase, the interest of Britain declines. The most capital article is that of fish, both cod and whale, and therefore I shall give it the first examination; as it includes more particularly their great navigation—commerce with foreign nations—and the employment of seamen; all which being of the greatest importance to Britain, we ought to enquire whether they are the same in the hands of the colonies. And this I shall do in the words of a late author, who has attended much to this subject.

We are told by Dr. Mitchel[l],[1] that the British planta-

---

[1] *The Present State of Great Britain and North America with Regard to Agriculture, Population, Trade, and Manufactures* (London, 1767).

tions maintain 45,000 seamen, and employ near 2,000 sail of ships. Now as we have found the number which Britain *possesses* to be about 12,000, consequently their own amounts to about 33,000. A North American writer likewise calculates the ships at 2,000. That these accounts are not exaggerated, there is some reason to believe from an assertion of another writer, who, speaking of the consequences of the regulations of the colonies in 1763, says that 20,000 seamen and fisher-men were turned out of employment there. Now if 20,000 were at once *out* of employment, the total *in* as well as *out* cannot be less than 33,000 especially as the fisheries were not affected. And if we come to remark the sentiments of various writers upon *particular branches* of their trade, there will be more reasons equally strong for supporting this total not far from the reality. Gee,[2] who wrote about 40 years ago, says the vessels belonging to New England alone, employed in the fishery and coasting trade (without including that to Europe) amounted to 800. So prodigiously as they have in-creased since, the reader will easily believe them to be much more numerous of late years; and yet that number, at 22 men each, employed 17,600 seamen. To double the number would bring it much nearer the truth at present. The fishery of the colonies, says Dr. Mitchel[1], is already much greater than that of Britain: the fishery of New England alone amounts to 255,000£. a year, which is equal to the amount of the British fishery. And yet New York and Philadelphia, with many other places to the northward, have large shares of this fish-ery; so that the whole must make a very great amount.

Without turning to more authorities (although a multitude might be produced) for proving a point which seems so

[2] Joshua Gee, distinguished London merchant, published in 1729 a work entitled *The Trade and Navigation of Britain Considered.*

strongly to prove itself, there will not be any danger, according to these several accounts, in determining the navigation *of the colonies* to employ 33,000 seamen; but lest any objections unseen should arise, I shall call the number only 30,000. It may possibly be expected that I should enlarge upon the vast consequences of such a number of seamen to a maritime power, and especially after what one of the best of the North American writers has observed with a degree of rapture. "In another century the greatest number of Englishmen will be on this side the water. What an accession of power to the British empire, by *sea* as well as by *land!* What increase of trade and navigation! What numbers of ships and seamen! We have been here but little more than 100 years, and yet the force of our privateers in the late war (1750) united, was greater both in men and guns than that of the whole British navy in queen Elizabeth's time."[3] What therefore must they have been in the last war? But notwithstanding all this, I am very far from placing to the account of Britain one jot of all these fine doings. And very clear I am, that the employment of the 12,000 seamen first mentioned, is of twenty times the consequence to this country of all the 30,000 kept by the colonies themselves. The more this subject is enquired into, the more evidently and clearly will it appear, that the production of staple commodities is the *only* business proper for colonies: whatever else they go upon, it is absolutely impossible that they should by any employment whatever make up for the want of the one really necessary. For want of this capital

---

[3] This statement was made by Benjamin Franklin when in his *Observations Concerning the Increase of Mankind, Peopling of Countries, etc.,* he undertook in philosophical fashion to answer the British iron masters who complained about the manufacture of iron in Pennsylvania. See A. H. Smyth, *The Writings of Benjamin Franklin* (New York, 1903–1907), III, 63–73.

foundation of a colony, our northern settlements, we have found, are full of farmers, manufacturers, merchants, fishermen, seamen—but no planters. This is precisely the case with Britain herself; consequently a rivalry between them must inevitably take place. This in the article of the fisheries we find fully taken place; for the northern colonies have nearly beaten us out of the Newfoundland fisheries, that great nursery of seamen! insomuch that the share of New England alone exceeds that of Britain. Can any one think from hence, that the *trade* and *navigation* of our colonies are worth one groat to this nation?

There is not one branch of commerce carried on by these trading settlements but might just as well be in the hands of the inhabitants of this kingdom, the supplying the sugar islands with lumber alone excepted, and that we have already seen is a trifle. Thus the trading part of the colonies rob this nation of the invaluable treasure of 30,000 seamen, and all the profits of their employment; or in other words, the northern colonies, who contribute nothing either to our riches or our power, deprive us of more than twice the amount of all the navigation we enjoy in consequence of the sugar islands, the southern, continental, and tobacco settlements! The freight of the staples of those setts of colonies bring us in upwards of a million sterling; that is, the navigation of 12,000 seamen: according to which proportion we lose by the rivalry of the northern colonies in this single article TWO MILLIONS AND AN HALF sterling! The hackneyed argument which has been copied from writer to writer, that let the colonies get what they will, it all centers in Britain, will doubtless here be extended; and they will say, if the northern colonies get so much money, that money to them is the same as staples to the southern ones, and equally laid out in merchandize with

Britain. But facts prove the very contrary: the consumption of British commodities in them I have shewed cannot be more than to the amount of 108,000£. They export thither in staples to the amount of 98,000£. Now, one of the warmest advocates above quoted asserts the fisheries of New England *alone* to be 255,000£.; according to this reasoning, they would purchase of us only for these two articles to the amount of 353,000£., which being more than three times over false, sufficiently proves that they may acquire riches without expending them with Britain.

No one, who has enquired the least into the state of the colonies, can be ignorant that these northern commercial ones carry on a very considerable illicit trade. A late writer says it amounted to a third of the actual imports.[4] Now under the title of their imports is included *all* they receive from Britain and the West Indies, or in value to upwards of 917,000£., a vast sum! and [one which] must in the nature of things be nearly so much taken out of the pockets of their mother country. Another writer lets us somewhat more into their illicit trade—"The colonies to the northward (of the tobacco ones) have very little direct trade with Great Britain; I mean they have nothing with which they can repay us for the commodities they draw from hence: they only trade with England circuitously; either through the West Indies, which is to us the most advantageous part of their trade, or through foreign European countries, which, however necessary, is a dangerous and suspicious channel. Our English ships meet others with the same commodities at the same markets; and if these markets happen to be overstocked, we interfere with and consequently hurt each other. But what is still more material, there

[4] John Mitchell, *The Present State of Great Britain and North America with Regard to Agriculture, Population, Trade, and Manufactures* (London, 1767), pp. 271 ff.

is much reason to suspect that no small part of the benefit of our North American trade is by this means *left to* [*taken from*] *the mother country, and passes to foreigners, and sometimes to enemies.* These northern provinces are in effect not subject to the act of navigation, because they do not trade in any of the commodities enumerated in that act. They are therefore neither obliged directly to bring their goods to England, nor when they have carried them to other countries, are they necessitated to take England in their way home. Whereas all the colonies which produce any of the enumerated commodities, under whatever relaxations, are always subject to one or other of these regulations. For instance, ships from Boston may carry fish, corn, and provisions to France and Italy, and return again directly to Boston laden with foreign commodities, subject to no other check than what must be considered as none, that of a custom-house officer in their own colony.* These ships, however, carry out something else besides corn and fish; for the governor of Massachuset[t]s' Bay, in 1733, writes word to the Lords of Trade, that *vast quantities* of hats are exported from thence to Spain and Portugal: thus they carry out their own to *cramp our* market, and bring home French goods to *enlarge* that of *our enemies.*† The general turn of reasoning through this passage is certainly just, though some particular sums are probably erroneous. The consumption of British manufactures in the northern colonies probably much exceeds 108,000£. but that they consume all they import, is most certainly contrary to every article of good intelligence that can be gained in the whole affair.

* *Examination of the Commercial Principles of the Late Navigation.* [Attributed to William Burke and published in 1762. Ed.]

† *Political Essays.* [As already noted, these were penned by Arthur Young. Ed.]

That fisheries and navigation are improper employments
for colonies, and detrimental to the interests of the mother
country appears clearly enough from hence; and I may add
to these reasons that the practice of the French, whose fishery
employs 20,000 seamen while ours maintains only 40,000,
proves strongly that *planted* settlements are by no means
necessary for success in fishing. When they had Louisburg, it
was only a place of arms; a security to their fishery, and by
no means a *colony;* and their fishery is now carried on in full
perfection, without so much as that: thus no argument can
be more false than that which pretends that our colonies have
not robbed Britain, but only created a new fishery from the
advantageousness of their situation. We see the fishery of
Britain is declined greatly, which, with the increase of that of
New England, proves the fact sufficiently. We are told that
of New England alone is greater than Britain's; suppose the
seamen 5,000; can any one imagine the employment of those
men, with all the trades they set to work, not to be of the
highest value to this kingdom, and the country that has gained
them so far [not to be] rivals and enemies? What advantage
do we reap from New England equal to this single loss?

The second article which I was to consider is that of corn
and provisions, which are exported from all these northern
colonies to the West Indies and to Europe. How far these are
to be considered as staples, a short enquiry will shew. As to
all that are sent to Europe, we may safely determine it to be
as pernicious a trade as any the colonies can go into, since it
is directly rivalling and even destroying one of the most
advantageous branches of the exports of Britain. American
corn cannot come to an European market without doing mischief to the corn trade of England. This trade is not like that

of most other commodities, which are usually exported in certain quantities and to certain markets; on the contrary, it is extremely uncertain in its destination, the quantity in demand depends on the accidents of crops, sometimes it is to one country, sometimes to another, and the circulation of the trade greatly depending on the surplus quantity which certain countries possess. Poland, England, and Barbary may be called the exporting countries. The latter from the uncertainty of its governments rarely makes the most of the fertility of its soil, proving but a weak rival to England: this leaves all the south of Europe open to the export of that country [England], and very advantageous the circumstance has been, as we have more than once experienced, both to Portugal, Spain, the south of France, and Naples. Let therefore any person judge of the propriety of introducing another rival into this trade, which is far more likely to drive us out of it, than all the others we can have in Europe. Wheat, for many years, sold at 20s. a quarter in America, which was their exporting price; the freight to Marseilles or Naples is 12s. more, the price therefore, delivered, has been 32s. a quarter; a price at which we have never yet sold in those markets, even with the assistance of the bounty. If this does not shew the great impropriety, not to use a harsher expression, of planting colonies in climates that will not produce staple commodities, surely nothing can. It may be said, perhaps, that importation from these colonies, even to Britain herself, may be an advantageous measure in dear years; but I cannot but consider such an idea as very fatal: it implies a dependance on America, which may grow into a neglect of our agriculture at home; than which a more fatal event can never happen. Britain should never look forward to scarcities of corn; if she does, she will be sure to find them. Let her, on the contrary, have no other idea but that of exporting, which will be the means of always keeping it cheap, as we have found for near a century.

There is another evil attending this exportation of American corn to Europe; it is the largeness of the market; while the North Americans were confined to the demand of the West Indies, they could look no farther, and raise no more wheat than sufficient for that demand; but having the European market to go to increases this culture among them prodigiously: the consequence of which is to draw them off from the culture of staples, and from those other professions which are more beneficial to the mother country. If the demand for wheat was not large—and the farmers raising little more than sufficient for their families, they have no encouragement to extend their culture—and the profit on the husbandry is small, in this situation many farmers had great inducements to move to the southward and turn planters; as many did. But when exportation finds a regular market for all they grow, in a country where land is so plentiful, it makes the common husbandry as profitable as planting, and instead of farmers turning planters, planters turn farmers, than which nothing can be more fatal to the interests of Britain.

In the second place, as to the supply of the West Indies, the same objections do not lie; for as the islands find planting too profitable to allow them to attend to common husbandry, there certainly can be no objection to the northern colonies answering the demand—any more than to their supplying them with lumber; but let me here make a remark that I do not recollect ever hearing from any quarter, or reading in any of the numerous works that have been published on this subject. It is that Britain in good policy ought to have kept this supply entirely to herself, instead of the uncertain corn trade she has had with Europe. For this, I think, many reasons are to be given; the demand which there has been in Europe for British corn has never been regular; it has been on the contrary very uncertain; and even in years, when exportation has run very high, it has not been answerable to the surplus of our crop, as we may judge from the price at home continuing so low that the farmers could in several countries scarcely live. Now the supply of the West Indies is the most beneficial market that is known in the world; for it is perfectly regular, and absolutely to be depended upon. Nowhere else are such considerable bodies of people as the inhabitants of those islands to be found, that depend for their daily bread on importation, that attempt to raise scarce anything that they eat. Britain therefore might have depended absolutely on this market; and the supply of it would have been more beneficial than the corn trade she has at fits and starts carried on in Europe: but the encouragement her agriculture would have received by this *regular* demand would have so animated it, that larger quantities of corn than ever would have been produced, and she would have found no difficulty in supplying the European demand also. This might have been done with great ease, by only laying a duty in the islands, because there are many ports for exporting corn from Britain, and many corn merchants in every port; so that there would never have been any reason to fear [the lack of] a plentiful supply, and at a fair price—and if the rate at which the corn came to them was judged too high, the same bounty on the export, or even a larger, if necessary, than what is given at present, would have remedied the inconvenience. As to the distance and freight, we are certain there would have been no material objection, from what we know to be the case at present, which is the supply the islands at present receive from England of beans, and from Ireland of beef. If beans will answer such a freight, most certainly wheat would.

Such a measure as this at present would be perhaps a dangerous one, because all sudden changes in matters of commerce are ever hazardous: but nothing would have been easier than to have established it before the exports from the northern colonies were so large, while the trade was low, and the supply not considerable; the measure might have been brought about by degrees, and nothing is clearer to me than its proving infinitely advantageous to Britain. It would have given an annual certain export to her; it would have rendered common husbandry so little profitable in North America, that the northern colonies, from whom we have so much to apprehend, would not probably have been one fourth so populous; instead of which we should have had many more people than we have to the south of Pennsylvania, and consequently larger products of true staple commodities. It should not be forgotten that one man employed upon tobacco is of far more worth to Britain than forty New England farmers. It appears therefore sufficiently clear, that we may determine corn and provisions to be improper commodities for a colony to deal in, and by no means to be ranked with staples.

Thus does it plainly appear that a very strong distinction is always to be made between the colonies north of Maryland and those to the south, in their importance to the mother country; a distinction which should never be forgotten, as it will remain a lesson to all succeeding ages in what climates to plant colonies. The writer I before quoted, justly remarks on this subject—"That the staple productions of our colonies decrease in value, in proportion to their distance from the sun. In the West Indies, which are the hottest of all, they make to the amount of 8£. 12s. 1d. per head. In the southern continental ones to the amount of 5£. 10s. In the central ones to the amount of 9s. 6d. ½. In the northern settlements to that of 2s. 6d. This scale surely suggests a most important lesson —to avoid colonizing in northern latitudes! Eighteen pounds the export of Nova Scotia after several years settlement, after the utmost attention from the government, after a million sterling of the public money being expended upon it, is an example one would think sufficient to deter the boldest projector! But if our colonies to the north produce such trifling staples, those to the south, on the contrary, are immensely valuable—indeed of such infinite importance to this nation, that *general expressions* of the benefit of our settlements should never be indulged; let provisoes ever come of—*those to the south.* We have found in the preceding enquiries, that those colonies which most abound with manufactures have the fewest staples; and this is a necessary consequence, for nothing but such products as bear a large price in Europe will yield a return from thence of the necessary manufactures, and much less of superfluous ones. But if a colony is situated in a climate which denies such productions, or from a want of due attention in the mother country they are not improved or suffered to decline, does it therefore follow that the inhabitants of such province are to go without cloaths, furniture, and tools? By no means; wherever there are people, they will most assuredly enjoy those necessaries; if they raise nothing from their soil which will purchase them in exchange, they will certainly make them themselves. And if they are a populous flourishing people, they will find very little difficulty in the attempt. Indeed it is not, properly speaking, an *attempt,* but the regular course of things; a concatenation of causes and effects, which take place imperceptibly. And in proportion as they grow more and more populous their manufactures will increase beyond the proportion of the people, until they come to work for exportation. It is ever to be remarked, that a people *cannot fully* supply themselves with any commodity without more than doing it—some exportation must take place, or the home consumption will not be regularly satisfied. It likewise appears, contrary to the ideas of several modern writers, that it is very possible for cultivation alone to supply a people with *all* the necessaries of life without any assistance from *trade* or *manufactures;* and that [may be done] under the disadvantage of exporting the raw material, and importing the manufacture, by a long and expensive voyage, under the subjection of duties, and consequently under complicated charges. The inhabitants of the West India islands and the southern continental colonies wear not a rag of their own manufacturing; drive not a nail of their own forging; eat not out of a platter or a cup of their own making; nay, the former produce not even bread to eat; and if that was the case with all the rest, provided Britain could regularly supply the deficiency (which under a certain system of policy she undoubtedly might), it would be so much the better for her—so entirely do these colonies depend on the mother country for all manufactures! and all from possessing beneficial staples. Of such vast consequence is it to the country to plant new colonies, or extend our old ones, only in climates which will allow of such capital advantages."[5]

In this enquiry I have endeavoured to shew not only the importance of the American colonies to Britain, but at the same time to explain wherein that importance consists; we find it lies in the climate of the colony being different from that of the mother country, as therein consists the only prob-

[5] Arthur Young, *Political Essays.* Young stressed the same point of view in many of his other writings.

ability of the people going upon staple commodities. The northern settlements might be made of much more advantage than they are at present; but it would be anticipating the subject to consider that point here, as I shall in another essay endeavor more particularly to explain it.

CHAPTER XXXV

MANUFACTURES

State of the colony manufactures—Difficulties under which they lie—Means of putting them down—Buy up the raw materials—Bounties—Finding other employments —New colonies—Observations

MUCH has been written concerning the bad effects of the American colonists going into manufactures, but no satisfactory account has been given of the amount of such fabrics, which has been owing to parliament's never having ordered a return of them to be laid before them. Some late writers have urged strongly the magnitude to which these manufactures have arisen, but it has been from calculations founded on dubious authority.[1] In this case the general idea of the necessity of *making* that [which] we cannot *buy* would be satisfactory did we know the amount of their consumption and that of their means of satisfying it.

In considering this point we are to drop the idea, explained in the preceding chapter, of the ill consequences to Britain which resulted from their trade and fisheries, and here merely

[1] Among these writers were, James Marriott, *Political Considerations* (London, 1762); Josiah Tucker, *The Laws and Policy of England Relating to Trade* (London, 1765); William Burke, *Remarks on the Letter Addressed to Two Great Men* (London, 1760); Joseph Massie, *Brief Observations Concerning the Management of the War* (London, 1761). See G. L. Beer, *British Colonial Policy, 1754–1765* (New York, 1922), chap. viii.

take them as means of acquiring wealth wherewith to purchase manufactures.

By manufactures are not to be understood the fabrics of
private families who work only for their own use, but those
only that are wrought for sale, and which are the only or
principal livelihood of the persons concerned and employed
in them. This is a distinction which our writers have not attended to sufficiently; for tho' the population of a settlement
that entirely supports itself is of little or no value to Britain,
yet as it is passive, and no more than supports itself, it is much
to be preferred to another branch of population, which is employed in cloathing, &c. itself and others too—that is, manufacturing for sale. As to the first evil, no remedy in the world
can be applied to it that will be effectual; nor is it an object
which can ever claim the attention of the mother country.

It is from hence clear that the object of enquiry is not the
probable total consumption of all the people in the colonies,
but of those only who do not work up their own manufactures:
when the northern settlements are compared with the southern ones, it is of consequence to shew the great superiority of
the latter; but as that superiority was fully shewn in the last
chapter, it is not to the purpose here. The only consumption
to be considered is that of the ranks which *buy* in order to consume. Their making the purchase shews that they have wherewith to pay; and then comes in properly the pretensions of
the mother country, *if you buy, I expect you* [*to*] *buy of me.*

Nothing is more difficult than to discover the amount of
their manufactures for sale: we are to consider that there are
other articles in their imports besides manufactures, wine,
rum, sugar, India commodities, &c. all which amount to considerable sums. The means by which they can purchase those

and [also] manufactures are their exports, the produce of
their lands, the produce of their fisheries, and the profits of
their commerce; the two first are pretty well known, but the
latter, open and clandestine, is very great, and no guess can
be given of its amount.[2]

That the manufactures for sale are not so great as some
have imagined, may be conceived from the vast number of
inhabitants who in all probability work entirely for themselves; in a country where the minute division of landed
property is so great as in the most populous of the northern
colonies, and in a climate that will yield little valuable, it is
impossible that the people should be able to *purchase* manufactures: poor countrymen in England do it because all their
income is paid them in money, whatever may be their work;
but in America day-labourers are rarely to be found except in
the neighbourhood of great towns; on the contrary, the man
who in England would be a labourer, would there be a little
freeholder, who, probably raising for many years but little
for sale, is forced to work up his wool in his family, his
leather, and his flax, after which, the rest of his consumption
is scarce worth mentioning. The number of people in the
northern colonies who come under this denomination is very
great, and consequently the deductions to be made from the
total consumption very considerable: it is not a difficult matter
to calculate how much a head would supply the total of a
people with manufacturers; this has been calculated; but it is
extremely difficult to guess the amount of *purchased* manufactures, which is the only important point.

In this enquiry we should not confine ourselves to the
northern colonies, but take into the account that part of the

---

[2] On this important question see C. P. Nettels, *The Roots of American
Civilization* (New York, 1938), pp. 612–17.

population of the tobacco ones which is not employed on tobacco; a considerable proportion of the total: as any person may judge who recollects that soon after the peace the number of people in Virginia and Maryland was calculated at 800,000, the export of tobacco therefore is not much above 20s. a head; instead of which, those who are employed by that staple are able, in all probability, to consume 5, 6, or 8£. a head in imported commodities, and the rest of the people scarcely any thing, as they must, like their brethren to the north, manufacture almost every thing they use. If the imported commodities in these colonies are assigned to 200,000 people, there will remain 600,000, whose purchased consumption is small; and if the common calculation is taken, of their being at the peace 1,000,000 of people in the northern colonies, we then find 1,600,000 souls, among whom the imports are in some proportion or other to be divided. The exports from Great Britain are as follow:

	£.
Canada	105,000
Nova Scotia	26,500
New England	407,000
New York	531,000
Pennsylvania	611,000
	1,680,500

If the population of these was 1,000,000, they imported about 32s. 6d. a head: if we allow 5£. a head for all that *purchased* their consumption, the number this importation supplied is 336,000, at which rate (to speak nothing of West Indian and foreign imports), 664,000 persons manufactured for themselves, besides the proportion of the tobacco settlements. Hence if these data are just, we may suppose one third of the people to consume purchased commodities, and two thirds to manufacture for themselves; but this supposes their own fabrics for sale to be inconsiderable, and that 5£. a head is for only a partial consumption.

There is yet another light in which this point is to be viewed, which is a different classing of the people; for the sake of explaining the clearer what I mean, I will suppose a division of the million of people in the northern colonies.

	£.
200,000 who consume of foreign manufactures, &c. only 2s. 6d. a head.	
500,000 who consume a head 40s.	
300,000 who consume 5£.	
The first	25,000
The second	1,000,000
The third	1,500,000
	2,525,000
Import from Britain	1,680,000
According to this account, they must buy of foreigners, or work among themselves .	844,500

For in this idea the fabrics worked in private families have no place; if they were taken in, the poorest would consume far more than 2s. 6d. There is nothing extravagant in this account; nor can it be supposed that the manufactures of the northern colonies amount to less than 844,500£. In case the consumption of the classes here stated is greater, then this amount will of course be proportionably larger.

Supposing this sum to be the fact, or near it—or if we call their manufactures for sale a million—I do not think it an amount that ought greatly to alarm the mother country, provided she took proper measures to obviate their ill effects, which measures would be very easily planned and executed. It is to be remembered that a very considerable portion of this sum must be expended in fabrics, the whole of which Britain cannot expect to furnish—and which in fact she does not furnish to any colony; for the last hand [finishing touches] to a variety of articles cannot be put at London, but must necessarily be executed in America, and the labours of those workmen and artizans is there blended with the price of the manufacture.

All that this kingdom can expect from the northern colonies, is to keep down public manufactories, which take the wool from the sheeps' back, and convert it into cloth; the flax from the ground, and make it into linen and lace; the skin off the beast, and turn it to finished fabrics of leather; the iron from the ore, and convert it into the variety of utensils which Sheffield and Birmingham exhibit; and the same in other instances: but this reasoning must not be carried too far in any of these articles; there are objects which when completed from wool, leather, and iron, will still be of such small value that the very freight from Britain and carriage to the consumer would be twice the worth; such we may be sure will be wrought in the colony. But when we see them making cloth of 12s. a yard, linen of 5s., hats of 16s. each, locks, keys, and curious articles of hardware, which is the case, we may then be certain that the policy of this kingdom is deficient; and that without violence, such manufactures might be put down.

We are to remember that the colonists are under great difficulties in their attempts to raise manufactures for sale. The mother country has the power of introducing her own fabrics as cheap as she pleases and under whatever advantages of bounties or premiums she likes to grant; which she can do in her exportation of them to no other market. Everywhere else they meet with duties on importation, and perhaps prohibitions; but in America the manufactories of Britain are openly in every market without duty or clog. In the next place the price of labour is very great, greater take the year through than in Britain, which is a material article; this must necessarily be the case where land can be had for nothing; workmen may be gained for high wages, but those high wages will presently enable them to set up for planters in a country where twenty pounds is a fortune sufficient to begin with; thus the master manufacturers can never keep the men after they have got them, which must lay them under almost insuperable difficulties, or subject them to expences which will make their manufactures much dearer than those of Britain.

The long winters and severe season which stops most employment, have been urged as reasons why they may manufacture largely for sale: but I am not of this opinion. Those who are conversant in our fabrics well know that in very sharp frosts many of our manufactures are at a stand; what therefore would [it] be at Boston or New York, where the frosts are in common 20 degrees sharper than the most severe we feel in England, and where the whole winter is frost and snow—people can scarce keep their extremities from freezing who attend to nothing else—how therefore could the finer sorts of manufactures be carried on? What sort of work would a weaver make, whose fingers were numbed with cold; or a workman in steel, whose flesh froze to his manufacture? In such a climate manufactures must be carried on in mild or warm weather, and then the workmen may have what they will ask in the field, and all the advantages here stated are at once given up. Under such circumstances no fabrics can be made cheap enough to under-sell Britain but such as come extravagantly dear from her and can be made reasonable in

America, or others so inferior in kind that freight and carriage make a large proportion of the whole value.

But supposing the manufactures of these provinces, notwithstanding these inconveniences, did not get to any height (which in some articles is the case), then Britain might, without having recourse to what governor Pownall[3] hints at—excises—take measures that would bring them down. The easiest and most adviseable way would be to raise the price of their raw materials by buying it [them] up for the British market: the obvious way to bring about any such transaction as that is by giving bounties upon the import into Great Britain, and if they are large enough, they certainly will effect any thing. But the objection is, that, in order to create a new trade, the expence by way of bounty may be greater than if done by other methods. I would propose to force the import of wool from the colonies into Great Britain to such a point as would be sufficient to burthen the woollen manufactures of America, by raising the price of their raw materials: at the same time that this laid a tax on the American fabrics, it would give a bounty on the British ones, by lowering the price of their raw materials by the import from the colonies.

The employment of factors, agents, or contractors would be less adviseable far than giving a bounty, provided the latter would have the effect; but as the wool-dealers in the colonies must be thrown into a different channel, and as the merchants there must open new correspondences, a bounty, in order to force such a new business, must probably be a greater expence than if government did the business, at least for a time, through the merchants; but when once the business was brought near a regular train, a small bounty would have a greater effect than a large one at first.

[3] See supra p. 405, footnote 7.

Such a transaction would be very heavy upon the manufactures of the Americans; for under the disadvantages which I before stated the colonists to lie, a rise of price in their wool would have the same effect as laying an excise upon their manufactures, but which would be brought about without the heartburnings and disputes inevitable with a new tax. The idea of importing wool from America is not a new one; Dr. Mitchell some years ago remarked—"The wool of the colonies is better than that of the English; it is of the same kind with the Spanish wool, or curled and frizzled like that, and might be rendered as fine by the same management. By the step which the colonies have lately taken to raise all the sheep they can, they will have plenty of wool. With this they have already made cloth worth 12s. a yard, which is as good as any that is made of English wool. Some of their wool has been sent to England, where it sold for the price of the best. This may perhaps be looked upon as a loss to England; but if she would study to make a right and proper use of her colonies, this might be of more service to her than any one thing they are capable of producing. If the Spaniards succeed in their attempts to manufacture their wool, England may want it from the colonies more than any other commodity, as it is well known there is not a single piece of fine cloth made in England without Spanish wool."[4] This observation came from a person perfectly well versed in American affairs from a long residence there, and shews how expedient the conduct would be, with a view to the goodness of the wool, as well as the design with which I propose it to be done.

The same conduct might be pursued with some other raw

[4] John Mitchell, *The Present State of Great Britain and North America with Regard to Agriculture, Population, Trade, and Manufacture* (London, 1767), pp. 142–43.

materials, such as skins, hemp, and flax, all which are valuable articles to be imported into Great Britain; some of them are so already, and if our demand was a little quickened, it would certainly be laying a difficulty upon the American manufacturers that work them. It is true that in both these cases the price would rise upon ourselves as well as them, but this I do not apprehend would be of a bad consequence equal to the advantages on the other side of the question; since there is no object in the policy of Britain which is of near such importance as putting down or at least preventing all increase in the manufactures of the colonies.

There is another method of effecting this great purpose, which in some respects would answer better, though worse in others: it would be giving a bounty on the export of such British manufactures *to America* as the colonists have made the greatest progress in erecting—and this bounty should be sufficient to enable the merchant importer in America to under-sell the manufacturer there: this would be a very simple operation, and might be made perfectly effectual; but it would have this needless expence, it would supply the West Indies and the southern continental colonies with the same fabrics as cheap as the northern colonies, which, though an effect of no ill consequence in itself, would add to the expence without making an equal return for it: not however that it would be without any return, for those British goods being so much cheaper in those markets would extend the consumption of them, and certainly increase the trade in them which is carried on in the West Indies.

Whether this method or the first was chosen would not be material, provided the thing was done: but that some method should be taken to effect it cannot be doubted, since the grand interest of Britain in her colonies is defeated and perverted by their setting up manufactories for sale, a step which, in the natural course of it if left to itself, must inevitably bring on their independance.

But here it will naturally be remarked that to put down the manufactures of the colonies, and thereby throw people out of employment, would be a very iniquitous scheme, unless some provision was at the same time made in an increase of other employments; and certainly no person can dispute the truth of this; but this part of the work would be very easy; among the true staples of the northern colonies have been mentioned skins, drugs, ships, pitch, potash, timber, flax-seed, copper, and iron, all which articles, particularly timber, ships, pitch, and iron, may be had in any quantities, provided due encouragement was given to procure them. At the same time that measures were taken to lessen their manufactures, we ought also to increase the quantity of these staples, not only to give employment to the people instead of manufacturing, but also to supply the country in general with as much or more wealth than they made by that employment. Among these articles none have oftener exercised the pens of ingenious men than that of naval stores, which we import from the Baltic at so large an expence, and pay for almost entirely with bullion: our northern settlements produce all sorts of timber in as great or greater perfection and plenty than the east country; this is a point acknowledged by all; masts, boltsprits, plank, deals of all kinds, and some articles of timber much more valuable than what we import. Great objections used formerly to be made, for want of saw mills being erected; but that is no longer the case, for there are many of them now upon almost all the rivers of America; so that every thing is done that could facilitate the supply, was the article of freight got over. *Gee,* in his *Navigation of Great*

Britain considered, says, "Our plantations in America abound with vast quantities of timber, and the navigation from New England, Nova Scotia, or Newfoundland is not more tedious nor at a greater distance from us, than the bottom of the Bothnic gulph, or Petersburgh. But those places having been long in trade and having a constant demand from us for that commodity, they always have great stocks of timber ready squared and boards lying ready to load a ship of five or six hundred tons in ten or twelve days; but hitherto we have never had stocks lying ready in our plantations, nor any encouragement for building large bulky ships, such as are used by the Danes and Swedes, who sail with a few hands and at a small charge. What timber we have had hitherto come directly to England has been rather put on board to fill up, when tobacco or other merchandize has not been to be had [that is, available], and therefore no care has hitherto been taken to make it a regular trade."[5] But this is not at present the case; for I am well informed that there are large stocks of timber lying in many of our plantations ready for the West Indies, and proportioned to that demand, consequently the quantity would of course increase, with any increase of demand, and no difficulties of that sort would be found. But Mr. Gee is mistaken in his assertion of the length of navigation; for this is seen in the freight: that from Riga to England is not above 25s. calculated at the rate per load at which it is paid for; whereas the freight from Nova Scotia is 40s. to 50s. This difference will, I believe, generally be found; and another circumstance in favour of the Baltic is the price of labour, which is not half what it is in our colonies; these are the only superiorities of the east country. But on the other hand, our American

[5] Joshua Gee. *The Trade and Navigation of Britain Considered* (London, 1729).

timber comes duty free, and even with a small bounty, though
an insufficient one; the only object therefore to get over is the
freight; and this can only be done by giving a bounty per ton
on all ships belonging to Great Britain that bring timber or
naval stores from the colonies. Let us suppose the freight per
ton from the Baltic 1£. 5s. and that from Nova Scotia 3£.,
which we may venture to state as an average, though 2£. 10s.
or even 2£. may be sometimes taken; in this case, a bounty of
2£. per ton would turn the scale of freight by 5s. which, with
the duties on the Baltic timber, would at once change the course
of all the timber and iron trade. By various accounts it has been
found that our import in iron is 27,500 tons [which] at 12£.
is 314,000£., and timber 200,000£.; these two articles amount
therefore to more than half a million sterling, not to speak
of increase in the other branches of their staples. I before
shewed, that the manufactures for sale in the northern colonies probably amounted to more than 800,000£. a year; now
we find that in these two articles of iron and timber they
might earn of Britain alone above 500,000£. which would
enable her to take proper measures to sink their manufactures
to that amount, and at the same time leave them with as much
wealth as they had before—no hardships would be found
from it in the colonies, but the interest of this country would
be prodigiously advanced; instead of paying half a million
to the Baltic in cash, we should send to the same amount in
manufactures to America, the difference of which is very
great; and at the same time we should effectually prevent
the increase of manufacturing in America, which in future
would prove of much more consequence than can at first be
imagined.

The expence to the public at which these beneficial effects
might be brought about would not be large. One hundred

thousand pounds a year would pay the bounty on 50,000 tons of shipping, that is, 100 sail at 500 tons each. We may venture to assert that this navigation would answer the purpose, if confined to that alone; and the expence of such a sum would bear no proportion to the immense advantages that must inevitably accrue from it to this country.

By the export of naval stores the colonies would find employment for that surplus of their population which has driven them to manufactures—by the import of British manufactures in consequence, and the buying up of their raw materials, their own fabrics would be put down—the manufacturing interest of Britain would be most highly advanced, and the export of bullion to the Baltic would be stopped; all these advantages would surely be well worth the sum they would cost the public in the bounties, which would not be lost to the nation or paid to foreigners, but distributed among her own people at home, to the invigoration of their industry. A late writer, after starting some proposals similar to this, remarks, "These sentiments are founded in reason, and tend to render Great Britain independant of the effects of that prodigious commercial manufacturing spirit which is now arose in all Europe. There are many peculiar motives for importing wool from these colonies with the other articles already specified. It would be a great assistance to our own woollen manufactures, and at the same time have the best effect we could wish upon that of the colonies. No *importations* are more beneficial than raw commodities, to be worked into manufactures; and no *exportations* so pernicious to a manufacturing country as that of such raw commodities; for which reason Britain should wish to import wool from these colonies; and were the system of policy I am now sketching thoroughly executed, such importation might very easily be effected. Every particular of this system is the link of a chain, and all equally connected; the more iron, timber, potash, and madder were imported, the more likewise you might have of wool, for the more would the colony woollen manufacture suffer, and consequently the less would be their demand for that commodity, and then the additional demand from Britain, at a time when the British manufactures were poured into every market, would completely give her the command of all the American wool. This importation might be made to extend to a very large sum annually.

"As to ships, some may perhaps think the benefit resulting from them to the mother country more equivocal; but in a certain degree I should apprehend the supply from the colonies highly advantageous. In many cases it might be found advantageous to build men of war there. But leaving them out of the question, let us consider the repeated outcries and complaints that have been made in this kingdom for so many years, of the want of timber for ship-building; and that such complaints are not ill grounded, everybody agree[s]. Now would it not be a very prudent measure, to reserve the timber in this island for the use of the navy alone, and depend on America for that for merchantmen? It is by no means advantageous to this country, whose agriculture is of such immense importance, to have any land occupied by wood that is good enough to yield corn, and consequently no more [wood] should be raised than is necessary; and supposing it necessary to raise all that is requisite for the royal navy, that is certainly the most; for there is no occasion to extend it to all that is used in merchant ships. The latter had better all be built in America. Nor would there be any necessity to lose the manufacturing of the hemp with which such ships were rigged, since we might import it raw from the new colonies, manu·

factured into sail cloth with as little expence as much of the hemp lies under, now used by New England, &c. If Britain builds annually 40,000 tons of shipping (I am only stating a supposition), this at 3£. 10s. per ton would alone amount to 140,000£. a year. Nor can I see why the northern colonies should not build for all Europe. The building trade might easily be carried to the under-selling all other countries, and especially when the culture of hemp and the working the iron mines are carried to perfection; for then there is no country in the world that will unite all the requisites for building cheap so completely as our colonies in North America; and that at the same time while all the benefit redounds to Britain alone, and without there being the least danger to her from such natural advantages in them. The danger would be great, if at the same time she suffered them to be traders and fishermen; but I laid it down as a rule to proceed upon, that trade, fishing, and manufacturing were put an entire stop to among them. Now the trade of ship-building has not only the advantage of selling timber (a mere drug in America) to great advantage, but of obliging those who bought it, at the same time to purchase some quantity of our hemp and iron. Thus if we built 100,000 tons of shipping annually for foreigners in our northern colonies, it would make up the former amount 500,000£. and I am very well persuaded that this might be easily effected. Supplying other nations with shipping cheaper than they have it at present would be no objection to this plan, since all the benefits they would reap therefrom are not comparable to those which we should receive from taking their money. Nor do I think in true politics it would be the least adviseable to refuse French gold for men of war thus built: for we may lay it down as a maxim, that the French will never want as many or more men of war than they can man; experience shews this; so that our enemy will not meet us with a ship the more for our selling them. And most assuredly we had better take his money than let it be given either to the Swedes or the Genoese."[6]

The reader will here observe that this point of employing the northern colonists upon staples (or commodities which answer the same purpose, by way of enabling them to do without manufacturers) would in the nature of things lower their fabrics, and take off all that eagerness for making a progress in them which has of late been so strong among the Americans. Give them employments more advantageous than manufacturing (which all that I have named would prove), and they will, in the nature of things, apply at once to them with as much avidity as ever they did to manufactures; for in the course of affairs in the colonies, it can only be the *surplus* of population that can found manufactories for sale.

And here it is necessary to observe that this system of destroying the fabrics of the colonies by buying up their raw materials, giving a bounty on the export of the British manufactures, and employing the colonists on staples, might be vastly assisted by the measures before explained of planting new colonies in better climates: this would draw off yet greater numbers than the above mentioned employment on iron, timber, ships, &c. The population that is to be commanded for manufactories can only be had when there is a surplus which the lands do not take off. The northern settlements are very populous—the best lands taken up—new grants only to be had in spots which possess not the advan-

[6] Arthur Young, *Political Essays Concerning the Present State of the British Empire* (London, 1772), pp. 396-98.

tages which settlers necessarily are desirous of: when such difficulties increase, and at the same time the people [are] vastly increased, it is the nature of things that the application to manufactures must increase proportionably; and the necessity of counter-acting the ill effect every day must be more and more evident. That [i.e., this] surplus of population arises merely for want of lands worth taking up, as the very term [surplus] implies, for no such thing can be found while land is so plentiful as to yield an immediate and beneficial maintenance to every family that applies for it: hence it is that manufactories are established, and hence the propriety of finding new employments on staples for the people, instead of manufactures. The same principles act in pointing out the necessity of such new colonies: that every man without employment may meet with every possible inducement to settle as a planter rather than as a manufacturer: and while any such [men] exist, we may be certain what choice will be made; the country life in America has too much independancy, too much plenty, and too many conveniencies not at all times to be embraced in preference to the business of manufacturing, which in every circumstance is so much inferior.

When land is difficult to be had or not good, owing to the extension of the settlements or to the monopolies of the country, the poor must be driven to other employments than those which depend on land; manufacturing, commerce, fisheries, &c. must then thrive in the natural course of things, unless some such measure as I have stated is put in practice in order to provide other employment. Such measures cannot be carried to the extent that is necessary with such an increasing people: the plan therefore to be adopted is certainly to prevent the future increase of the evil, by providing a motive for the fresh emigration of the people. Settling Canada, Nova Scotia, and Florida is not providing any such motive, as it has long been found that the people of the other colonies will not go to them; but colonies on the Ohio, Mississippi, and in the Illinois, would have this effect beyond any other measure in the world. The journey from New England, New York, Jersey, Pennsylvania, and Maryland is by means of the rivers in the back country, the Ohio, the Mississippi, and the lakes, as easy, cheap, and commodious, as can be wished: so that the people in those colonies who cannot get good land at home, may, at a very small expence, provide as much as they can desire in those territories, which are in every respect as excellent, in point of soil and climate, as can be wished. Water-carriage from the old colonies is absolutely necessary to such new ones as are designed to draw off the people from them. The inhabitants of America are so accustomed to do without expence, that they would consider a long land-carriage of their effects as an insurmountable obstacle to their removal; I mean the lower ranks of the people, whose emigration the system of policy I have just been stating would most concern. But the passage to the tracts of country I have mentioned is as commodious, especially by the Ohio, as they can wish, and would not fail to draw off a very great number of the people.

Here I have traced that system, the several parts of which could hardly fail of having the effects I have mentioned. In the first place, buying up their wool and other raw materials would lay a tax on their master manufacturers, at the same time that it would be an advantage to those of Britain. Secondly, giving a bounty upon the import in America of such British manufactures as the Americans had made the greatest progress in setting up, would enable us to under-sell them in all the towns in our colonies. Thirdly, buying up or giving a bounty on the tonnage of all ships that brought iron, timber, or naval stores from thence, would find employment for their people more beneficial than that of manufactures; which would not only prevent such people as are now employed on them from falling into distress, but would prevent others from engaging in them in future. Fourthly, planting new colonies in fertile and healthy countries would draw off that surplus of their population, which has hitherto thrown them into manufacturing; it would lessen their present numbers considerably, and be a drain to their future increase.

These several points of conduct aim at the same purpose—a purpose too important to admit of any delay, which on the contrary requires spirited endeavours, and such variations in the view as shall attack the evil on every side. One or two of these measures might do much good, but all of them are necessary, if a complete cure is intended, and prevention meant, in future, as well as present ease. Manufactures in these colonies have been owing to the increase of the people being beyond the proportion of fresh land to take off the surplus of population. Nothing can either put them down or prevent their increase, but [except] drawing off many of the inhabitants, by tempting them with a better country and plenty of land, and finding more profitable employments than manufacturing for such as stay at home. These are the grand objects: well pursued they would prove effectual in putting down all their manufactories for sale, and preventing new ones being erected; but if the work was not sufficiently executed thereby, the bounty on similar British fabrics would give the finishing stroke. The northern colonies under such a system of policy would no more have manufactures abounding among them of their own make, than the

West Indies or the southern colonies, excepting what was the private work of families; an object not of much jealousy to Britain, and even those would be much lessened by the same conduct. At the same time that this great and desirable effect took place, the manufacturing interest of the mother country would be amazingly advanced more than by any other measure that could be devised; for the export to America would be increased proportionably to the quantity made by the American manufactories for sale, and the import of naval stores; so that instead of paying a vast sum in bullion to the Baltic for those commodities, they would be bought of the colonies with manufactures, a difference infinitely great. The trade and navigation of Britain would be greatly encouraged—and her American affairs would be thrown on a footing that would, if well pursued, be effectual in preventing those many evils which cannot but arise from the establishment of manufactures among the colonists. Such advantages are rarely to be gained without trouble or expence; but in this case both would be small in comparison with the benefit: the small bounties already in being shew that our legislature think the thing extremely desirable; but if they would effect it, they must submit to a larger expence, in order to secure a profit of far more consideration than almost any expence.

CHAPTER XXXVI

INDEPENDANCY

*Great errors in the accounts given of the progress of popu-
lation in America—Principles of increase—Dependancy
connected with staples—Surplus of population—Power
of the colonies—Observations*

THIS is one of the most curious and interesting disquisi-
tions that can at any time demand the attention of this
kingdom. The colonies we have planted in America have
arisen to such a height of populousness, power, and wealth
that an idea of their future independancy starts into the mind
of almost every man on the very mention of them in conversation: some assert the period near at hand, while others
are willing to believe it yet at a distance. To enquire when
it is to happen is not of importance; but to examine those
circumstances whose tendency is either to accelerate or retard
it is an enquiry which is equally interesting and useful, since
from thence may be deduced the plan of conduct which it is
proper this nation should pursue, in order to secure a continuance of the advantages she at present enjoys, by means
of her settlements in America.

Virginia, from its first plantation, has doubled its number
of people every twenty years: this fact, which is well authen-
ticated by actual enumerations, has led many of our writers
into a most capital mistake concerning the progress of popu-

lation in America: they have transferred it from Virginia to our colonies on the continent in general, than which a greater blunder could scarcely be made. Virginia is a settlement where the people are spread all over the country, quite to the mountains, among the hills, and even over them; and have been so for many years, owing to the uncommon inland navigation all the country enjoys: but in the colonies to the south the people are confined to the unhealthy coast for the sake of cultivating rice, the most unwholesome employment under the sun. Tobacco and wheat, which are the grand products of Virginia, will not grow in swamps and marshes; though the former requires a rich moist soil, yet it must be free from wet, and dry lands do for it, provided they are fertile—rich woodlands, for instance, where oak, hickory, and locust trees are found—such lands in America are ever healthy; and as to wheat, it may be laid down as a maxim that wherever it thrives the climate and soil are salubrious to the human body. Another circumstance is the climate of Virginia, which at some distance from the coast is as fine as any in America; it is the medium between the cold of the northern colonies, and the heat of the southern ones, as its situation is between both. Further, Virginia is without towns; the people make such advantage by their agriculture that all are employed in it, consequently all are on the increase; they have neither merchants, manufacturers, nor fishermen among them.

If the reader considers these circumstances, he will find them extremely well adapted to increase the number of a people. The healthiness of the climate—the goodness, and at the same time dryness of the soil—the ease with which every man finds employment on the soil—the profit of agriculture exceeding that of any other profession. These are points which, when united with the plenty of land that most of our colonies enjoy, could not fail to occasion a very rapid increase of the people.

That this increase is not to be extended in idea to the rest of the colonies, will evidently appear from these circumstances in them being very different: in the north the climate is so very severe that it is impossible population should thrive in the same degree as a more temperate one, for the necessaries of life must be had with more difficulty. In the southern colonies, the heat is too excessive—in the low country on the coast, where the planters confine themselves on account of rice—for the people to increase as they do in Virginia: in the northern colonies the soil is not comparable to what it is in the tobacco ones, consequently provisions cannot be had with equal ease. The same observation is applicable to the planted parts of the southern settlements, and will continue so till the back country is cultivated. In the northern colonies agriculture is far from being attended with that profit which results from the culture of staple commodities; the consequence of which is a large proportion of the people applying to other professions, which are far from having that tendency to increase which is found in classes maintained by the soil: thus the people gather into towns; populous cities are met with, the bane of increase; trade, manufactures, and fisheries flourish: and although such may be thought to increase the people, it is a great mistake; those employments only find business for the surplus of agriculture; where is a town full of those professions, in the most healthy climate, that doubles its number from its own increase in twenty years? Yet is this done in Virginia: on the contrary, all great towns would be presently depopulated, if they were not supplied by the country. Another circumstance is the considerable tracts of country in the northern settlements that are fully peopled, and where land is as dear as in the cultivated parts of Great Britain. In such there cannot be that increase which is found in Virginia, where the people are spread so much more over the country.

It is here necessary to attend particularly to the progress of population in a newly planted country, in order to see from what principles the increase of the people arises, and what are the circumstances that draw them from the professions which depend on agriculture. The great increase found in Virginia has been owing to the plenty of good land in a climate that will allow of the culture of a staple. A man there who fixes upon a plantation breeds his family of course to a knowledge of agriculture; the sons marry early, because they no sooner form a connection with the daughters of a neighboring planter than they think of marrying. It is the same in England, but what puts it aside [there] is the difficulty of supporting a family; the young couple, as much as they may wish it, are obliged by prudence and their parents to wait till they be settled advantageously, which often is till the chance of a numerous family is half cut off. In Virginia, and those parts of the other colonies circumstanced in the same manner, the connection is no sooner formed than the marriage ensues. The man takes up a grant of land, his father gives him a little stock, and assists him in building a house: money is wanting for but very few things, and a small sum all that is necessary; the business is then done, and the future success of the family undoubted. Such a state of the case not only brings on marriages early, but also early courtships; for in thickly peopled countries men are retarded in their ideas of connecting themselves, for fear of that poverty they are always in danger of: an unmarried young man in parts of the colonies is a prodigy.

Here therefore we deduce the first principle, which is plenty of land to be had for asking, and under the payment only of some slight fees: the second is, that land being good, and well situated; if it is not good, too much expence and difficulty will attend the cultivation of it; for if subsistence for a family be not easily and speedily to be gained, with some surplus, by the sale of which other necessaries may be purchased, [then] more money must be had in readiness before a plantation is undertaken; and if the situation is not within a due distance of water-carriage, it will be in vain to raise products for sale, as they cannot be sold.

From hence we find there must be a difference in the progress of the population of different provinces proportioned to these circumstances; the land in Virginia is much better than in the northern colonies; and it is in general far nearer to navigation; these are points of superiority which cannot fail of rendering the increase much quicker in the former than in the latter.

The third observation to be made here is concerning the climate; the soil must not only be good, but the climate must be warm enough to yield products that are of a value sufficient to make agriculture more profitable than either manufactures, commerce, or fisheries. In Virginia the culture of tobacco is much more beneficial than any other employment; the crop yields a certain and ready value, by means of which they are able to purchase such manufactures and necessaries as their lands will not produce, and at the same time afford a good profit to the planter; so circumstanced, they have no inducement to change their way of life—their sons have no other business before their eyes by which they can better themselves even in idea. But all this is different in the northern colonies; agriculture there is nothing more than the culture of provisions, which, though, when prices are high and a market ready, is very profitable, yet is it not that regular profit which attends a staple; this want of a regular market for commodities rarely to be sent to Europe, renders other means of getting money necessary, such as commerce, fishing, and manufactures; and when once these are but partly established, they must necessarily draw off many people from the culture of the earth. The success which attends some of these—and the inclinations of individuals, which, *when there is a choice*, will necessarily operate with many—by degrees leads more and more into pursuits entirely different from agriculture—circumstances owing originally almost entirely to a want of staple products. When once there is a population formed independant of agriculture, the people are divided; one part increase proportionably to the circumstances above-described, but the other have no increase, or probably require the support of the country to keep up their numbers.

We find therefore that the first requisite is plenty of land in a healthy climate; the second, fertility and a convenient situation; and the third, the climate's yielding a staple product. If we examine the rest of the colonies with Virginia, unless it be in places either not fertile, or in inconvenient situations, the navigation of Virginia is infinitely superior to that of any other colony: New England has very little inland navigation; and in point of fertility, the soil in the tobacco provinces much exceeds that of any of the rest. Respecting the product of staples, the northern colonies have none, and therefore have been driven to every profession as well as agriculture. And in the southern ones, where there are both staples and good land, the rice culture has fixed the principal part of the people on the coast, where the climate is so unhealthy, that, instead of breeding people, it is formed for destroying them.

From these considerations it is very evident that the increase of people in Virginia must be far greater than in the rest of the colonies, and consequently, that those writers who have supposed the whole of our settlements to increase in people as quick as that colony, must have erred very considerably in their calculations.

This is a material point: it is a very good thing for Britain that the colonies which have not staples do not increase so quick, for if they did, their manufactures, &c., would increase proportionably; but that increase in other colonies brings on a corresponding increase of the staple products, and also a proportionable consumption of British manufactures.

The independancy of the colonies, whenever it may happen, must turn on this point, *the increase of people in those settlements which have not staples*. The increase in those which have staples, must always be for the advantage of the mother country. It is therefore of consequence to know the truth of so important a matter: the northern colonies are most populous, but it does not therefore follow that their present increase is equal to that of Virginia.

Dr. Mitchel[1] says the number of people in the tobacco colonies soon after the peace was 800,000; in the northern colonies near 1,500,000;[1] the total I do not apprehend at that time to be so great. The melancholy circumstance in this account is the number in those settlements which produce no staples. If the total, as some authors assert, be 2,000,000 at the peace, the number in the northern colonies could not be above 1,000,000 or 1,100,000.

[1] *The Present State of Great Britain and North America with Regard to Agriculture, Population, Trade, and Manufactures, impartially considered* (London, 1767), pp. 214–16.

It is no difficult matter to explain how the danger of America's becoming independant does not lie in mere population, but in the territories where that population is found. A people spread over a vast extent of fertile country, and employed in raising staples so valuable as to pay well for the freight to Europe and distant countries—the raising which is attended with more profit than any other employment—such a people, it is very evident, can find little or no inducement to oppose the designs of the mother country. The latter finds a ready and certain market for all the staples of the former, and sells in return every article of manufacture or other commodities that can be wanted, at the same fair price she fixes on them in all other markets: at the same time that this friendly and mutually beneficial intercourse subsists between them, the mother country is at all times ready and able to protect the colony against all enemies and invaders. In such a situation it is evident that both parties must remain satisfied with each other, until one of them is guilty of some great indiscretion or false politics; and we may venture to assert, that such false steps, in all probability, will come from the mother country, that is, from the active and superior party. This is the true description of a colony founded upon just principles, and the great object to be attended to is the people's employing themselves in a business wherein they cannot interfere with Britain.

Now if we turn our eyes to the northern colonies, we shall find that the case is extremely different. As the climate will not produce staples of value enough to purchase manufactures, &c. the inhabitants are necessitated to apply to other professions; these are commerce, fisheries, and manufactures; the moment they get into this train, they engage in a rivalship with the mother country; both are in the same pursuits;

they meet each other in the same markets, and with the same commodities; when once the mother country *feels* the effect of such a competition, jealousies, heart-burnings, restraints, opposition, and a number of effects of rivalry arise, and are the forerunners of that independancy of which we are treating at present.

It is not that the northern colonies are without a considerable and a profitable agriculture; the distinguishing circumstance is the product of the agriculture. In the tobacco colonies, &c., the staple is a commodity that is wanted in Europe, and yields a good price; consequently the planters can sell to the British merchants a product that regularly supplies them with a return of British manufactures. But the agriculture of the northern provinces, that is, of all the settlements north of the tobacco colonies yields only corn and provisions; valuable articles, it is true, but not sufficiently so to bear the freight to Europe, except in years when they are very cheap in America, and very dear in Europe: consequently the sale of them to the merchants of Britain must, in the nature of things, be a mere uncertainty, a contingency depending on accident: whereas the sale which is to pay for the import of manufactures must be regular, and absolutely to be depended upon.

Now the want of such staple products must have the consequence of obliging the inhabitants of such colonies to make those fabrics they cannot buy, or else to apply to such businesses as may have the effect which the agriculture of other colonies produces.

But, say some, why cannot these settlements apply to manufactures, commerce, and fisheries, without such an application bringing on their independancy? Because those employments, by whatever people they are carried on, occasion wealth, military power, and that surplus of population from which armies may, on any occasion be raised. When the general business of a colony is the same as that of the mother country to the degree of rivalship, disputes and quarrels must arise; and when these become inflamed by a continuation of the same disputes, the possession of a great body of seamen, many ships, with every sort of naval stores, arms, and ammunition for the equipment of fleets, armies, and their attendants, with a great surplus of population for the recruit of both; manufactures in number sufficient to take off a dependance on others, and commerce for a general supply; when this is the case, it must surely be apparent at first sight that colonies in such a situation possess the principal means of becoming independant; in such a situation they will have little compunction at disputes with their superior, and every day feel less and less dread at any open hostilities.

The difference is extremely great between such and others that are in a different predicament; among whom we find no surplus of population, no ships, no seamen, no magazines of naval stores, nor any great cities, to plan, direct, and head the discontents that may arise from the causes I have just set forth. While the natural tendency of the soil, climate, productions, and navigation is to spread the people over a whole country, their increase does not make them powerful; add millions to Virginia, and spread over the Ohio, Illinois, and Mississippi, they will be no more powerful with four millions than with one, because, as long as fresh land is plentiful, there will be no surplus of population to gather into towns; without the same surplus there can be no manufacture, nor any possibility of raising armies or navies. A colony not a fourth so populous, but possessing a surplus of population apparent in its cities, and consequent employments independant of agriculture, would be far more dangerous to Britain. Hence we find how ill judged a conduct that was in the British government which lead it to attempt to force a capital in Virginia: every means were used to lead the people to flock into Williamsburg, and magnificent edifices erected to adorn it; miserable want of foresight! Instead of which, had great restrictions been laid on towns increasing, in the infancy of Boston, New York, and Philadelphia, this country would at present have been in the possession of perhaps 20,000 seamen more than she now enjoys; and all the trade depending on them. A modern author observes, "The navigation then of our American colonies has been more once exerted in actual feats of power, in carrying a war—against the enemies of Britain indeed; but the same power might be exerted against her, and in the case of a revolt most certainly would."[2] "We have been here," says an American writer, "but little more than one hundred years, and yet the force of our privateers in the late war (that of 1744), united was greater, both in men and guns, than that of the whole British navy in queen Elizabeth's reign."[3]

What therefore must it have been in the late war! Besides such a formidable naval force, they have raised, paid, and armed great armies. During the late war they kept an army of above 30,000 men on foot. They have founderies of cannon, magazines of

[2] See Arthur Young, *Political Essays Concerning the Present State of the British Empire* (London, 1772), p. 421.

[3] See A. H. Smyth, *The Writings of Benjamin Franklin* (New York, 1903–1907), III, 63–73. This is from Franklin's *Observations concerning the Increase of Mankind*, published in 1755 after having been submitted to members of the American Philosophical Society. Taken by itself, the sentence here quoted might lead one to conclude that Franklin was boasting. Rather, he was concerned with the whole problem of colonization and the relation of the American colonies to Great Britain. This document contained the principles which colored much of Franklin's later social thought and action. Cf. Carl Van Doren, *Benjamin Franklin* (New York, 1938), p. 216.

war, arsenals, forts, and fortifications, and even victorious generals amongst their own troops. They have a standing militia; and constantly have the means of raising and arming a formidable body of forces. Let it not be imagined that I am drawing a comparison between the power of Britain and her colonies; far from it; I am only touching upon a few concurrent circumstances, which add to the grand ones of an independant agriculture and manufactures. Supposing that the latter are of capital importance to a people about to throw off the dominion of another, the former are likewise of vast consequence to the attempts, and would render the execution much easier than it could be without them: and how much likewise would depend on the situation of Britain at the time! For instance, whether she was in the midst of a successful or an unsuccessful war;—in the midst of a secure peace or a doubtful contest. A certain concatenation of events might give the colonies an opportunity of not only striking the blow, but preventing all future hopes in the mother country of reversing it. The effect of external circumstances therefore must be great.[4]

[4] This lengthy quotation is taken from Arthur Young's *Political Essays Concerning the Present State of the British Empire* (London, 1772) pp. 421–22.

There is no indication in the text of *American Husbandry* of the omission of many lines following the sentence "Supposing that the latter are of capital importance . . . and would render the execution much easier than it could be without them." This marks the end of a paragraph. The omitted portion of the original follows: "But perhaps it will be said, If these circumstances concur so strong at present, why do they not throw off the dominion of Britain; or rather, why did they not, when they were so exasperated at the act of parliament which taxed them in stamps? To which I answer; that, powerful as these several circumstances undoubtedly are, yet the general foundation upon which their operation must be laid is the number of people. All I have asserted is, that in all cases an independent agriculture and manufactures are necessary; and the other circumstances of trade, navigation, and military force by sea and land, of great importance. But it does not from thence result, that these uniting among a million of people, spread over an immense breadth of country, will enable them to throw off the dominion of such a nation as Britain; or among two or even three million people. All I have attempted to prove is, that these circumstances combined, most undoubtedly may enable our colonies, when arrived at a certain degree of population, to become an independent nation. But

Seeing the principles upon which the danger of this independancy lies, we may, without great difficulty, examine and
point out the means of preventing it as long as possible: we
have found that the situation which most threatens it is the
populousness of those colonies which have no staples: hence
therefore all those measures I before pointed out as a remedy
against the manufactures of America are equally applicable
to the present case; since in their operation they cannot lessen
the fabrics of the northern colonies without either lessening
the number of their people, or in giving them employments
which shall have the effect of staples. In proportion as these
objects were effected, the greater would be the difficulty of
their becoming independant; and in that chain of conduct no
link is more important than the establishment of new colonies
in such a climate as will yield staples, and in situations which
will admit an easy emigration from the northern settlements
to them. Such new colonies, among which that of the Ohio
will be foremost, would have the effect of drawing off that
surplus of population which in a country most of which is
cultivated, applies to manufactures, commerce, or fisheries;
and as long as such surplus could be made to flow in this new
channel, we should be in no greater danger of the independancy of America than we are at present, and perhaps
not in so much.

I have shewn that the general increase of people in the
colonies is not near what the generality of writers make it:

precisely to fix the degree of populousness, would be absurd; since even
the effect of that would and must depend on external circumstances: A
union of several, peculiarly favourable to the event, would render the execution easier to three millions of people than it might otherwise be to fix—
Thirty thousand seamen, twenty sail of the line, a possibility of collecting
twenty thousand veteran troops, a train of artillery, and magazines of
military stores, the existence or non-existence of these circumstances would,
it is very evident, prodigiously accelerate or retard the execution . . ."

instead of doubling all their numbers in 25 years, their present number will not probably be doubled in 50 years; and
then the next doubling may take 120 years, and so on; a consideration too much overlooked by all authors that have
treated of American affairs. But granting the increase to be
quicker than I have stated it, yet it is not the numbers, as I
before observed, but the surplus of agriculture that we are
to fear.

Suppose the total fifteen millions, but spread over the continent so much that the manufactures, commerce, and fisheries were no greater than at present—in that case I assert, that
we should be in no greater danger of their independance
than we are at present. But on the contrary, if their numbers
had filled all that part of the continent which will yield staples, so that fresh land for a small expence could no longer
be had for new settlers, then of course that surplus of population which used to be taken off continually by new cultivation, must necessarily have recourse to other employments;
then cities arise, commerce and manufactures flourish, the
arts are introduced, and a mother country established instead
of remaining a colony.

Here we may make an observation, which, though at first
sight it may appear greatly distant, yet deserves attention,
whenever population has advanced to such a degree in our
colonies: it is, that we must then, at all events, make the
acquisition of Louisiana, on the west of the Mississippi, to
supply that necessary quantity of fresh land which will be
wanting to prevent the surplus of population applying to any
other profession than agriculture: if the preceding principles
are admitted, and they can hardly be rejected, then this observation will not have the appearance of wildness. The au-

thor above quoted gives an idea of British policy similar to this: he remarks,

That she should abide by the boundaries fixed already to the old colonies, that of the rivers' heads; and all further settling to be in *new colonies* wherever they were traced.—That she should keep the inland navigation of the continent, that is, of all the great lakes and navigable rivers, to herself, and not suffer any setts of men to navigate them, and thereby communicate from one part of the continent to another.—That she should never suffer any provincial troops or militia to be raised, but reserve entirely to herself the defense of the frontiers.—That she should throw whatever obstacles she could upon all plans of communication from colony to colony, or conveniences from place to place.— That in proportion as any colony declined in staples and threatened not to be able to produce a sufficiency of them, the inhabitants should receive such encouragement to leave it, as more than to drain its natural increase, unless new staples were discovered for it.—A people, circumstanced as the North Americans would be, if such a system was fully and completely executed, could not possibly even *think* of withdrawing themselves from the dominion of Britain until their staples failed them and they were drove, in spite of all laws and prohibitions, to herd together in towns for the purposes of manufacturing those necessaries which their staples would not pay for. No matter what their numbers might be, they would remain subject to the mother country as long as she could supply them with staples, and that principally would depend upon providing their increase with fresh land. It is true she would find an end of her territory at last, and then the natural course of things would form towns and manufactures of that increase, which she before took off by means of plenty of land. A connection would then arise between town and town and colony and colony; *numbers* would feel that strength which results from *connection* alone, and the influence of the mother country would be too weak to oppose the consequences.[5]

[5] See Arthur Young, *Political Essays Concerning the Present State of the*

If a contrary conduct in Britain should be pursued, which it must be owned is but too likely, the independancy of America may happen in no distant period; for as such progress has been made in the northern colonies towards general manufactures, and the possession of great fisheries and an extensive commerce, the effect will every day be an increase of those employments proportioned to the surplus of population in the settlements; and this increase must necessarily bring on a degree of power, which will enable them, on the first fair opportunity, to throw off their obedience to the British government. Or affairs may gradually go on in such a train, as will bring on the same independency by slow degrees, and at last rest in the completion of it without any acts of violence against Britain—by rising into too powerful a people for the mother country to think of controlling.

British Empire (London, 1772), pp. 428–29. Only part of this long excerpt is quoted directly. In fact, all that part preceding "A people circumstanced . . ." consists of a combination of propositions set down by Young in short paragraphs.

CHAPTER XXXVII

REPRESENTATION

Of a union between Great Britain and her colonies—Objections which have been made—Answers—Difficulties—Observations

THAT different parts of the same empire ought to be united as closely as possible by all the ties of political interest is a maxim, which as it has never been denied, so one might imagine it would never be necessary to prove the cases in which it ought particularly to be applied. But in this of our American colonies such difficulties have been started, and such objections have been made that have made many persons to think truth no longer truth—or that a strong exception is here found to a maxim otherwise infallible.

Mr. Pownall, who resided long in America, and was supposed to be well acquainted with American affairs, started the plan of an union in a more direct manner than any other writer of credit had done before, showing that an American representation might take place without very great difficulties: and the late Mr. Grenville went pretty much into the same idea when he planned the stamp act, but from that blundering execution which was seen in all his schemes, he totally defeated the plan by beginning at the wrong end.

A very able and lively author, in the *Observation on a late*

State of the Nation,[1] took Mr. Grenville's scheme to pieces, and ridiculed it with great severity. His objections turn chiefly, if not entirely, upon the distance of America and the uncertainty of that navigation, from length of voyage, shipwrecks, and war, which must bring the American representatives to Great Britain: in all which he displays much wit and great ridicule. But I am one of those who do not think that wit is reason, or that he who gets the laugh must infallibly be on the right side; since this would be nothing more than saying that a man's conduct is always right in proportion to the wit with which he can defend it. We are not therefore to see nothing but impossibilities in a matter which at most abounds with only difficulties; and a resolution to conquer difficulties ought always to be taken in proportion to the benefits which will result from the victory.

The difficulty of the distance, I think, may be got over by several means. Suppose the members from America, who may be there chosen either by the freeholders of the provinces, or by the present representatives in the provincial assemblies, should always be elected for an uncertain duration; that is, the member resident at London should continue the sitting member either till another landed who was to succeed him, or till his own re-election was noticed. I think this plan would at once answer many of the objections which the above-mentioned ingenious gentleman has started. Nor do I see to what material ones the plan is open: if it is said that the member in England cannot support his interest in case of new elections in America, I reply, neither can the member of our own parliament, in case he is abroad; which often

---

[1] See Edmund Burke, *Observations on a Late State of the Nation* (Dublin, 1769). In this document Burke severely criticized William Knox's pamphlet *The Present State of the Nation* (London, 1768).

happens, and yet we see his friends exerting themselves near as effectually: but granting the fact, of what consequence is it to either Britain or America, whether Mr. George or Mr. Thomas be the member? As long as there must be a sitting one, the necessity is fully answered by either; and if some individual happens to be of singular merit or popularity, he will of course be re-elected. This uncertain duration of a member's sitting may appear strange at first sight, but upon a little reflection there will be found nothing objectionable in it, as the term will be fixed by no ministerial artifice, nor by the artifice of any other man: if a member is not re-elected, it will of course be the business of his successor to take his seat as soon as he can; and if on the way he should be taken by the Spaniards, and carried to Lima, it will be a disagreeable adventure to him, but public business will suffer nothing by it.

But there is another circumstance which answers a great part of the objections which have been made to American representation: English counties elect Scotch members—Scotch towns elect English members—and both of them Irish ones; why not upon the same principles elect British members for America? They will be equally eligible. At present the provinces appoint agents and give them salaries; their seat will render a salary unnecessary, and they will be much more able to advance the business and defend the interest of their constituents: it would be at the option of the electors of America either to chuse some person among themselves, or else upon the same principles as they make choice of their agents, to chuse some person of reputation or knowledge in Britain. There does not appear to be any insuperable objections to any part of such a business.

As to the arrangement of the electors in America, it would have no more difficulties in it than that of the same thing in

Scotland—it would only be necessary to take care that the increasing population of that vast country should be represented, which would be well enough secured by decreeing all freeholders, whose freeholds were above the value of ten pounds sterling, should have a vote, both such as were in being at the time of the union and also such as should be gained or erected afterwards. And if the representation of towns was entirely dropped, it would be so much the better, and be taking a proper hint from the experience of electors in England.

Objections have likewise been raised upon the score of difficulties in contested elections, from the tediousness and expence of trials at the bar of the house, when witnesses are to be brought, and all their attendants, across the Atlantic ocean: but as well might we object to the representation of the Highlands of Scotland, because such evils were infinitely greater than with Middlesex—there are boroughs in Scotland from whence it is near as difficult and expensive to get a tribe of people to London on such a business, as it would be from parts of America. If objections against extending legislation throughout the empire are stated merely from the extent of the empire, it is so weak a plea that one might almost reply to it by saying, you should get rid of what you cannot govern. You can send governors, deputies, surveyors, marshals, registers, and placemen of every denomination to America; it is a pretty joke to imagine they cannot as well return us representatives.

Concerning the general expediency of this measure, I recollect nothing material that has been urged against it. On the contrary, very many reasons have been offered to shew that it is not only proper but necessary. It should be considered that the danger of the American colonies throwing off what is commonly called the yoke of their mother country turns principally upon points of government in which the one party is supposed to be aggrieved by the laws enacted in the other. Nor can we well state a case in which there is any probability of a revolt, but what arises from this circumstance.

If the union was to take place, and all the provinces of our American dominion represented in the British parliament, there would be a tye and a connection of a very different nature from what at present subsists between them. Acts of legislature would then be acts to which themselves had given their consent; a point of vast importance, and by no means treated in a satisfactory manner, by speaking of a virtual representation.

Let us suppose the administration of our government to be so unexceptionable in regard to all American measures as to prevent any open revolt among that part of the subjects in our empire, in what manner then could America become independant? I reply, by the connection gradually falling off until it became of no consequence—this connection is merely commercial. Its declension would be proportionate to the colonists supplying their own markets with manufactures, after which the remaining connection would be too inconsiderable to deserve a thought: hence therefore we find a natural and easy death to every advantage which can result from America to Britain. But if the former was represented in the parliament of Britain—and if that representation formed an entire new legislative power, to which they gave unrestrained obedience, the *connection* between them, which has been found of such importance, would be properly perpetual—as secure as the connection between Scotland and England.

If in any future time the population and importance of

America become what we have reason to suppose they will be, then it might be expected that a change in the place of parliamentary meetings might ensue, and America become the head of the empire, as far as the residence of government could make it so; a revolution which might be much more advantageous to this country than a total separation would be, under many circumstances which might attend so great a change. But as this idea is in reference only to a period extremely distant, no arguments to be drawn from it can be conclusive in the present inquiry.

INDEX

INDEX

Hispaniola, exchanged for Louisiana, 468

Histoire de la nouvelle France (Charlevoix), 368*n*

History of America (Mitchell), xli; excerpts, xlv–xlvi, xlviii.

Hoeing, *see* Hand-hoeing; Horse-hoeing

Hogs, 41, 42, 98, 102, 112, 156, 232, 241, 243, 255, 258, 266, 269, 347, 393, 414, 451, 455, 464; products of America adapted for, 451

Holing, 415, 419

Holly, 268

Hops, 115, 152, 166, 384

Hornbram trees, 267, 384

Horse-hoeing husbandry, 38, 57, 115, 165, 222, 316, 326; value in sugar culture, xviii, lv, 419–25, 463

Horse-Hoeing Husbandry (Tull), 38*n*

Horses, 17, 42, 43, 59, 98, 119, 190, 393, 414, 451; bad treatment, 59; expense of, compared with man labour, 222

Hospitality an obligation, 351

Houses, attention that should be given to situation and building of, 225; how built, 135, 343; of tobacco planters, 170; *see also* Buildings

Huakiki (Kankakee) river, 403*n*

Hudson river, 71, 72, 75; plantation on, 79–85; unpatented land tracts, 77

Hudson's Bay, 493

Hunting, *see* Game

Huron, Lake, 401, 402

Hurricanes, violence of, 410; West Indian, 409, 444, 458, 464

Husbandry, effect of land plenty of, 106, 122; importance of diversity of products, 331; increase of cul-

tivation the colonist's advantage, 85, 86, 139, 149, 175, 302; large capitalized English farms, 306*n*; northern colonies, 5, 6, 16, 24 ff., 37 ff., 55 ff., 78, 79, 93 ff., 104 ff., 113, 122 ff., 143 ff.; southern colonies, 188 ff., 242, 243, 248 ff., 315 ff., 346; *see also* Agriculture; Products

Iberville, Pierre Moyne Sieur d', 381

Ice on Hudson, 72

Illinois country, 400–407; beauty, 401, 402, 403; capable of becoming granary of Louisiana, 404; climate, 404, 407; communication with New Orleans, 406; exports, 216, 406; forests, 401, 403; government, 400, 405; importance to Britain, 407; location, 400, 404, 407; navigation, rivers, 400, 402; products, 406; soil, 404; staples, 407; territory in, 400; travellers' accounts of, 400–406

Illinois river, 380, 400, 403

Implements and tools, 60; cultivator, 166; cotton mills, 391; machine for tobacco culture, 249; used in sugar production, 416, 418, 419, 420; *see also* Horse-hoeing

Imports, British, from colonies, 292; British, from foreign countries, which should be produced in colonies, 356–59; consumption in colonies, 511; duties repealed, 100*n*; northern colonies, 498 f.; southern colonies, 491

Indentured servants, 54, 121

Independancy, 529–44; as result of falling off of connection with Britain, 549; must turn on increase of population where no staples, 535 ff.

Indian corn, *see* Maize

Indian hemp, 117*n*